D0502458

THE CHILDREN'S HOUR

IN FIFTEEN VOLUMES

ILLUSTRATED

VOLUME III

" It is strange that they let that dog lie there " (page 356)

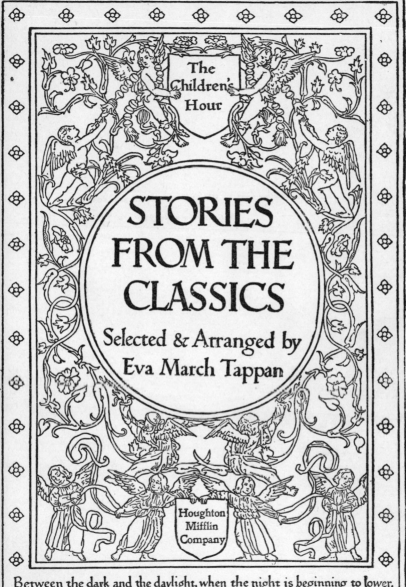

The
Children's
Hour

STORIES
FROM THE
CLASSICS

Selected & Arranged by
Eva March Tappan

Houghton
Mifflin
Company

Between the dark and the daylight, when the night is beginning to lower,
Comes a pause in the day's occupations, that is known as the Children's Hour.

NOTE

A LL rights in stories in this volume are reserved by the holders of the copyrights. The publishers and others named in the subjoined list are the proprietors, either in their own right or as agents for the authors, of the stories taken from the works enumerated, of which the ownership is hereby acknowledged. The editor takes this opportunity to thank both authors and publishers for the ready generosity with which they have allowed her to include these stories in "The Children's Hour."

"The Wonder-Book," and "Tanglewood Tales," by Nathaniel Hawthorne; published by Houghton, Mifflin & Company.

"Old Greek Folk Stories," by Josephine Preston Peabody; published by Houghton, Mifflin & Company.

"The Odyssey of Homer," English prose version by George Herbert Palmer; published by Houghton, Mifflin & Company.

NOTE

A   author's thanks are due to the owners of the
copyrights. The publishers and those
named in the following list and the writers, or others, their
representatives or agents for the use of the material therein
used. No work is reproduced of which the copyright is in the
writer's hand.   The editor desires especially to thank the
several authors and publishers for the ready generosity with
which they have allowed her to include these stories, etc.:—

Dr. Talbot's Home.

"The Wonder-Book" and "Tanglewood Tales," by Nathaniel Hawthorne, published by Houghton, Mifflin & Company.

"The Birds' Christmas," by Josephine Preston Peabody; published by Houghton, Mifflin & Company.

"The Odyssey of Homer," English prose version by
George Herbert Palmer; published by Houghton, Mifflin &
Company.

CONTENTS

CONTENTS

CONTENTS

ILLUSTRATIONS

TO THE CHILDREN

THE greater part of this book is made up of stories from the poems of Homer and Virgil. Homer is thought to have lived in Greece about three thousand years ago, and yet his poems never seem old-fashioned and people do not tire of reading them. Boys and girls almost always like them, because they are so full of stories. If you want to read about giants or mermaids or shipwrecks or athletic contests or enchanters or furious battles or the capture of cities or voyages to strange countries, all you have to do is to open the Iliad and the Odyssey, and you will find stories on all of these subjects. Homer can describe a foot-race or the throwing of a discus so that you hold your breath to see who will win; and he can picture a battle so vividly that you almost try to dodge the arrows and spears. He can make the tears come into your eyes by telling you of the grief of the warrior's wife when he leaves her and their baby son to go to battle; and he can almost make you shout, "Hurrah for the brave champion!" when he tells you what wonderful deeds of prowess have been done. He can describe a shield so minutely that you could make one like it; and he can paint a scene of feasting so perfectly that you feel as if you had been in the very room.

How is it that Homer makes his stories seem so real? There are several reasons, but one of the strongest is because he tells the little things that writers often forget to put in. When he describes the welcome given to two strangers at the house of the lost Ulysses, by Telemachus, son of the wanderer, he begins, "When they were come within the lofty hall, he carried the spear to a tall pillar and set it in a well-worn rack." That one word, "well-worn," gives us the feeling that Homer is not making up a story, but that he has really seen the rack and noticed how it looked. The same sentence shows why it is that people do not tire of reading Homer. It ends, "where also stood many a spear of hardy Ulysses." This reminds the reader that in spite of the hero's long years of absence, no one has been allowed to remove his weapons from their old place. From this one phrase, then, we can realize how much his wife and son love him, and how they have mourned for him. Telemachus welcomes the strangers, but we can feel how eager he is for them to be made comfortable as soon as possible so he can talk of his father and learn whether they have chanced to meet him in their wanderings. Homer's poems are full of such sentences as these; and, no matter how many times one reads them, some thought, unnoticed before, is ever coming to light. That is why they are always fresh and new and interesting.

There is a tradition that Homer was blind, and that he wandered about from one place to another, singing or reciting his poems; but this is only tradition, and there is little hope that we shall ever be able to find out whether it is true or not.

Homer's great poem, the Iliad, is the account of the Trojan War. His Odyssey relates the adventures of the hero Ulysses, or Odysseus, as the Greeks called him, in many years of wandering at the close of the war before his enemies among the Gods would permit him to return to his home. There were Trojan heroes, however, as well as Greek, and Æneas was one of them. Virgil, the Latin poet, has told in the Æneid the story of his troubles and adventures. Æneas, too, was driven over the waters, for the Gods had told him it was the will of Jupiter, or Zeus, as it is in Greek, for him to seek Italy and there found a city. Part of his journey is the same as that of Ulysses. He, too, stops at the country of the one-eyed giants and has to row as fast as he can to escape the rocks that they throw at his vessel. He, too, hears the thunders of Mount Ætna and sees the flashing of the fires of the volcano. His sailors point to it in fear and whisper to one another, "That is the giant Enceladus. He rebelled against the Gods and they piled the mountain on top of him. The fires of Jupiter burn him, and he breathes out glowing flames. When he tosses from one side to the other, the whole island of Sicily is shaken with a mighty earthquake."

Virgil was no homeless singer; he was one of the great literary men of Rome, and he read his poems aloud to the Emperor Augustus. He had a handsome villa and a troop of friends. He enjoyed everything that was beautiful and seemed as happy when a friend had written a good poem as if he had composed it himself. He was never satisfied with his verse till he had made every line as perfect as possible. When he was ill and knew that he could not recover, he made a will, and in it he ordered the Æneid to be burned, because it was not so polished as he wished. "I meant to spend three years more on it," he said. Fortunately for all the people who enjoy a great poem, the Emperor forbade that this part of the will should be carried out. He gave the manuscript to three friends of Virgil, all of them poets, with orders to strike out every phrase that they believed Virgil would have struck out on revision, but not to add one word. This is the way that the Æneid was saved for us. If it had been destroyed, we should have lost the work of one of the best storytellers that have ever lived.

Livy, too, was a friend of the Emperor Augustus. He lived in Rome, enjoying his companions, the libraries of the city, and, most of all, his independence. Even Virgil was ready to insert a few lines here and there in a poem to gratify his friends, or to choose a subject that he knew would please the Emperor; but Livy wrote on the subject that pleased him and treated it just as he believed to be best. His great work was his history, and this he begins with a little preface, as independent as it is graceful. "Whether I shall gain any share of glory," he says, "by writing a history of the Roman people, I do not know. The work, however, will be a pleasure to me; and even if any fame that might otherwise be mine should be hidden by the success of other writers, I shall console myself by thinking of their excellence and greatness." No such thing happened, however, for the kindly historian was so praised and his work so fully appreciated that he said he had all the fame he could wish.

TO THE CHILDREN

Herodotus was a Greek who liked to travel. The world was very small in his day, for little of it was known except some of the lands bordering on the Mediterranean. To visit Tyre, Babylon, Egypt, Palestine, and the islands of the eastern Mediterranean, as he did, made a man a great traveler five centuries before Christ. Herodotus enjoyed all these wanderings, but they also "meant business" to him. Whenever he came to a place of historical interest, he stayed awhile. He explored the country thereabouts, he measured the important buildings, he talked with the people who knew most about the place. Then, when he came to write of its history, he did not write like a man who had read an article or two in an encyclopædia and was trying to recite what he had learned, but like one who knew the place which he was describing and liked to talk about it, and about what had happened there. It is no wonder that his history has always been a favorite; and to be a favorite author for twenty centuries is no small glory.

Ovid was a Latin poet who knew how to tell a story. He could not only invent a tale, but he could tell it so well that the reader feels as if it must be true. His most interesting stories, however, he did not invent, for they are a rewriting of the old mythological tales. In one respect he is like Homer; he never forgets the little things, and he tells so many details that we can hardly believe he is imagining them. In his story of Baucis and Philemon, for instance, Ovid does not forget to say that the cottage door was so low that the two gods had to stoop to pass through it; that Baucis hurried to brighten the fire with dry leaves and bits of bark; that one leg of the table was too short and had to be propped up with a piece of tile. He tells us that the kindhearted couple tried to catch their one goose so as to cook it for the supper of their guests; but that they were so old, and the goose so nimble of wing, that he escaped them and flew to the Gods for refuge. We are so accustomed to think of Latin as a grave, dignified language that almost every line of Ovid's "Metamorphoses" is a pleasant surprise. The stories that he tells, "The Miraculous Pitcher" (page 67), "The Golden Touch" (page 92), "The Pomegranate Seeds" (page 114), and others, retold by Hawthorne, are favorites among the boys and girls of to-day, and they must have been liked just as well by the Roman children. In Rome the children read the great poets in school, and I fancy that they were always glad when the hour came to read the "Metamorphoses."

STORIES FROM HERODOTUS

LADRONIUS, THE PRINCE OF THIEVES

Retold by G. H. Boden and W. Barrington d'Almeida

MANY hundreds of years ago, not long after the Greeks returned from the famous siege of Troy, there lived a king of Egypt, whose name was Rhampsinitus. So great a king was he, that he kept a small army constantly employed in supplying the royal household with food, and another small army was required to keep the gardens of the palace in order. And had any one been bold enough to doubt the greatness of the king, he need only have looked at his magnificent dress to set all doubts at rest forever. Upon the neck of the king was a heavy necklace, glittering with priceless jewels, and on his arms were massive bracelets of pure gold. A golden serpent, the symbol of royalty, gleamed from his forehead, and his golden breastplate showed the sacred beetle worked in precious stones, to protect him from evil spirits. Whenever he appeared in the streets of his capital, he was borne in the royal chair on the shoulders of eight of his courtiers, while on each side walked a great noble carrying a fan, shaped like a palm leaf, with a long, straight stem. In front marched the bodyguard of Sardinians, men with fair skins and blue eyes, who looked very much out of place among the

3

swarthy Egyptians; and last of all came the grim, black guards from Ethiopia, with their sabres flashing in the sun. And all the people fell on their faces and kissed the dust before their royal master. Moreover, King Rhampsinitus erected several enormous statues of himself, as well as many fine palaces and a beautiful temple, bearing inscriptions which related all his great and glorious deeds, so that the people who lived after him might know how great a king he had been.

But, in spite of all his greatness, there was one thing that prevented King Rhampsinitus from being a happy man. He had so many treasures — masses of silver, nuggets of gold, and bags of gold-dust, jewelry, precious stones, and carvings in ivory — that he lived in constant fear of being robbed. He had all his treasures packed in large jars and strong chests, which were securely fastened, sealed up, and stowed away in a strong room of the palace; but even then he did not feel comfortable, for might not the palace be broken into by a clever thief and part of his treasure stolen, while he slept? Besides, there was so much treasure packed away already, that it was difficult to find a safe place for any more. His anxiety made the king so unhappy, and caused him so many sleepless nights, that he determined at last to build a large chamber of stone, with walls too thick for any thief to break through. He sent for his chief architect, who collected a great multitude of workmen and set to work building the chamber without delay. Whole villages were compelled to join in the work; even the old men and children were employed in carrying away rubbish, bringing water and clay, and

4

doing other work that was not too hard for them. The stronger and more skillful workmen hewed great blocks of granite, which were dragged to the place on wooden sledges; and, as they had no cranes to lift the stones into their places on the walls, they were obliged to build mounds of sand and rough bricks, and roll up each stone gradually with wooden levers, until they got it into its proper place. It was terribly hard work, but there were so many workmen, and the foremen used their whips so unmercifully, that the walls rose very rapidly.

Now the architect was a cunning man, and guessed what the chamber was intended to hold. He therefore fitted one stone in such a way that it would slide down and leave a hole just large enough for a man to crawl through; and yet, when you looked at the wall, there was no sign at all by which the secret could be discovered. Nor did the architect think it necessary to mention the secret opening to his majesty, when he showed the chamber to him and told him that it was as strong as he could make it.

Rhampsinitus lost no time in moving his treasures into the new treasure-chamber. The key he kept with him night and day, so that at last he could sleep peacefully, knowing that any one who wished to pass the solid, brass-bound door, must first prevail upon him to unlock it.

For some time all went well. The king went to the treasury every morning, and found everything in its place. Evidently he had been too clever for the thieves.

In the mean time the architect was lying ill in bed,

and day by day he grew weaker and weaker; until at length he knew that his end was approaching, and, calling his two sons to his bedside, he told them of the secret way into the treasure-chamber.

"I have little of my own to leave you, my sons," he said, "and I have but little influence at court; but by the aid of this secret, which I devised for your sake, you may become rich men, and hold the office of king's treasurers for life."

The young men were delighted at his words, and so impatient were they to enjoy their good fortune, that on the very night of their father's funeral they stole away quietly to the place where the treasure-house stood. They found the sliding stone exactly as their father had described it. The younger and slimmer of the two brothers crawled through the opening and found himself in a dark chamber, surrounded by heavy chests and jars with sealed covers. Breaking open one of the latter, he put in his hand and drew out a handful of gold, which sparkled and twinkled at him even in the faint light which came through the hole in the wall. Handful after handful he drew out and passed to his brother, at the same time filling the bags he had brought with him, until both had as much as they could conveniently carry. Then they replaced the stone, and returned to lay the treasure before their mother; for in those days stealing was considered rather a clever trick, and even the thief's mother did not scold him, so long as he was not so clumsy as to be caught.

Imagine the consternation of King Rhampsinitus when he visited the chamber the following morning!

Everything seemed as secure as ever, and yet, when he opened the door, there lay one of the great jars turned over and empty, while the lid of one of the chests was broken open and part of the contents scattered on the floor. He examined every nook and cranny of the chamber from floor to ceiling, and there was no sign of any one's having forced an entrance. The fastenings of the door were firm, and the lock was one which it was perfectly impossible to pick. For greater security, however, Rhampsinitus sent at once for a locksmith, and commanded him to fit the door with a second lock, the key of which he kept with the other.

Notwithstanding this precaution, the treasure-chamber was robbed again on the next night, and this time the thieves had broken open a great many of the chests, and carried away some of the most valuable jewels. On the following night a sentinel was posted, and still the treasury was robbed. The sentinel vowed that he had stood with his back to the door all night, and there is little doubt that he spoke the truth, though the poor fellow was accused of sleeping at his post, and punished for his negligence.

Then the king took counsel of the fan-bearer on the right hand, who was also prime minister. He made a long speech, beginning with his regret that his majesty had not thought fit to consult him earlier, and concluding with a learned discourse on the habits of rats.

"This is all very interesting," said Rhampsinitus, "but I do not see that it helps very much to protect my treasure."

"I crave your majesty's pardon," the prime minister

answered. "I was about to observe that the best way to catch a rat is first to study the habits and tastes of the rat, and next to apply the knowledge so gained in setting a trap."

From which one may see that the prime minister was a very learned man, and could not be expected to come to the point all at once. The king thanked him for his valuable advice, and procured two or three powerful man-traps, which he placed within his treasure-chamber.

Night came on, and the two thieves set to work as before, but no sooner had the younger brother disappeared through the hole in the wall than he began to utter loud cries of agony.

"Peace, brother! You will rouse the guard," said the elder. "What can have befallen you?"

The other controlled himself, and said with a groan, "Ladronius, we are ruined. I am held fast in a trap, and I think my leg is broken. O Horus, Lord of Life, deliver me!"

With some difficulty Ladronius crawled through the opening to aid his brother, for, though a thief, he was no coward.

"Go back, Ladronius, go back!" cried his brother. "Leave me to my fate! I think I hear the cries of the guard. No, brother, waste no more time!" he entreated, as Ladronius tugged in vain at the cruel teeth of the trap. "One thing remains to be done. Cut off my head, and take it away with you, that I may not be recognized and so we both perish! I hear the footsteps of men approaching. Do not rob our mother of both her sons!"

And Ladronius, seeing that there was nothing else to be done, drew his sword, cut off his brother's head, and escaped through the opening, not forgetting to replace the stone behind him. He was only just in time, for scarcely had he gained the cover of a clump of trees, when the soldiers of the guard came running to the place and began to belabor the door. To their surprise they found everything quiet and nothing displaced. They examined the outside of the building thoroughly, and then, supposing that they had been roused by a false alarm, they returned to the palace.

In the morning, Rhampsinitus paid his daily visit to the chamber, and discovered the headless body in the trap. He was more puzzled than ever. He examined the fastenings of the door and the whole of the chamber over and over again, and no hole nor crevice could he find.

"Nevertheless," said he, "I have now bait for my trap. What can I do better than set a thief to catch a thief?"

So he ordered the body to be hung from the outer wall of the chamber, and placed sentinels to guard it, strictly charging them to bring before him any one who showed pity or sorrow for the dead.

When the mother heard of her son's death and how the body had been treated, she reproached Ladronius bitterly for his cowardice, and implored him with many tears to bring back the body for proper burial. For the Egyptians thought that unless a man's body were properly embalmed and buried whole, he could have no life in the next world; so that it would be a

9

terrible misfortune if the head and the body were buried separately. Ladronius attempted to comfort his mother, but did not dare to carry off his brother's body so long as the sentinels were watching. In vain his mother wept and entreated him, until at last her grief was turned to anger, and she vowed that, if he did not obey her, she would go to the king and tell him the whole story. Then Ladronius, seeing her so determined, promised to do as she wished, and set his wits to work to invent some means of carrying off the body without being caught by the sentinels. At last he thought of a plan, which seemed to have some chance of success. He hired two donkeys, and having bought some wineskins, which were used in the place of bottles, he filled them with strong wine and placed them on the donkeys' backs.

Thus equipped, and dressed up to look like an old merchant, he set out for the place where his brother's body was suspended. When he drew near to the sentinels, he secretly loosened some of the strings which fastened the necks of the wineskins, and then whipping the donkeys and letting them run on a little way in front, he pursued them with loud cries.

"Oh, miserable wretch that I am!" he cried, beating his head and looking the very picture of despair. "All my good wine wasted on the ground! What shall I do? Oh, what shall I do? Stop, most ungrateful of donkeys, children of Set, that devour my substance and waste my wine as if it were water! May Tefnet plague you with gadflies, and Renenutet poison the thistles! Oh dear! oh dear! I am a ruined man."

10

The soldiers, supposing it to be a genuine accident, laughed loudly at the fellow's distress, and while some chased and caught the donkeys, the others brought bowls and pitchers and began to drink the wine, as it ran out of the skins.

"Never mind, worthy sir!" they said to Ladronius. "The wine is serving a very good purpose. Here is to our future friendship and your excellency's very good health!"

Ladronius pretended to fly into a great passion, and called them thieves and monsters of iniquity for robbing a poor man of his wine.

"Ay, laugh away!" he cried. "But a day of reckoning will come for your wickedness. See how the law treats robbers!" And he pointed to his brother's body hanging on the wall.

"Now, by Anubis, the fellow speaks truth," said one of the soldiers. "We are but sorry fellows to drink away a poor man's living, and if this were to come to the ears of the king, we should be in evil case for leaving our duty."

The others laughed good-humoredly, as they tied up some of the skins, and did their best to put the merchant into a good temper. Ladronius, after a little more grumbling, appeared to be pacified, and, as a sign of good-will, presented a wineskin to the soldier who had first spoken in his favor.

"May you never want a young friend to speak for you in your old age," said he, "and may you meet with no worse companions than these; for though they seem to be somewhat headstrong, yet I perceive that I spoke hard words in my anger."

11

The soldiers, who by this time had sat down on the grass and were passing the wineskin from one to another, declared that the merchant was a good-hearted old fellow and invited him to come and drink their health.

"Nay, my masters," said Ladronius, pretending to adjust the straps on the donkeys' backs. "I have far to go, and I am but a little way on my journey."

But, as they pressed him, he consented to drink one cup with them before he went. "Though in truth," he added, "if I mistake not, the skin is emptied already. I see that you would force me to part with another, before I set out."

As he spoke, he produced another wineskin, and the soldiers, who were growing merry, greeted him with a shout of delight, and insisted on his sitting down with them. Ladronius, still declaring that he could stay only long enough to drink one cup with them, allowed himself to be placed in the midst, where he presently proved himself so good a companion and told so many merry tales that the soldiers would not hear of his departure. They drank more and more heavily, until at length a third skin was opened, and one by one the sentinels were overpowered by the strong wine, and all lay asleep on the ground.

By this time it had grown dark, and Ladronius, who had pretended to be as drunk as the rest, cautiously raised his head, and finding that all the sentinels were snoring, he took down his brother's body and carried it off. But, before he went, he shaved the right side of the head of each of the sentinels, to show his contempt for the king's precautions.

12

The king was furious when he discovered the failure of his plan and the insult offered to his guards, all of whom were beheaded for their disobedience to his orders. He was more determined than ever to catch the thief, and after taking counsel once more with his prime minister, he decided upon another plan. He caused a proclamation to be made, in which he promised the hand of his daughter to the man whom she should consider the cleverest and most wicked of all men. He commanded the princess to sit on a throne in the temple of Ra, the sun-god, and to speak to all who came to pay their homage to her, asking them what was the cleverest and most wicked deed they had done. But secretly Rhampsinitus told her that, if any one related the story of the robbing of the treasury, she was to seize him by the hand, and hold him till the guards came and secured him.

The moment Ladronius heard the proclamation, he saw that it was another trick to catch him, but he was so daring and so fond of adventure that he could not resist the temptation to outdo the king in cunning once more. He determined actually to put his head in the lion's mouth — in other words, to go boldly to the temple and talk to the princess. He took with him under his cloak the strangest of presents, an arm cut from a dead man's body.

When he entered the temple, he beheld the princess seated on her throne, looking very beautiful in her royal robes, with her dark curls flowing over her shoulders, and the golden vulture of Egypt spreading his wings over her head. She looked a little pale and weary too,

13

for she had talked with many scores of suitors, all of whom had told her tales which were very much alike and nothing at all to do with her father's treasure-chamber. And when the princess looked up and saw Ladronius standing there, with his bold, handsome face, and resolute eyes, she had a suspicion that this was the robber of the treasury. At the same time she felt some pity for the young man, whom she was to be the means of punishing for his bravery. However, she could only obey her father, and motioning to Ladronius to approach, she addressed him with great courtesy, saying, "You seem, sir, by your bearing, to be a man of some strength and courage. Tell me now, what is the most wicked thing, and what the cleverest, you ever did in your life?"

And Ladronius looked her straight in the face and answered, "Most gracious princess, the most wicked thing I ever did in my life was to cut off my brother's head in His Majesty's treasure-house, and the cleverest was when I made the sentinels drunk and carried off my brother's body."

Scarcely were the words out of his mouth, when the princess jumped up and caught him, as she supposed, by the arm, at the same time crying out for the guards, who were concealed behind the throne. But, to her dismay, the arm seemed to part company with the rest of the body, and she was left with the cloak of Ladronius and the arm of the dead man, while Ladronius himself was out of the temple before she had recovered from her surprise; nor could the guards find any trace of him outside.

14

The princess went back to her father in fear and trembling, and related how Ladronius had escaped once more; but the king was so amazed at the daring and skill of the young man, that he quite forgot to be angry.

The picture of the princess holding the arm that had no body attached to it, and gazing blankly after the departing figure of Ladronius, so took his fancy, that he lay back on his couch, and laughed till his sides ached.

"Bast!" he cried at length. "If the youth is really as clever as this, I would rather have him my friend than my enemy. Such a man should be rewarded and not punished for his genius. So he made you a present of his cloak too, did he?" And the king collapsed once more.

"And what manner of youth is he?" he asked the princess; the princess answered, with a blush, that he looked like a brave young man.

"That I am sure he is," said the king. "I have learnt it to my cost. And he is not ill-looking?"

"No," said the princess; she would not describe him as ill-looking.

"Ah! well," said the king dryly, "we must see whether we cannot find some means of securing his friendship."

So King Rhampsinitus ordered another proclamation to be made, promising that if the robber would present himself to the king and confess how he had broken into the treasury, the king would grant him a free pardon and a great reward beside.

Ladronius was not long in making up his mind. He knew that kings were not always above treachery, but he had survived so many dangers that he determined to risk this also. He arrayed himself, therefore, in his best attire, and boldly presented himself to the king, who was delighted with his courage and bade him relate the whole story fearlessly. And when Rhampsinitus heard of the secret way into his treasury, he would not rest until he had seen the sliding stone and moved it for himself. He laughed heartily when he remembered how he had put another lock on the door, and how he had posted a sentinel in the one place where he could see nothing of the thieves. Then he returned to the palace, and sent for the princess, his daughter. Presently she entered with her train of maidens, and Ladronius was so overcome by her fresh, girlish beauty, that he could hardly find voice enough to reply to the king's questions. The king rose and embraced his daughter, and then, addressing Ladronius before the assembled courtiers, he said, "Ladronius, the Egyptians are the most cunning of all nations on the face of the earth, and you have proved yourself more cunning than all the Egyptians. And now, after robbing me of so many treasures, you are about to rob me of the best and most priceless of all."

So saying, he took his daughter by the hand, and led her to Ladronius.

"Take her, my son!" he said. "A good and obedient daughter should make a faithful and loving wife."

The princess stood with her eyes cast down, blushing very prettily, and Ladronius looked very handsome

16

as he knelt and kissed her hand. Then the trumpets began to blare, the drums rattled, the cymbals clashed, and the courtiers shouted, "Long live our gracious princess! Long live Rhampsinitus and his son-in-law Ladronius!" The royal minstrel brought his harp and sang a solemn chant, all about the beauty of the princess and the bravery of Ladronius; and the maids of honor performed a graceful dance to the music, winding wreaths of lotus flowers about the bride and bridegroom. As the music ceased, the venerable High Priest of Ra, a tall old man with his head clean-shaven, came forward to bless and anoint them, and to tell how he had foreseen it all from the beginning.

So Ladronius and the beautiful princess were married, and, though it is not in the story, there can be no doubt that they lived very happily for the rest of their lives.

ARION AND THE DOLPHIN

Retold by G. H. Boden and W. Barrington d'Almeida

IT happened once upon a time, in the olden days, that
a young man, Periander of Corinth, started from a
port in the south of Greece to sail to Miletus. Being
caught in a storm, the boat was carried out of her course
as far as the island of Lesbos, where she stayed for several days, in order that the damage caused by the storm
might be repaired. In the mean time Periander landed,
and occupied himself in wandering about the island
and watching the inhabitants. In his wanderings, he
came one evening upon a group of men and women,
the sight of whom made him pause with a longing to
join them. They had been working hard all day, gathering the grapes, and pressing them in big, wooden vats,
to extract the wine for which Lesbos was famous; and
now, in the beautiful autumn evening, they were making merry after their labors.

No wonder Periander stayed to watch them, for they
made a very pretty picture, — the handsome youths,
with their bronzed faces and strong, fine limbs; the
women with their gay dresses and bare feet, that seemed
to have been made for dancing; the vine-clad hill at the
back, and, over it all, the glow of the setting sun. In

the centre of the dancers sat a boy, playing upon a small lute with seven strings. To this accompaniment the dancers chanted a song in praise of Dionysus, the god of the vine. Gradually the music went faster and faster; and faster and faster the feet of the dancers sped over the ground, until they were all out of breath, and lay laughing on the grass.

Then, as the boy struck another chord, all laughter was hushed, and he began to sing; it was a simple, plaintive little song, but there was a magic in his voice which held the listeners spellbound. The last rays of the setting sun played about his golden curls, and lit up his sweet, childish face, as he sang: —

> "Why should you grieve for me, my love,
>   When I am laid to rest?
> Our lives are shaped by the gods above,
>   And they know best.
> What though I stand on the farther shore,
> Others have crossed the stream before —
>   Why weep in vain?
> Life is but a drop in the deep,
> Soon we wake from the last, lone sleep,
>   And meet again."

As the last note died away, a sigh came from the listeners; some of the women turned away their faces, and the young men began to talk hastily, as if to hide their emotion.

Periander waited until the group began to break up. Then he stepped forward and laid his hand on the boy's shoulder. The boy looked up with a smile.

"What is your name, my fair minstrel?" asked Periander.

"My name is Arion," answered the boy, as if he were used to being questioned. "I come from Methymna beyond the hills, where I used to tend the goats." And he told Periander that his mother and father died before he could remember, and that he was brought up by an old goat-herd; until a traveling minstrel, who happened one day to hear him singing on the hills, took charge of him and taught him to play the lute.

"That was one of his own songs I was singing," said Arion. "He always liked me to sing his songs; but, when I am a man, I shall make my own songs, and sing them in the great cities over the sea."

"And so you shall," said Periander. "Now, listen to me, Arion! Some day, perhaps, I also may be a great man, able to help you to become a great singer. Remember, when you have need of a friend, that Periander of Corinth will help you, if he can!"

And, when he departed, Periander left a sum of money with a worthy old couple, who promised to look after the boy, and see that he wanted nothing.

After some years, Periander became king of Corinth, and having a love of everything beautiful, he soon gathered about him a little band of poets, artists, and musicians. One day, when he was listening to one of the court musicians, something — it might have been a chord in the music — reminded him of the little Lesbian Arion. He seemed to see once more the boy with the golden light on his curls, and the upturned faces of the peasants grouped around him; and the very words of the song ran in his head.

"By Apollo!" he cried, so suddenly that the musician nearly fell off his seat. "We will have the little Lesbian at court, and make a famous singer of him. Where is Glaucus? Ho, there! Bid Glaucus attend the king!"

When Glaucus appeared, the king bade him take a boat and sail for Lesbos. "There you will make search for one Arion, a singer," he said. "And when you have found him, say, 'Periander of Corinth has need of his friend Arion.' And see that you bring him safely to Corinth!"

Glaucus did as he was bidden, and in due time found Arion, now grown into a tall, graceful youth. Arion, when he heard the message, consented to accompany Glaucus to Corinth, where he was greeted with great kindness by Periander. He very soon became a great favorite among the Corinthians, and all the musicians envied him his beautiful voice and his skill in playing on the lute. No one had such power to soothe the king in his black moods; nor was it at court alone that his fame as a singer was known, for he was ever ready to sing to the people, who idolized him and called him the son of Apollo. Among other things he taught them the song and dance of the Lesbians in honor of Dionysus and the vine; it afterwards became one of the most famous songs of Greece.

Many years Arion stayed with Periander, who held him in high honor and loaded him with costly presents. His fame spread as far as Italy and Sicily, and he had many requests that he would go over and sing to the people there. At length, he determined to make the journey, not only from curiosity to see new countries,

but also because he had heard of the songs sung by the
Sicilian shepherds, and had a great desire to study
them. Periander tried to dissuade him, but, finding
him resolved, he assisted him in his preparations, and
on his departure exacted from him a promise that he
would return to Corinth.

Arion traveled about Italy and Sicily for a long time,
and made a great fortune by his singing. But growing
tired at last of the wandering life, he went to Tarentum
to find a ship which would take him back to Corinth.
There were two or three ships ready to make the journey, among them one named the Nausicaa, which was
manned by a crew of Corinthians. This he chose, being
somewhat nervous about the large sum of money he
was carrying, and thinking that he could trust the
Corinthians, whom he knew, better than a crew of
foreigners.

The Nausicaa was a strange-looking vessel, with a
single sail, and long oars pulled by men who sat on
benches along the side. The prow, which was carved
to represent the maiden Nausicaa, stood well out of
the water, and the bulwarks descended in a graceful
curve to rise again at the stern, where the captain stood
and shaped his course by means of a broad paddle,
which was hung over the side.

The voyage began happily enough, the wind being
favorable, and the captain and crew all deference and
politeness. But when they were well out to sea, the
behavior of the crew changed; they answered Arion's
questions with scant politeness, and held many whispered consultations, which, from the black glances

cast at him, made him uneasy as to his safety. On the second evening, waking out of a light sleep, he heard them conspiring to throw him overboard and divide his wealth among them. Arion started up and implored them not to carry out their evil purpose, offering to hand over all his wealth, if they would spare his life. His entreaties and promises were all in vain.

"We give you a fair choice," said the captain brutally. "Either leap into the sea at once, or kill yourself in some other way, and we will bury you decently on shore."

Abandoning his vain appeals for mercy, Arion begged them, as a last favor, to let him sing once more before he died.

"That we will not refuse," the captain answered; "though, if you think to move us by your wailing, let me tell you that you waste your breath!" In reality, he was not displeased to have an opportunity of hearing the most famous singer in the world.

Arion put on his sacred robes, in which he used to sing in the temple of Apollo, and taking his lute he stepped firmly to the prow of the vessel. There he stood, pale and calm, in the silvery light of the moon, his fair hair playing with the wind, while the little waves lifted themselves to look at him, and then ran playfully into the shadow of the boat, to dash their heads against the beams and be broken into spray. The sailors were awed in spite of themselves, as that beautiful voice rose on the breeze. He sang the old song which he had sung in the Lesbian vineyards when Periander saw him first. And when he came to the last lines, —

"Life is but a drop in the deep,
Soon we wake from the last, lone sleep,
And meet again,"

Arion leapt over the side of the vessel, just as he was.

The captain, fearing that some of the crew might be moved to lend him assistance, gave the order to make all speed ahead. Had he waited, he might have seen a most wonderful sight. For, as Arion fell into the sea, the water seemed to become alive beneath him, and he felt it lifting him up, and carrying him rapidly away from the ship. Then he discovered that he was seated astride on a great, black fish, which was swimming very rapidly on the top of the water, and he knew it must be a dolphin, which had been attracted by his singing; for the dolphins, unlike most things that live in the sea, have sharp ears, and are very fond of music. He touched his lute, to see if the strings had suffered from the water, and, as he did so, the great back quivered beneath him. Finding, therefore, that the dolphin liked the music, and thinking that he owed it some return for saving his life, Arion began to sing, and sang song after song; whenever he stopped, the dolphin ceased from swimming, as if to inquire the reason; and when Arion began again, the dolphin bounded through the water with great strokes of his broad tail. A strange sight it must have been, had there been any one there to see! But the dolphin went straight across the open sea, where no ships were to be seen; for the sailors of that day did not care to lose sight of the coast, but would sail all the way round a large bay rather than straight across it. So it was that Arion came to Tænarus in Greece, without having been seen by any man. The dolphin took him close to the shore, where he bade it good-by, and watched it swim away disconsolately.

From Tænarus he made his way on foot to Corinth. Periander was overjoyed to see him once more; and when he marveled at the strange costume in which Arion had traveled, Arion related the whole story.

Periander listened attentively, and, when it was finished, remarked gravely, "Are you then so little satisfied with your victories over the musicians, Arion, that you have determined to be king of story-tellers also?"

"Does your majesty intend to throw doubt on my story?" asked Arion.

"Far be it from me!" answered Periander. "The story pleases me well, and if you will tell me another such, I will take pains to believe that also."

"Then Zeus be my witness! I will find means to prove it," cried Arion.

"Have I not said that I doubted not?" asked Periander. "Yet I would gladly see the proof. My crown to your lute upon the issue!"

"So be it!" said Arion. "But first I must ask your majesty that none may speak of my return; and when the ship *Nausicaa* comes to port, let the seamen be dealt with as I shall appoint!"

The king assented laughing, for he deemed the tale impossible. After some days, however, it was announced that the ship *Nausicaa* was in the harbor. Periander summoned the captain and all the crew to the palace, and asked them whether they had brought any news of his minstrel Arion. The captain replied that men said at Tarentum that Arion was still in Italy, traveling from place to place, and received everywhere with great honor. The rest of the sailors confirmed the story, and one of them added that Arion was said to prefer Italy to Greece, nor had he any intention of returning to Corinth.

At that moment a curtain was drawn and disclosed Arion, standing in his sacred robes and holding his lute, just as they had seen him last in the prow of the ship. The sailors, supposing that they beheld his spirit, were seized with terror, and fell at the king's feet, confessing all their wickedness and begging for mercy. But Periander was filled with indignation, and spurned them angrily. Arion interposed, urging the king to be merciful, now that the seamen had seen their wickedness, and were willing to make restitution. Periander, however, would not hear of mercy.

"Your compassion bears witness to your noble spirit, Arion," he replied. "But these men have planned a most cruel and cowardly murder, and cruelly shall they suffer for it. Seize me these men, guards, and bind them!"

The guards came forward and began to lead away the trembling wretches.

"Stay!" cried Arion. "It is I who am king. Did not your majesty stake your crown against my lute, and can the royal word be broken? Back, guards! I claim my wager."

Periander could not refrain from laughter, but confessed himself beaten by this piece of strategy. "The wit of Arion," he said, "is stronger than the tears of repentance. Release the prisoners!"

ARION AND THE DOLPHIN

"That being so," said Arion, "and seeing that I find myself more easy with the lute, I will restore the royal crown to Periander."

So the men were set at liberty, after having restored the property of Arion, and departed full of gratitude, invoking blessings on his head.

And lest any man should doubt the truth of the story in time to come, Arion erected at Tænarus a statue in bronze, representing a man riding on a dolphin's back.

STORIES FROM LIVY

ROMULUS, FOUNDER OF ROME

Adapted by Alfred J. Church

ÆNEAS of Troy, coming to the land of Italy, took to wife Lavinia, daughter of King Latinus, and built him a city, which he called Lavinium, after the name of his wife. And, after thirty years, his son Ascanius went forth from Lavinium with much people, and built him a new city, which he called Alba. In this city reigned kings of the house and lineage of Æneas for twelve generations. Of these kings the eleventh in descent was one Procas, who, having two sons, Numitor and Amulius, left his kingdom, according to the custom, to Numitor, the elder. But Amulius drove out his brother, and reigned in his stead. Nor was he content with this wickedness, but slew all the male children of his brother. And the daughter of his brother, that was named Rhea Silvia, he chose to be a priestess of Vesta, making as though he would do the maiden honor, but his thought was that the name of his brother should perish, for they that serve Vesta are vowed to perpetual virginity.

But it came to pass that Rhea bare twin sons, whose father, it was said, was the god Mars. Very wroth was Amulius when he heard this thing; Rhea he made fast in prison, and the children he gave to certain of his servants that they should cast them into the river.

Now it chanced that at this season Tiber had overflowed his banks, neither could the servants come near
to the stream of the river; nevertheless they did not
doubt that the children would perish, for all that the
overflowing of the water was neither deep nor of a
swift current. Thinking, then, that they had duly performed the commandment of the king, they set down
the babes in the flood and departed. But after a while
the flood abated, and left the basket wherein the children had been laid on dry ground. And a she-wolf, coming down from the hill to drink at the river (for the
country in those days was desert and abounding in wild
beasts), heard the crying of the children and ran to
them. Nor did she devour them, but gave them suck;
nay, so gentle was she that Faustulus, the king's shepherd, chancing to go by, saw that she licked them with
her tongue. This Faustulus took the children and gave
them to his wife to rear; and these, when they were
of age to go by themselves, were not willing to abide
with the flocks and herds, but were hunters, wandering through the forests that were in those parts. And
afterward, being now come to full strength, they were not
content to slay wild beasts only, but would assail troops
of robbers, as these were returning laden with their
booty, and would divide the spoils among the shepherds. Now there was held in those days, on the hill
that is now called the Palatine, a yearly festival to the
god Pan. This festival King Evander first ordained,
having come from Arcadia, in which land, being a land
of shepherds, Pan, that is the god of shepherds, is greatly
honored. And when the young men and their company

(for they had gathered a great company of shepherds about them, and led them in all matters both of business and of sport) were busy with the festival, there came upon them certain robbers that had made an ambush in the place, being very wroth by reason of the booty which they had lost. These laid hands on Remus, but Romulus they could not take, so fiercely did he fight against them. Remus, therefore, they delivered up to King Amulius, accusing him of many things, and chiefly of this, that he and his companions had invaded the land of Numitor, dealing with them in the fashion of an enemy and carrying off much spoil. To Numitor, therefore, did the king deliver Remus, that he might put him to death. Now Faustulus had believed from the beginning that the children were of the royal house, for he knew that the babes had been cast into the river by the king's command, and the time also of his finding them agreed thereto. Nevertheless he had not judged it expedient to open the matter before due time, but waited till occasion or necessity should arise. But now, there being such necessity, he opened the matter to Romulus. Numitor also, when he had the young man Remus in his custody, knowing that he and his brother were twins, and that the time agreed, and seeing that they were of a high spirit, bethought him of his grandsons; and, indeed, having asked many questions of Remus, was come nigh to knowing of what race he was. And now also Romulus was ready to help his brother. To come openly with his whole company he dared not, for he was not a match for the power of King Amulius; but he bade

sundry shepherds make their way to the palace, each
as best he could, appointing to them a time at which
they should meet. And now came Remus also, with
a troop of youths gathered together from the household of Numitor. Then did Romulus and Remus
slay King Amulius. In the meanwhile Numitor gathered the youth of Alba to the citadel, crying out that
they must make the place safe, for that the enemy
was upon them; but when he perceived that the young
men had done the deed, forthwith he called an assembly of the citizens, and set forth to them the wickedness which his brother had wrought against him, and
how his grandsons had been born and bred and made
known to him, and then, in order, how the tyrant had
been slain, himself having counseled the deed. When
he had so spoken the young men came with their company into the midst of the assembly, and saluted him
as king; to which thing the whole multitude agreeing
with one consent, Numitor was established upon the
throne.

After this Romulus and his brother conceived this
purpose, that, leaving their grandfather to be king at
Alba, they should build for themselves a new city in
the place where, having been at the first left to die,
they had been brought up by Faustulus the shepherd.
And to this purpose many agreed both of the men of
Alba and of the Latins, and also of the shepherds that
had followed them from the first, holding it for certain
all of them that Alba and Lavinium would be of small
account in comparison of this new city which they should
build together. But while the brothers were busy with

these things, there sprang up afresh the same evil thing which had before wrought such trouble in their house, even the lust of power. For though the beginnings of the strife between them were peaceful, yet did it end in great wickedness. The matter fell out in this wise. Seeing that the brothers were twins, and that neither could claim to have the preference to the other in respect of his age, it was agreed between them that the gods that were the guardians of that country should make known by means of augury which of the two they chose to give his name to the new city. Then Romulus stood on the Palatine hill, and when there had been marked out for him a certain region of the sky, watched therein for a sign; and Remus watched in like manner, standing on the Aventine. And to Remus first came a sign, six vultures; but so soon as the sign had been proclaimed there came another to Romulus, even twelve vultures. Then they that favored Remus clamored that the gods had chosen him for king, because he had first seen the birds; and they that favored Romulus answered that he was to be preferred because he had seen more in number. This dispute waxed so hot that they fell to fighting; and in the fight it chanced that Remus was slain. But some say that when Romulus had marked out the borders of the town which he would build, and had caused a wall to be built round it, Remus leapt over the wall, scorning it because it was mean and low; and that Romulus slew him, crying out, "Thus shall every man perish that shall dare to leap over my walls." Only others will have it that though he perished for this cause Romulus slew him not, but a certain Celer. This much is certain, that Romulus gained the whole kingdom for himself, and called the city after his own name.

And now, having first done sacrifice to the Gods, he called a general assembly of the people, that he might give them laws, knowing that without laws no city can endure. And judging that these would be the better kept of his subjects if he should himself bear something of the show of royal majesty, he took certain signs of dignity, and especially twelve men that should continually attend him, bearing bundles of rods, and in the midst of the rods an axe; these men they called *lictors*. Meanwhile the city increased, for the king and his people enlarged their borders, looking rather to the greatness for which they hoped than to that which they had. And that this increase might not be altogether empty walls without men, Romulus set up a sanctuary, to which were gathered a great multitude of men from the nations round about. All that were discontented and lovers of novelty came to him. Nor did he take any account of their condition, whether they were bond or free, but received them all. Thus was there added to the city great strength. And the king, when he judged that there was strength sufficient, was minded to add to the strength counsel. Wherefore he chose a hundred men for counselors. A hundred he chose, either because he held that number to be sufficient, or because there were no more that were fit to bear this dignity and be called Fathers, for this was the name of these counselors.

After this the people bethought themselves how they

should get for themselves wives, for there were no women in the place. Wherefore Romulus sent ambassadors to the nations round about, praying that they should give their daughters to his people for wives. "Cities," he said, "have humble beginnings even as all other things. Nevertheless they that have the Gods and their own valor to help become great. Now that the gods are with us, as ye know, be assured also that valor shall not be wanting." But the nations round about would not hearken to him, thinking scorn of this gathering of robbers and slaves and runaways, so that they said, "Why do ye not open a sanctuary for women also that so ye may find fit wives for your people?" Also they feared for themselves and their children what this new city might grow to. Now when the ambassadors brought back this answer the Romans were greatly wroth, and would take by force that which their neighbors would not give of their free will. And to the end that they might do this more easily, King Romulus appointed certain days whereon he and his people would hold a festival with games to Neptune; and to this festival he called all them that dwelt in the cities round about. But when many were gathered together (for they were fain to see what this new city might be), and were now wholly bent on the spectacle of the games, the young men of the Romans ran in upon them, and carried off all such as were unwedded among the women. To these King Romulus spake kindly, saying, "The fault is not with us but with your fathers, who dealt proudly with us, and would not give you to us in marriage. But now ye shall be held in all honor as our wives, and shall have your portion of all that we possess. Put away therefore your anger, for ye shall find us so much the better husbands than other men, as we must be to you not for husbands only but parents also and native country."

In the meanwhile the parents of them that had been carried off put on sackcloth, and went about through the cities crying out for vengeance upon the Romans. And chiefly they sought for help from Titus Tatius, that was king of the Sabines in those days, and of great power and renown. But when the Sabines seemed to be tardy in the matter, the men of Cære first gathered together their army and marched into the country of the Romans. Against these King Romulus led forth his men and put them to flight without much ado, having first slain their king with his own hand. Then, after returning to Rome, he carried the arms which he had taken from the body of the king to the hill of the Capitol, and laid them down at the shepherds' oak that stood thereon in those days. And when he had measured out the length and breadth of a temple that he would build to Jupiter upon the hill, he said, "O Jupiter, I, King Romulus, offer to thee these arms of a king, and dedicate therewith a temple in this place, in which temple they that come after me shall offer to thee like spoils in like manner, when it shall chance that the leader of our host shall himself slay with his own hands the leader of the host of the enemy." And this was the first temple that was dedicated in Rome. And in all the time to come two only offered in this manner, to wit, Cornelius Cossus that slew Lars Tolumnius, king of Veii, and Claudius Marcellus that slew Britomarus, king of the Gauls.

After this, King Tatius and the Sabines came up against Rome with a great army. And first of all they gained the citadel by treachery in this manner. One Tarpeius was governor of the citadel, whose daughter, Tarpeia by name, going forth from the walls to fetch water for a sacrifice, took money from the king that she should receive certain of the soldiers within the citadel; but when they had been so received, the men cast their shields upon her, slaying her with the weight of them. This they did either that they might be thought to have taken the place by force, or that they judged it to be well that no faith should be kept with traitors. Some also tell this tale, that the Sabines wore great bracelets of gold on their left arms, and on their left hands fair rings with precious stones therein, and that when the maiden covenanted with them that she should have for a reward that which they carried in their left hands, they cast their shields upon her. And other say that she asked for their shields having the purpose to betray them, and for this cause was slain.

Thus the Sabines had possession of the citadel; and the next day King Romulus set the battle in array on the plain that lay between the hill of the Capitol and the hill of the Palatine. And first the Romans were very eager to recover the citadel, a certain Hostilius being their leader. But when this man, fighting in the forefront of the battle, was slain, the Romans turned their backs and fled before the Sabines, even unto the gate of the Palatine. Then King Romulus (for he himself had been carried away by the crowd of them that fled) held up his sword and his spear to the heavens, and cried aloud, "O Jupiter, here in the Palatine didst thou first, by the tokens which thou sentest me, lay the foundations of my city. And lo! the Sabines have taken the citadel by wicked craft, and have crossed the valley, and are come up even hither. But if thou sufferest them so far, do thou at the least defend this place against them, and stay this shameful flight of my people. So will I build a temple for thee in this place, even a temple of Jupiter the Stayer, that may be a memorial to after generations of how thou didst this day save this city." And when he had so spoken, even as though he knew that the prayer had been heard, he cried, "Ye men of Rome, Jupiter bids you stand fast in this place and renew the battle." And when the men of Rome heard these words, it was as if a voice from heaven had spoken to them, and they stood fast, and the king himself went forward and stood among the foremost. Now the leader of the Sabines was one Curtius. This man, as he drave the Romans before him, cried out to his comrades, "See, we have conquered these men, false hosts and feeble foes that they are! Surely now they know that it is one thing to carry off maidens and another to fight with men." But whilst he boasted himself thus, King Romulus and a company of the youth rushed upon him. Now Curtius was fighting on horseback, and being thus assailed he fled, plunging into a certain pool which lay between the Palatine hill and the Capitol. Thus did he barely escape with his life, and the lake was called thereafter

Curtius' pool. And now the Sabines began to give way to the Romans, when suddenly the women for whose sake they fought, having their hair loosened and their garments rent, ran in between them that fought, crying out, "Shed ye not each other's blood, ye that are fathers-in-law and sons-in-law to each other. But if ye break this bond that is between you, slay us that are the cause of this trouble. And surely it were better for us to die than to live if we be bereaved of our fathers or of our husbands." With these words they stirred the hearts both of the chiefs and of the people, so that there was suddenly made a great silence. And afterward the leaders came forth to make a covenant; and these indeed so ordered matters that there was not peace only, but one state where there had been two. For the Sabines came to Rome and dwelt there; and King Romulus and King Tatius reigned together. Only, after a while, certain men of Lanuvium slew King Tatius as he was sacrificing to the Gods at Lavinium; and thereafter Romulus only was king as before.

When he had reigned thirty and seven years there befell the thing that shall now be told. On a certain day he called the people together on the field of Mars, and held a review of his army. But while he did this there arose suddenly a great storm, with loud thunderings and very thick clouds, so that the king was hidden away from the eyes of all the people. Nor indeed was he ever again seen upon the earth. And when men were recovered of their fear they were in great trouble, because they had lost their king, though indeed the Fathers would have it that he had been carried by a whirlwind into heaven. Yet after a while they began to worship him as being now a god; and when nevertheless some doubted, and would even whisper among themselves that Romulus had been torn in pieces by the Fathers, there came forward a certain Proculus, who spake after this manner: "Ye men of Rome, this day, in the early morning, I saw Romulus, the father of this city, come down from heaven and stand before me. And when great fear came upon me, I prayed that it might be lawful for me to look upon him face to face. Then said he to me, 'Go thy way, tell the men of Rome that it is the will of them that dwell in heaven that Rome should be the chiefest city in the world. Bid them therefore be diligent in war; and let them know for themselves and tell their children after them that there is no power on earth so great that it shall be able to stand against them.' And when he had thus spoken, he departed from me, going up into heaven." All men believed Proculus when he thus spake, and the people ceased from their sorrow when they knew that King Romulus had been taken up into heaven.

HOW HORATIUS HELD THE BRIDGE

Adapted by Alfred J. Church

[King Tarquin had been driven from Rome because of his tyranny].

KING TARQUIN and his son Lucius (for he only remained to him of the three) fled to Lars Porsenna, king of Clusium, and besought him that he would help them. "Suffer not," they said, "that we, who are Tuscans by birth, should remain any more in poverty and exile. And take heed also to thyself and thine own kingdom if thou permit this new fashion of driving forth kings to go unpunished. For surely there is that in freedom which men greatly desire, and if they that be kings defend not their dignity as stoutly as others seek to overthrow it, then shall the highest be made even as the lowest, and there shall be an end of kingship, than which there is nothing more honorable under heaven." With these words they persuaded King Porsenna, who judging it well for the Etrurians that there should be a king at Rome, and that king an Etrurian by birth, gathered together a great army and came up against Rome. But when men heard of his coming, so mighty a city was Clusium in those days, and so great the fame of King Porsenna, there was such fear as had never been before. Nevertheless they were steadfastly purposed to hold out. And first all that were in the country fled into the city, and round about the city they set guards to keep it, part thereof being defended by walls, and part, for so it seemed, being made safe by the river. But here a great peril had well-nigh overtaken the city; for there was a wooden bridge on the river by which the enemy had crossed but for the courage of a certain Horatius Cocles. The matter fell out in this wise.

There was a certain hill which men called Janiculum on the side of the river, and this hill King Porsenna took by a sudden attack. Which when Horatius saw (for he chanced to have been set to guard the bridge, and saw also how the enemy were running at full speed to the place, and how the Romans were fleeing in confusion and threw away their arms as they ran), he cried with a loud voice, "Men of Rome, it is to no purpose that ye thus leave your post and flee, for if ye leave this bridge behind you for men to pass over, ye shall soon find that ye have more enemies in your city than in Janiculum. Do ye therefore break it down with axe and fire as best ye can. In the meanwhile I, so far as one man may do, will stay the enemy." And as he spake he ran forward to the farther end of the bridge and made ready to keep the way against the enemy. Nevertheless there stood two with him, Lartius and Herminius by name, men of noble birth both of them and of great renown in arms. So these three for a while stayed the first onset of the enemy; and the men of Rome meanwhile brake down the bridge. And when there was but a small part remaining, and they that brake it down

44

called to the three that they should come back, Horatius bade Lartius and Herminius return, but he himself remained on the farther side, turning his eyes full of wrath in threatening fashion on the princes of the Etrurians, and crying, "Dare ye now to fight with me? or why are ye thus come at the bidding of your master, King Porsenna, to rob others of the freedom that ye care not to have for yourselves?" For a while they delayed, looking each man to his neighbor, who should first deal with this champion of the Romans. Then, for very shame, they all ran forward, and raising a great shout, threw their javelins at him. These all he took upon his shield, nor stood the less firmly in his place on the bridge, from which when they would have thrust him by force, of a sudden the men of Rome raised a great shout, for the bridge was now altogether broken down, and fell with a great crash into the river. And as the enemy stayed a while for fear, Horatius turned him to the river and said, "O Father Tiber, I beseech thee this day with all reverence that thou kindly receive this soldier and his arms." And as he spake he leapt with all his arms into the river and swam across to his own people, and though many javelins of the enemy fell about him, he was not one whit hurt. Nor did such valor fail to receive due honor from the city. For the citizens set up a statue of Horatius in the market-place; and they gave him of the public land so much as he could plough about in one day. Also there was this honor paid him, that each citizen took somewhat of his own store and gave it to him, for food was scarce in the city by reason of the siege.

HOW CINCINNATUS SAVED ROME

Adapted by Alfred J. Church

IT came to pass that the Æquians brake the treaty
of peace which they had made with Rome, and,
taking one Gracchus Clœlius for their leader, marched
into the land of Tusculum; and when they had plundered the country thereabouts, and had gathered together much booty, they pitched their camp on Mount
Ægidus. To them the Romans sent three ambassadors,
who should complain of the wrong done, and seek re-
dress. But when they would have fulfilled their errand,
Gracchus the Æquian spake, saying, "If ye have any
message from the Senate of Rome, tell it to this oak,
for I have other business to do;" for it chanced that
there was a great oak that stood hard by, and made a
shadow over the general's tent. Then one of the ambassadors, as he turned to depart, made reply, "Yes,
let this sacred oak and all the gods that are in heaven
hear how ye have wrongfully broken the treaty of
peace; and let them that hear help us also in the day
of battle, when we shall avenge on you the laws both
of gods and of men that ye have set at nought."

When the ambassadors had returned to Rome the
Senate commanded that there should be levied two
armies; and that Minucius the Consul should march
with the one against the Æquians on Mount Ægidus,

and that the other should hinder the enemy from their plundering. This levying the tribunes of the Commons sought to hinder; and perchance had done so, but there also came well-nigh to the walls of the city a great host of the Sabines plundering all the country. Thereupon the people willingly offered themselves, and there were levied forthwith two great armies. Nevertheless when the Consul Minucius had marched to Mount Ægidus, and had pitched his camp not far from the Æquians, he did nought for fear of the enemy, but kept himself within his entrenchments. And when the enemy perceived that he was afraid, growing the bolder for his lack of courage, they drew lines about him, keeping him in on every side. Yet before that he was altogether shut up there escaped from his camp five horsemen, that bare tidings to Rome how that the Consul, together with his army, was besieged. The people were sorely dismayed to hear such tidings; nor, when they cast about for help, saw they any man that might be sufficient for such peril, save only Cincinnatus. By common consent, therefore, he was made Dictator for six months, a thing that may well be noted by those who hold that nothing is to be accounted of in comparison of riches, and that no man may win great honor or show forth singular virtue unless he be well furnished with wealth. For here in this great peril of the Roman people there was no hope of safety but in one who was cultivating with his own hand a little plot of scarcely three acres of ground. For when the messengers of the people came to him they found him ploughing, or, as some say, digging a ditch. When they had greeted each the other, the messengers said, "May the Gods prosper this thing to the Roman people and to thee. Put on thy robe and hear the words of the people." Then said Cincinnatus, being not a little astonished, "Is all well?" and at the same time he called to his wife Racilia that she should bring forth his robe from the cottage. So she brought it forth, and the man wiped from him the dust and the sweat, and clad himself in his robe, and stood before the messengers. These said to him, "The people of Rome make thee Dictator, and bid thee come forthwith to the city." And at the same time they told how the Consul and his army were besieged by the Æquians. So Cincinnatus departed to Rome; and when he came to the other side of the Tiber there met him first his three sons, and next many of his kinsfolk and friends, and after them a numerous company of the nobles. These all conducted him to his house, the lictors, four and twenty in number, marching before him. There was also assembled a very great concourse of the people, fearing much how the Dictator might deal with them, for they knew what manner of man he was, and that there was no limit to his power, nor any appeal from him.

The next day before dawn the Dictator came into the market-place, and appointed one Lucius Tarquinius to be Master of the Horse. This Tarquinius was held by common consent to excel all other men in exercises of war; only, though, being a noble by birth, he should have been among the horsemen, he had served, for lack of means, as a foot soldier. This done he called an assembly of the people and commanded that all the shops in the city should be shut; that no man should concern himself with any private business, but all that were of an age to go to the war should be present before sunset in the Field of Mars, each man having with him provisions of cooked food for five days, and twelve stakes. As for them that were past the age, they should prepare the food while the young men made ready their arms and sought for the stakes. These last they took as they found them, no man hindering them; and when the time appointed by the Dictator was come, all were assembled, ready, as occasion might serve, either to march or to give battle. Forthwith they set out, the Dictator leading the foot soldiers by their legions, and Tarquinius the horsemen, and each bidding them that followed make all haste. "We must needs come," they said, "to our journey's end while it is yet night. Remember that the Consul and his army have been besieged now for three days, and that no man knows what a day or a night may bring forth." The soldiers themselves also were zealous to obey, crying out to the standard-bearers that they should quicken their steps, and to their fellows that they should not lag behind. Thus they came at midnight to Mount Ægidus, and when they perceived that the enemy was at hand they halted the standards. Then the Dictator rode forward to see, so far as the darkness would suffer him, how great was the camp of the Æquians and after what fashion it was pitched. This done he commanded that the baggage should be gathered together into a heap, and that the soldiers should stand every man in his own place. After this he compassed about the whole army of the enemy with his own army, and commanded that at a set signal every man should shout, and when they had shouted should dig a trench and set up therein the stakes. This the soldiers did, and the noise of the shouting passed over the camp of the enemy and came into the city, causing therein great joy, even as it caused great fear in the camp. For the Romans cried, "These be our countrymen, and they bring us help." Then said the Consul, "We must make no delay. By that shout is signified, not that they are come only, but that they are already dealing with the enemy. Doubtless the camp of the Æquians is even now assailed from without. Take ye your arms and follow me." So the legion went forth, it being yet night, to the battle, and as they went they shouted, that the Dictator might be aware. Now the Æquians had set themselves to hinder the making of a ditch and rampart which should shut them in; but when the Romans from the camp fell upon them, fearing lest these should make their way through the midst of their camp, they left them that were with Cincinnatus to finish their entrenching, and fought with the Consul. And when it was now light, lo! they were already shut in, and the Romans, having finished their entrenching, began to trouble them. And when the Æquians perceived that the battle was now on either side of them, they could withstand no longer, but sent ambassadors praying for peace, and saying, "Ye have prevailed; slay us not, but rather permit us to depart, leaving our arms behind us." Then said the Dictator, "I care not to have the blood of the Æquians. Ye may depart, but ye shall depart passing under the yoke, that ye may thus acknowledge to all men that ye are indeed vanquished." Now the yoke is thus made. There are set up in the ground two spears, and over them is bound by ropes a third spear. So the Æquians passed under the yoke.

In the camp of the enemy there was found abundance of spoil. This the Dictator gave wholly to his own soldiers. "Ye were well-nigh a spoil to the enemy," said he to the army of the Consul, "therefore ye shall have no share in the spoiling of them. As for thee, Minucius, be thou a lieutenant only till thou hast learnt how to bear thyself as a consul." Meanwhile at Rome there was held a meeting of the Senate, at which it was commanded that Cincinnatus should enter the city in triumph, his soldiers following him in order of march. Before his chariot there were led the generals of the enemy; also the standards were carried in the front; and after these came the army, every man laden with spoil. That day there was great rejoicing in the city, every man setting forth a banquet before his doors in the street.

After this, Virginius, that had borne false witness against Cæso, was found guilty of perjury, and went into exile. And when Cincinnatus saw that justice had been done to this evil-doer, he resigned his dictatorship, having held it for sixteen days only.

THE STORY OF VIRGINIA

Adapted by Alfred J. Church

IT was agreed between the nobles and the commons that, to make an end of disputing about the laws, ambassadors should be sent into Greece, and especially to Athens (which city and its lawgiver, Solon, were held in high repute in those days), to learn what manner of laws and customs they had, and to bring back a report of them. And when the ambassadors had brought back their report, it seemed good to the people that in the following year there should be appointed neither consuls nor any other magistrate, but decemvirs only; that is to say, ten men, who should set in order the laws of Rome. Thus it came to pass in the ninety and first year from the driving out of the kings, that decemvirs were appointed in the stead of consuls, Appius Claudius being the chief of the ten.

For a while these pleased the people well, doing justice equally between man and man. And the custom was that each day one of the ten sat as judge with the twelve lictors about him, the nine others sitting with one minister only. Also they busied themselves with the ordering of the laws; and at last set forth ten tables on which these were written. At the same time they called the people together to an assembly, and spake to them thus: "The Gods grant that this undertaking may turn to the credit of the state, and of you, and of your children. Go, therefore, and read these laws which we have set forth; for though we have done what ten men could do to provide laws that should be just to all, whether they be high or low, yet the understandings of many men may yet change many things for the better. Consider therefore all these matters in your own minds, and debate them among yourselves. For we will that the Roman people should be bound by such laws only as they shall have agreed together to establish."

The ten tables were therefore set forth, and when these had been sufficiently considered, and such corrections made therein as seemed good, a regular assembly of the people was called, and the laws were duly established. But now there was spread abroad a report that two tables were yet wanting, and that when these should have been added the whole would be complete; and thence there arose a desire that the Ten should be appointed to hold office a second year. This indeed was done; but Appius Claudius so ordered matters that there were elected together with him none of the chief men of the state, but only such as were of an inferior condition and fortune.

After this the Ten began more and more to set aside all law and right. Thus whereas at the first one only on each day was followed by the twelve lictors, each of the Ten came daily into the market-place so attended, and whereas before the lictors carried bundles of rods only, now there was bound up with the rods an axe; whereby was signified the power of life and death. Their actions also agreed with this show, for they and their ministers plundered the goods and chattels of the people. Some also they scourged, and some they beheaded. And when they had so put a man to death, they would divide his substance among those that waited upon them to do their pleasure.

Among their misdeeds two were especially notable. There was a certain Sicinius in the host, a man of singular strength and courage, who took it ill that the Ten should thus set themselves above all law, and was wont to say to his comrades that the commons should depart from the city as they had done in time past, or should at the least make them tribunes to be their champions as of old. This Sicinius the Ten sent on before the army, there being then war with the Sabines, to search out a place for a camp; and with him they sent certain others, bidding them slay him when they should have come to some convenient place. This they did, but not without suffering much loss; for the man fought for his life and defended himself, slaying many of his enemies. Then they that escaped ran into the camp, saying that Sicinius had fallen into an ambuscade, and had died along with certain others of the soldiers. At the first, indeed, this story was believed; but afterward, when, by permission of the Ten, there went some to bury the dead, they found that none of the dead bodies had been spoiled, and that Sicinius lay with his arms in the midst, the others having their faces toward him; also that there was no dead body of an enemy in the place, nor any track as of them that had gone from the place; for which reasons they brought back tidings that Sicinius had certainly been slain by

THE STORY OF VIRGINIA

his own comrades. At this there was great wrath in
the camp; and the soldiers were ready to carry the
body of Sicinius to Rome, but that the Ten made a
military funeral for him at the public cost. So they
buried Sicinius with great lamentation; but the Ten
were thereafter in very ill repute among the soldiers.

Again, there was a certain centurion, Lucius Virginius by name, an upright man and of good credit
both at home and abroad. This Virginius had a daughter, Virginia, a very fair and virtuous maiden, whom
he had espoused to a certain Icilius that had once been
a tribune of the commons. On this maiden Appius
Claudius, the chief of the Ten, sought to lay hands,
and for this end gave commandment to one Marcus
Claudius, who was one of the clients of his house,
that he should claim the girl for a slave. On the morrow
therefore, as Virginia passed across the market-place,
being on her way to school (for the schools in those
days were held in the market-place), this Claudius
seized her, affirming that she was born of a woman that
was a slave, and was therefore by right a slave herself.
The maiden standing still for fear, the nurse that attended her set up a great cry and called the citizens
to help. Straightway there was a great concourse, for
many knew the maiden's father Virginius, and Icilius
to whom she was betrothed. Then said Claudius,
seeing that he could not take her by force, "There is
no need of tumult or of gathering a crowd. I would pro-
ceed by law, not by force." Thereupon he summoned
the girl before the judge. When they came to the judgment-seat of Appius the man told a tale that had al-

55

ready been agreed upon between the two. "This girl,"
he said, "was born in my house, and was thence secretly
taken to the house of Virginius, and passed off on the
man as his daughter. Of this I will bring proof sufficient,
such as will convince Virginius himself, who doubtless
has received the chief wrong in this matter. But in the
meanwhile it is reasonable that the slave should remain
in the house of her master." To this the friends of
the girl made answer, "Virginius is absent on the service of the state, and will be here within the space of
two days, if tidings of this matter be sent to him. Now
it is manifestly wrong that judgment concerning a man's
children should be given while he is himself absent.
Let the cause, therefore, be postponed till he come.
Meanwhile let the maiden have her freedom, according
to the law which Appius and his fellows have themselves established."

Appius gave sentence in these words: "That I am
a favorer of freedom is manifest from this law of which
ye make mention. Yet this law must be observed in
all cases and without respect of persons; and as to
this girl, there is none but her father only to whom her
owner may yield the custody of her. Let her father therefore be sent for; but in the meanwhile Claudius must
have custody of her, as is his right, only giving security
that he will produce her on the morrow."

At this decree, so manifestly unrighteous was it,
there was much murmuring, yet none dared to oppose
it, till Numitorius, the girl's uncle, and Icilius came forth
from the crowd. The lictor cried, "Sentence has been
given," and bade Icilius give place. Then Icilius turned

THE STORY OF VIRGINIA

to Appius, saying, "Appius, thou must drive me hence
with the sword before thou canst have thy will in this
matter. This maiden is my espoused wife; and verily,
though thou call hither all thy lictors and the lictors
of thy colleagues, she shall not remain in any house
save the house of her father."

To this Appius, seeing that the multitude was greatly
moved and were ready to break forth into open violence,
made this reply: "Icilius cares not for Virginia, but
being a lover of sedition and tumult, seeks an occasion
for strife. Such occasion I will not give him to-day.
But that he may know that I yield not to his insolence,
but have regard to the rights of a father, I pronounce
no sentence. I ask of Marcus Claudius that he will
concede something of his right, and suffer surety to be
given for the girl against the morrow. But if on the morrow the father be not present here, then I tell Icilius
and his fellows that he who is the author of this law
will not fail to execute it. Neither will I call in the lictors of my colleague to put down them that raise a
tumult. For this my own lictors shall suffice."

So much time being thus gained, it seemed good to
the friends of the maiden that the son of Numitorius
and the brother of Icilius, young men both of them
and active, should hasten with all speed to the camp,
and bring Virginius thence as quickly as might be. So
the two set out, and putting their horses to their full
speed, carried tidings of the matter to the father. As
for Appius, he sat awhile on the judgment-seat, waiting for other business to be brought before him, for
he would not have it seem that he had come for this

cause only; but finding that there was none, and indeed the people were wholly intent on the matter of Virginia, he departed to his own house. Thence he sent an epistle to his colleagues that were at the camp, saying, "Grant no leave of absence to Virginius, but keep him in safe custody with you." But this availed nothing, for already, before ever the epistle was brought to the camp, at the very first watch of the night, Virginius had set forth.

When Virginius was come to the city, it being then early dawn, he put on mean apparel, as was the custom with such as were in danger of life or liberty, and carried about his daughter, who was clad in like manner, praying all that he met to help and succor him. "Remember," said he, "that day by day I stand fighting for you and for your children against your enemies. But what shall this profit you or me if this city being safe, nevertheless our children stand in peril of slavery and shame?" Icilius spake in like manner, and the women (for a company of matrons followed Virginia) wept silently, stirring greatly the hearts of all that looked upon them. But Appius, so set was his heart on evil, heeded none of these things; but so soon as he had sat him down on the seat of judgment, and he that claimed the girl had said a few words complaining that right had not been done to him, he gave his sentence, suffering not Virginius to speak. What pretense of reason he gave can scarce be imagined, but the sentence (for this only is certain) was that the girl should be in the custody of Claudius till the matter should be decided by law. But when Claudius came to take the maiden,

THE STORY OF VIRGINIA

her friends and all the women that bare her company
thrust him back. Then said Appius, "I have sure
proof, and this not from the violence only of Icilius,
but from what is told to me of gatherings by night in
the city, that there is a purpose in certain men to stir
up sedition. Knowing this I have come hither with
armed men; not to trouble quiet citizens, but to punish
such as would break the peace of the state. Such as
be wise, therefore, will keep themselves quiet. Lictor,
remove this crowd, and make room for the master
that he may take his slave." These words he thundered
forth in great anger; and the people, when they heard
them, fell back in fear, so that the maiden stood without defense. Then Virginius, seeing that there were none
to help him, said to Appius, "I pray thee, Appius,
if I have said aught that was harsh to thee, that thou
wilt pardon it, knowing how a father must needs suffer
in such a case. But now suffer me to inquire somewhat
of this woman that is the girl's nurse, that I may know
what is the truth of the matter. For if I have been deceived in the matter, and am not in truth father to the
girl, I shall be more content." Then, Appius giving permission, he led his daughter and her nurse a little space
aside, to the shops that are by the temple of Cloacina,
and snatching a knife from a butcher's, said, "My
daughter, there is but this one way that I can make thee
free," and he drave the knife into her breast. Then he
looked back to the judgment-seat and cried, "With
this blood, Appius, I devote thee and thy life to per-
dition." There went up a great cry from all that stood
there when they saw so dreadful a deed, and Appius

59

commanded that they should seize him. But no man laid hands on him, for he made a way for himself with the knife that he carried in his hand, and they that followed defended him, till he came to the gate of the city. Then Icilius and Numitorius took up the dead body of the maiden and showed it to the people, saying much of the wickedness of him who had driven a father to do such a deed, and much also of the liberty which had been taken from them, and which, if they would only use this occasion, they might now recover. As for Appius, he cried out to his lictors that they should lay hands on Icilius, and when the crowd suffered not the lictors to approach, would himself have made a way to him, by the help of the young nobles that stood by him. But now the crowd had leaders, themselves also nobles, Valerius and Horatius. These said, "If Appius would deal with Icilius according to law we will be securities for him; if he mean to use violence, we are ready to meet him." And when the lictor would have laid hands on these two the multitude brake his rods to pieces. Then Appius would have spoken to the people, but they clamored against him, so that at last, losing all courage and fearing for his life, he covered his head and fled secretly to his own house.

Meanwhile Virginius had made his way to the camp, which was now on Mount Vecilius, and stirred up the army yet more than he had stirred the city. "Lay not to my charge," he said, "that which is in truth the wickedness of Appius; neither turn from me as from the murderer of my daughter. Her indeed I slew, thinking that death was better than slavery and shame; nor indeed had I survived her but that I hoped to avenge her death by the help of my comrades." Others also that had come from the city persuaded the soldiers; some saying that the power of the Ten was overthrown, and others that Appius had gone of his own accord into banishment. These words so prevailed with the soldiers that, without any bidding from their generals, they took up their arms, and, with their standards carried before them, came to Rome and pitched their camp on the Aventine.

Nevertheless, the Ten were still obstinate, affirming that they would not resign their authority till they had finished the work for which they had been appointed, namely, the drawing up of the twelve tables of the laws. And when the army perceived this they marched from the Aventine and took up their abode on the Sacred Hill, all the commons following them, so that there was not left in the city a single man that had ability to move; nor did the women and children stay behind, but all, as many as could move, bare them company; for Duilius, that had been tribune, said, "Unless the Senate see the city deserted, they will take no heed of your complaints." And indeed, when these perceived what had taken place, they were more urgent than before that the Ten should resign their office. And these at last consented. "Only," said they, "do not suffer us to perish from the rage of the commons. It will be an ill day for the nobles when the people shall learn to take vengeance on them." And the Senate so wrought that though at the first the commons in their great fury demanded that the Ten should be burned alive, yet they were persuaded to yield, it being agreed that each man should be judged by the law according to his deserts. Appius, therefore, was accused by Virginius, and being cast into prison, slew himself before the day appointed for the trial. Oppius also, another of the Ten, whom the commons hated for his misdeeds next after Appius, was accused and died in like manner. As for Claudius, that had claimed Virginia for his slave, he was condemned to be banished. And thus at the last, the guilty having been punished, the spirit of Virginia had rest.

THE SACRIFICE OF MARCUS CURTIUS

Adapted by Alfred J. Church

IN the three hundred and ninety-third year after the building of the city there was seen suddenly to open in the market-place a great gulf of a deepness that no man could measure. And this gulf could not be filled up, though all the people brought earth and stones and the like to cast into it. But at the last there was sent a message from the Gods that the Romans must inquire what was that by which more than all things the state was made strong. "For," said the soothsayer, "this thing must be dedicated to the Gods in this place if the commonwealth of Rome is to stand fast forever." And while they doubted, one Marcus Curtius, a youth that had won great renown in war, rebuked them, saying, "Can ye doubt that Rome hath nothing better than arms and valor?"

Then all the people stood silent; and Curtius, first beholding the temples of the immortal Gods that hung over the market-place and the Capitol, and afterward stretching forth his hands both to heaven above and to this gulf that opened its mouth to the very pit, as it were, of hell, devoted himself for his country; and so — being clothed in armor and with arms in his hand,

and having his horse arrayed as sumptuously as might be — he leapt into the gulf; and the multitude, both of men and women, threw in gifts and offerings of the fruits of the earth, and afterward the earth closed together.

STORIES FROM OVID

THE MIRACULOUS PITCHER

By Nathaniel Hawthorne

ONE evening, in times long ago, old Philemon and his old wife Baucis sat at their cottage door, enjoying the calm and beautiful sunset. They had already eaten their frugal supper, and intended now to spend a quiet hour or two before bedtime. So they talked together about their garden, and their cow, and their bees, and their grapevine, which clambered over the cottage wall, and on which the grapes were beginning to turn purple. But the rude shouts of children, and the fierce barking of dogs, in the village near at hand, grew louder and louder, until, at last, it was hardly possible for Baucis and Philemon to hear each other speak.

"Ah, wife," cried Philemon, "I fear some poor traveler is seeking hospitality among our neighbors yonder, and, instead of giving him food and lodging, they have set their dogs at him, as their custom is!"

"Well-a-day!" answered old Baucis, "I do wish our neighbors felt a little more kindness for their fellow-creatures. And only think of bringing up their children in this naughty way, and patting them on the head when they fling stones at strangers!"

"Those children will never come to any good," said Philemon, shaking his white head. "To tell you the truth, wife, I should not wonder if some terrible thing were to happen to all the people in the village, unless they mend their manners. But, as for you and me, so long as Providence affords us a crust of bread, let us be ready to give half to any poor, homeless stranger that may come along and need it."

"That's right, husband!" said Baucis. "So we will!"

These old folks, you must know, were quite poor, and had to work pretty hard for a living. Old Philemon toiled diligently in his garden, while Baucis was always busy with her distaff, or making a little butter and cheese with their cow's milk, or doing one thing and another about the cottage. Their food was seldom anything but bread, milk, and vegetables, with sometimes a portion of honey from their beehive, and now and then a bunch of grapes, that had ripened against the cottage wall. But they were two of the kindest old people in the world, and would cheerfully have gone without their dinners, any day, rather than refuse a slice of their brown loaf, a cup of new milk, and a spoonful of honey, to the weary traveler who might pause before their door. They felt as if such guests had a sort of holiness, and that they ought, therefore, to treat them better and more bountifully than their own selves.

Their cottage stood on a rising ground, at some short distance from a village, which lay in a hollow valley, that was about half a mile in breadth. This valley, in past ages, when the world was new, had probably been the bed of a lake. There fishes had glided to and fro in the depths, and water-weeds had grown along the margin, and trees and hills had seen their reflected images in the broad and peaceful mirror. But, as the waters subsided, men had cultivated the soil, and built houses on it, so that it was now a fertile spot, and bore no traces of the ancient lake, except a very small brook, which meandered through the midst of the village, and supplied the inhabitants with water. The valley had been dry land so long that oaks had sprung up, and grown great and high, and perished with old age, and been succeeded by others, as tall and stately as the first. Never was there a prettier or more fruitful valley. The very sight of the plenty around them should have made the inhabitants kind and gentle, and ready to show their gratitude to Providence by doing good to their fellow-creatures.

But, we are sorry to say, the people of this lovely village were not worthy to dwell in a spot on which Heaven had smiled so beneficently. They were a very selfish and hard-hearted people, and had no pity for the poor, nor sympathy with the homeless. They would only have laughed, had anybody told them that human beings owe a debt of love to one another, because there is no other method of paying the debt of love and care which all of us owe to Providence. You will hardly believe what I am going to tell you. These naughty people taught their children to be no better than themselves, and used to clap their hands, by way of encouragement, when they saw the little boys and girls run after some poor stranger, shouting at his heels, and pelting him with stones. They kept large and fierce dogs, and whenever a traveler ventured to show himself in the village street, this pack of disagreeable curs scampered to meet him, barking, snarling, and showing their teeth. Then they would seize him by his leg, or

by his clothes, just as it happened; and if he were
ragged when he came, he was generally a pitiable object
before he had time to run away. This was a very terrible thing to poor travelers, as you may suppose, especially when they chanced to be sick, or feeble, or lame,
or old. Such persons (if they once knew how badly these
unkind people, and their unkind children and curs,
were in the habit of behaving) would go miles and miles
out of their way, rather than try to pass through the
village again.

What made the matter seem worse, if possible, was
that when rich persons came in their chariots, or riding
on beautiful horses, with their servants in rich liveries
attending on them, nobody could be more civil and
obsequious than the inhabitants of the village. They
would take off their hats, and make the humblest bows
you ever saw. If the children were rude, they were
pretty certain to get their ears boxed; and as for the
dogs, if a single cur in the pack presumed to yelp, his
master instantly beat him with a club, and tied him up
without any supper. This would have been all very
well, only it proved that the villagers cared much about
the money that a stranger had in his pocket, and nothing
whatever for the human soul, which lives equally in the
beggar and the prince.

So now you can understand why old Philemon spoke
so sorrowfully, when he heard the shouts of the children
and the barking of the dogs, at the farther extremity
of the village street. There was a confused din, which
lasted a good while, and seemed to pass quite through
the breadth of the valley.

THE MIRACULOUS PITCHER

"I never heard the dogs so loud!" observed the good old man.

"Nor the children so rude!" answered his good old wife.

They sat shaking their heads, one to the other, while the noise came nearer and nearer; until, at the foot of the little eminence on which their cottage stood, they saw two travelers approaching on foot. Close behind them came the fierce dogs, snarling at their very heels. A little farther off ran a crowd of children, who sent up shrill cries, and flung stones at the two strangers, with all their might. Once or twice, the younger of the two men (he was a slender and very active figure) turned about and drove back the dogs with a staff which he carried in his hand. His companion, who was a very tall person, walked calmly along as if disdaining to notice either the naughty children or the pack of curs, whose manners the children seemed to imitate.

Both of the travelers were very humbly clad, and looked as if they might not have money enough in their pockets to pay for a night's lodging. And this, I am afraid, was the reason why the villagers had allowed their children and dogs to treat them so rudely.

"Come, wife," said Philemon to Baucis, "let us go and meet these poor people. No doubt, they feel almost too heavy-hearted to climb the hill."

"Go you and meet them," answered Baucis, "while I make haste within doors, and see whether we can get them anything for supper. A comfortable bowl of bread and milk would do wonders towards raising their spirits."

Accordingly, she hastened into the cottage. Philemon, on his part, went forward, and extended his
hand with so hospitable an aspect that there was no
need of saying what nevertheless he did say, in the
heartiest tone imaginable, —

"Welcome, strangers! welcome!"

"Thank you!" replied the younger of the two, in a
lively kind of way, notwithstanding his weariness and
trouble. "This is quite another greeting than we have
met with yonder in the village. Pray, why do you live
in such a bad neighborhood?"

"Ah!" observed old Philemon, with a quiet and
benign smile, "Providence put me here, I hope, among
other reasons, in order that I may make you what
amends I can for the inhospitality of my neighbors."

"Well said, old father!" cried the traveler, laughing;
"and, if the truth must be told, my companion and
myself need some amends. Those children (the little
rascals!) have bespattered us finely with their mud-balls;
and one of the curs has torn my cloak, which was ragged
enough already. But I took him across the muzzle with
my staff; and I think you may have heard him yelp,
even thus far off."

Philemon was glad to see him in such good spirits;
nor, indeed, would you have fancied, by the traveler's
look and manner, that he was weary with a long day's
journey, besides being disheartened by rough treatment
at the end of it. He was dressed in rather an odd way,
with a sort of cap on his head, the brim of which stuck
out over both ears. Though it was a summer evening,
he wore a cloak, which he kept wrapt closely about

him, perhaps because his under garments were shabby.
Philemon perceived, too, that he had on a singular pair
of shoes; but, as it was now growing dusk, and as the
old man's eyesight was none the sharpest, he could not
precisely tell in what the strangeness consisted. One
thing, certainly, seemed queer. The traveler was so
wonderfully light and active, that it appeared as if his
feet sometimes rose from the ground of their own accord, or could only be kept down by an effort.

"I used to be light-footed, in my youth," said Philemon to the traveler. "But I always found my feet grow
heavier towards nightfall."

"There is nothing like a good staff to help one along,"
answered the stranger; "and I happen to have an
excellent one, as you see."

This staff, in fact, was the oddest-looking staff that
Philemon had ever beheld. It was made of olive-wood,
and had something like a little pair of wings near the
top. Two snakes, carved in the wood, were represented
as twining themselves about the staff, and were so very
skillfully executed that old Philemon (whose eyes, you
know, were getting rather dim) almost thought them
alive, and that he could see them wriggling and twisting.

"A curious piece of work, sure enough!" said he.
"A staff with wings! It would be an excellent kind of
stick for a little boy to ride astride of!"

By this time Philemon and his two guests had reached
the cottage door.

"Friends," said the old man, "sit down and rest
yourselves here on this bench. My good wife Baucis
has gone to see what you can have for supper. We are

poor folks; but you shall be welcome to whatever we have in the cupboard."

The younger stranger threw himself carelessly on the bench, letting his staff fall, as he did so. And here happened something rather marvelous, though trifling enough, too. The staff seemed to get up from the ground of its own accord, and, spreading its little pair of wings, it half hopped, half flew, and leaned itself against the wall of the cottage. There it stood quite still, except that the snakes continued to wriggle. But, in my private opinion, old Philemon's eyesight had been playing him tricks again.

Before he could ask any questions, the elder stranger drew his attention from the wonderful staff, by speaking to him.

"Was there not," asked the stranger, in a remarkably deep tone of voice, "a lake, in very ancient times, covering the spot where now stands yonder village?"

"Not in my day, friend," answered Philemon; "and yet I am an old man, as you see. There were always the fields and meadows, just as they are now, and the old trees, and the little stream murmuring through the midst of the valley. My father, nor his father before him, ever saw it otherwise, so far as I know; and doubtless it will still be the same, when old Philemon shall be gone and forgotten!"

"That is more than can be safely foretold," observed the stranger; and there was something very stern in his deep voice. He shook his head, too, so that his dark and heavy curls were shaken with the movement. "Since the inhabitants of yonder village have forgotten the

74

affections and sympathies of their nature, it were better that the lake should be rippling over their dwellings again!"

The traveler looked so stern that Philemon was really almost frightened; the more so, that, at his frown, the twilight seemed suddenly to grow darker, and that, when he shook his head, there was a roll as of thunder in the air.

But, in a moment afterwards, the stranger's face became so kindly and mild that the old man quite forgot his terror. Nevertheless, he could not help feeling that this elder traveler must be no ordinary personage, although he happened now to be attired so humbly and to be journeying on foot. Not that Philemon fancied him a prince in disguise, or any character of that sort; but rather some exceedingly wise man, who went about the world in this poor garb, despising wealth and all worldly objects, and seeking everywhere to add a mite to his wisdom. This idea appeared the more probable, because, when Philemon raised his eyes to the stranger's face, he seemed to see more thought there, in one look, than he could have studied out in a lifetime.

While Baucis was getting the supper, the travelers both began to talk very sociably with Philemon. The younger, indeed, was extremely loquacious, and made such shrewd and witty remarks that the good old man continually burst out a-laughing, and pronounced him the merriest fellow whom he had seen for many a day.

"Pray, my young friend," said he, as they grew familiar together, "what may I call your name?"

"Why, I am very nimble, as you see," answered the

traveler. "So, if you call me Quicksilver, the name will fit tolerably well."

"Quicksilver? Quicksilver?" repeated Philemon, looking in the traveler's face, to see if he were making fun of him. "It is a very odd name! And your companion there? Has he as strange a one?"

"You must ask the thunder to tell it you!" replied Quicksilver, putting on a mysterious look. "No other voice is loud enough."

This remark, whether it were serious or in jest, might have caused Philemon to conceive a very great awe of the elder stranger, if, on venturing to gaze at him, he had not beheld so much beneficence in his visage. But undoubtedly here was the grandest figure that ever sat so humbly beside a cottage door. When the stranger conversed, it was with gravity, and in such a way that Philemon felt irresistibly moved to tell him everything which he had most at heart. This is always the feeling that people have when they meet with any one wise enough to comprehend all their good and evil, and to despise not a tittle of it.

But Philemon, simple and kind-hearted old man that he was, had not many secrets to disclose. He talked, however, quite garrulously, about the events of his past life, in the whole course of which he had never been a score of miles from this very spot. His wife Baucis and himself had dwelt in the cottage from their youth upward, earning their bread by honest labor, always poor, but still contented. He told what excellent butter and cheese Baucis made, and how nice were the vegetables which he raised in his garden. He said, too, that, because they loved one another so very much, it was the wish of both that death might not separate them, but that they should die, as they had lived, together.

As the stranger listened, a smile beamed over his countenance, and made its expression as sweet as it was grand.

"You are a good old man," said he to Philemon, "and you have a good old wife to be your helpmeet. It is fit that your wish be granted."

And it seemed to Philemon, just then, as if the sunset clouds threw up a bright flash from the west, and kindled a sudden light in the sky.

Baucis had now got supper ready, and, coming to the door, began to make apologies for the poor fare which she was forced to set before her guests.

"Had we known you were coming," said she, "my good man and myself would have gone without a morsel, rather than you should lack a better supper. But I took the most part of to-day's milk to make cheese; and our last loaf is already half eaten. Ah me! I never feel the sorrow of being poor, save when a poor traveler knocks at our door."

"All will be very well; do not trouble yourself, my good dame," replied the elder stranger kindly. "An honest, hearty welcome to a guest works miracles with the fare, and is capable of turning the coarsest food to nectar and ambrosia."

"A welcome you shall have," cried Baucis, "and likewise a little honey that we happen to have left, and a bunch of purple grapes besides."

"Why, Mother Baucis, it is a feast!" exclaimed

Quicksilver, laughing; "an absolute feast! and you shall see how bravely I will play my part at it! I think I never felt hungrier in my life."

"Mercy on us!" whispered Baucis to her husband. "If the young man has such a terrible appetite, I am afraid there will not be half enough supper!"

They all went into the cottage.

And now, my little auditors, shall I tell you something that will make you open your eyes very wide? It is really one of the oddest circumstances in the whole story. Quicksilver's staff, you recollect, had set itself up against the wall of the cottage. Well, when its master entered the door, leaving this wonderful staff behind, what should it do but immediately spread its little wings, and go hopping and fluttering up the doorsteps! Tap, tap, went the staff, on the kitchen floor; nor did it rest until it had stood itself on end, with the greatest gravity and decorum, beside Quicksilver's chair. Old Philemon, however, as well as his wife, was so taken up in attending to their guests that no notice was given to what the staff had been about.

As Baucis had said, there was but a scanty supper for two hungry travelers. In the middle of the table was the remnant of a brown loaf, with a piece of cheese on one side of it, and a dish of honeycomb on the other. There was a pretty good bunch of grapes for each of the guests. A moderately sized earthen pitcher, nearly full of milk, stood at a corner of the board; and when Baucis had filled two bowls, and set them before the strangers, only a little milk remained in the bottom of the pitcher. Alas! it is a very sad business, when a

78

"I AM AFRAID THERE WILL NOT BE HALF ENOUGH SUPPER"

bountiful heart finds itself pinched and squeezed among narrow circumstances. Poor Baucis kept wishing that she might starve for a week to come, if it were possible, by so doing, to provide these hungry folks a more plentiful supper.

And, since the supper was so exceedingly small, she could not help wishing that their appetites had not been quite so large. Why, at their very first sitting down, the travelers both drank off all the milk in their two bowls, at a draught.

"A little more milk, kind Mother Baucis, if you please," said Quicksilver. "The day has been hot, and I am very much athirst."

"Now, my dear people," answered Baucis, in great confusion, "I am so sorry and ashamed! But the truth is, there is hardly a drop more milk in the pitcher. O husband, husband, why did n't we go without our supper?"

"Why, it appears to me," cried Quicksilver, starting up from table and taking the pitcher by the handle, "it really appears to me that matters are not quite so bad as you represent them. Here is certainly more milk in the pitcher."

So saying, and to the vast astonishment of Baucis, he proceeded to fill, not only his own bowl, but his companion's likewise, from the pitcher that was supposed to be almost empty. The good woman could scarcely believe her eyes. She had certainly poured out nearly all the milk, and had peeped in afterwards, and seen the bottom of the pitcher, as she set it down upon the table.

"But I am old," thought Baucis to herself, "and

apt to be forgetful. I suppose I must have made a mistake. At all events, the pitcher cannot help being empty now, after filling the bowls twice over."

"What excellent milk!" observed Quicksilver, after quaffing the contents of the second bowl. "Excuse me, my kind hostess, but I must really ask you for a little more."

Now Baucis had seen, as plainly as she could see anything, that Quicksilver had turned the pitcher upside down, and consequently had poured out every drop of milk, in filling the last bowl. Of course, there could not possibly be any left. However, in order to let him know precisely how the case was, she lifted the pitcher, and made a gesture as if pouring milk into Quicksilver's bowl, but without the remotest idea that any milk would stream forth. What was her surprise, therefore, when such an abundant cascade fell bubbling into the bowl, that it was immediately filled to the brim, and overflowed upon the table! The two snakes that were twisted about Quicksilver's staff (but neither Baucis nor Philemon happened to observe this circumstance) stretched out their heads, and began to lap up the spilt milk.

And then what a delicious fragrance the milk had! It seemed as if Philemon's only cow must have pastured, that day, on the richest herbage that could be found anywhere in the world. I only wish that each of you, my beloved little souls, could have a bowl of such nice milk, at supper-time!

"And now a slice of your brown loaf, Mother Baucis," said Quicksilver, "and a little of that honey!"

Baucis cut him a slice accordingly; and though the loaf, when she and her husband ate of it, had been rather too dry and crusty to be palatable, it was now as light and moist as if but a few hours out of the oven. Tasting a crumb, which had fallen on the table, she found it more delicious than bread ever was before, and could hardly believe that it was a loaf of her own kneading and baking. Yet, what other loaf could it possibly be?

But oh, the honey! I may just as well let it alone, without trying to describe how exquisitely it smelt and looked. Its color was that of the purest and most transparent gold; and it had the odor of a thousand flowers; but of such flowers as never grew in an earthly garden, and to seek which the bees must have flown high above the clouds. The wonder is, that, after alighting on a flower-bed of so delicious fragrance and immortal bloom, they should have been content to fly down again to their hive in Philemon's garden. Never was such honey tasted, seen, or smelt. The perfume floated around the kitchen, and made it so delightful, that, had you closed your eyes, you would instantly have forgotten the low ceiling and smoky walls, and have fancied yourself in an arbor, with celestial honeysuckles creeping over it.

Although good Mother Baucis was a simple old dame, she could not but think that there was something rather out of the common way in all that had been going on. So, after helping the guests to bread and honey, and laying a bunch of grapes by each of their plates, she sat down by Philemon, and told him what she had seen, in a whisper.

"Did you ever hear the like?" asked she.

"No, I never did," answered Philemon, with a smile. "And I rather think, my dear old wife, you have been walking about in a sort of a dream. If I had poured out the milk, I should have seen through the business at once. There happened to be a little more in the pitcher than you thought, — that is all."

"Ah, husband," said Baucis, "say what you will, these are very uncommon people."

"Well, well," replied Philemon, still smiling, "perhaps they are. They certainly do look as if they had seen better days; and I am heartily glad to see them making so comfortable a supper."

Each of the guests had now taken his bunch of grapes upon his plate. Baucis (who rubbed her eyes, in order to see the more clearly) was of opinion that the clusters had grown larger and richer, and that each separate grape seemed to be on the point of bursting with ripe juice. It was entirely a mystery to her how such grapes could ever have been produced from the old stunted vine that climbed against the cottage wall.

"Very admirable grapes these!" observed Quicksilver, as he swallowed one after another, without apparently diminishing his cluster. "Pray, my good host, whence did you gather them?"

"From my own vine," answered Philemon. "You may see one of its branches twisting across the window, yonder. But wife and I never thought the grapes very fine ones."

"I never tasted better," said the guest. "Another

cup of this delicious milk, if you please, and I shall then have supped better than a prince."

This time, old Philemon bestirred himself, and took up the pitcher; for he was curious to discover whether there was any reality in the marvels which Baucis had whispered to him. He knew that his good old wife was incapable of falsehood, and that she was seldom mistaken in what she supposed to be true; but this was so very singular a case, that he wanted to see into it with his own eyes. On taking up the pitcher, therefore, he slyly peeped into it, and was fully satisfied that it contained not so much as a single drop. All at once, however, he beheld a little white fountain, which gushed up from the bottom of the pitcher, and speedily filled it to the brim with foaming and deliciously fragrant milk. It was lucky that Philemon, in his surprise, did not drop the miraculous pitcher from his hand.

"Who are ye, wonder-working strangers!" cried he, even more bewildered than his wife had been.

"Your guests, my good Philemon, and your friends," replied the elder traveler, in his mild, deep voice, that had something at once sweet and awe-inspiring in it. "Give me likewise a cup of the milk; and may your pitcher never be empty for kind Baucis and yourself, any more than for the needy wayfarer!"

The supper being now over, the strangers requested to be shown to their place of repose. The old people would gladly have talked with them a little longer, and have expressed the wonder which they felt, and their delight at finding the poor and meagre supper prove so much better and more abundant than they hoped. But the elder traveler had inspired them with such reverence that they dared not ask him any questions. And when Philemon drew Quicksilver aside, and inquired how under the sun a fountain of milk could have got into an old earthen pitcher, this latter personage pointed to his staff.

"There is the whole mystery of the affair," quoth Quicksilver; "and if you can make it out, I'll thank you to let me know. I can't tell what to make of my staff. It is always playing such odd tricks as this; sometimes getting me a supper, and, quite as often, stealing it away. If I had any faith in such nonsense, I should say the stick was bewitched!"

He said no more, but looked so slyly in their faces, that they rather fancied he was laughing at them. The magic staff went hopping at his heels, as Quicksilver quitted the room. When left alone, the good old couple spent some little time in conversation about the events of the evening, and then lay down on the floor, and fell fast asleep. They had given up their sleeping-room to the guests, and had no other bed for themselves, save these planks, which I wish had been as soft as their own hearts.

The old man and his wife were stirring, betimes, in the morning, and the strangers likewise arose with the sun, and made their preparations to depart. Philemon hospitably entreated them to remain a little longer, until Baucis could milk the cow, and bake a cake upon the hearth, and, perhaps, find them a few fresh eggs, for breakfast. The guests, however, seemed to think it better to accomplish a good part of their journey before the heat of the day should come on. They, therefore, persisted in setting out immediately, but asked Philemon and Baucis to walk forth with them a short distance, and show them the road which they were to take.

So they all four issued from the cottage, chatting together like old friends. It was very remarkable, indeed, how familiar the old couple insensibly grew with the elder traveler, and how their good and simple spirits melted into his, even as two drops of water would melt into the illimitable ocean. And as for Quicksilver, with his keen, quick, laughing wits, he appeared to discover every little thought that but peeped into their minds, before they suspected it themselves. They sometimes wished, it is true, that he had not been quite so quick-witted, and also that he would fling away his staff, which looked so mysteriously mischievous, with the snakes always writhing about it. But then, again, Quicksilver showed himself so very good-humored, that they would have been rejoiced to keep him in their cottage, staff, snakes, and all, every day, and the whole day long.

"Ah me! Well-a-day!" exclaimed Philemon, when they had walked a little way from their door. "If our neighbors only knew what a blessed thing it is to show hospitality to strangers, they would tie up all their dogs, and never allow their children to fling another stone."

"It is a sin and shame for them to behave so, — that it is!" cried good old Baucis vehemently. "And ·

I mean to go this very day, and tell some of them what naughty people they are!"

"I fear," remarked Quicksilver, slyly smiling, "that you will find none of them at home."

The elder traveler's brow, just then, assumed such a grave, stern, and awful grandeur, yet serene withal, that neither Baucis nor Philemon dared to speak a word. They gazed reverently into his face, as if they had been gazing at the sky.

"When men do not feel towards the humblest stranger as if he were a brother," said the traveler, in tones so deep that they sounded like those of an organ, "they are unworthy to exist on earth, which was created as the abode of a great human brotherhood!"

"And, by the by, my dear old people," cried Quicksilver, with the liveliest look of fun and mischief in his eyes, "where is this same village that you talk about? On which side of us does it lie? Methinks I do not see it hereabouts."

Philemon and his wife turned towards the valley, where, at sunset, only the day before, they had seen the meadows, the houses, the gardens, the clumps of trees, the wide, green-margined street, with children playing in it, and all the tokens of business, enjoyment, and prosperity. But what was their astonishment! There was no longer any appearance of a village! Even the fertile vale, in the hollow of which it lay, had ceased to have existence. In its stead, they beheld the broad, blue surface of a lake, which filled the great basin of the valley from brim to brim, and reflected the surrounding hills in its bosom with as tranquil an image as if it had been there ever since the creation of the world. For an instant, the lake remained perfectly smooth. Then a little breeze sprang up, and caused the water to dance, glitter, and sparkle in the early sunbeams, and to dash, with a pleasant rippling murmur, against the hither shore.

The lake seemed so strangely familiar, that the old couple were greatly perplexed, and felt as if they could only have been dreaming about a village having lain there. But, the next moment, they remembered the vanished dwellings, and the faces and characters of the inhabitants, far too distinctly for a dream. The village had been there yesterday, and now was gone!

"Alas!" cried these kind-hearted old people, "what has become of our poor neighbors?"

"They no longer exist as men and women," said the elder traveler, in his grand and deep voice, while a roll of thunder seemed to echo it at a distance. "There was neither use nor beauty in such a life as theirs; for they never softened or sweetened the hard lot of mortality by the exercise of kindly affections between man and man. They retained no image of the better life in their bosoms; therefore, the lake, that was of old, has spread itself forth again, to reflect the sky!"

"And as for those foolish people," said Quicksilver, with his mischievous smile, "they are all transformed to fishes. There needed but little change, for they were already a scaly set of rascals, and the coldest-blooded beings in existence. So, kind Mother Baucis, whenever you or your husband have an appetite for a dish of broiled trout, he can throw in a line, and pull out half a dozen of your old neighbors!"

"Ah," cried Baucis shuddering, "I would not, for the world, put one of them on the gridiron!"

"No," added Philemon, making a wry face, "we could never relish them!"

"As for you, good Philemon," continued the elder traveler, — "and you, kind Baucis, — you, with your scanty means, have mingled so much heartfelt hospitality with your entertainment of the homeless stranger, that the milk became an inexhaustible fount of nectar, and the brown loaf and the honey were ambrosia. Thus, the divinities have feasted, at your board, off the same viands that supply their banquets on Olympus. You have done well, my dear old friends. Wherefore, request whatever favor you have most at heart, and it is granted."

Philemon and Baucis looked at one another, and then — I know not which of the two it was who spoke, but that one uttered the desire of both their hearts.

"Let us live together, while we live, and leave the world at the same instant, when we die! For we have always loved one another!"

"Be it so!" replied the stranger, with majestic kindness. "Now, look towards your cottage!"

They did so. But what was their surprise on beholding a tall edifice of white marble, with a wide-open portal, occupying the spot where their humble residence had so lately stood!

"There is your home," said the stranger, beneficently smiling on them both. "Exercise your hospitality in yonder palace as freely as in the poor hovel to which you welcomed us last evening."

The old folks fell on their knees to thank him; but, behold! neither he nor Quicksilver was there.

So Philemon and Baucis took up their residence in the marble palace, and spent their time, with vast satisfaction to themselves, in making everybody jolly and comfortable who happened to pass that way. The milk-pitcher, I must not forget to say, retained its marvelous quality of being never empty, when it was desirable to have it full. Whenever an honest, good-humored, and free-hearted guest took a draught from this pitcher, he invariably found it the sweetest and most invigorating fluid that ever ran down his throat. But, if a cross and disagreeable curmudgeon happened to sip, he was pretty certain to twist his visage into a hard knot, and pronounce it a pitcher of sour milk!

Thus the old couple lived in their palace a great, great while, and grew older and older, and very old indeed. At length, however, there came a summer morning when Philemon and Baucis failed to make their appearance, as on other mornings, with one hospitable smile overspreading both their pleasant faces, to invite the guests of over-night to breakfast. The guests searched everywhere, from top to bottom of the spacious palace, and all to no purpose. But, after a great deal of perplexity, they espied, in front of the portal, two venerable trees, which nobody could remember to have seen there the day before. Yet there they stood, with their roots fastened deep into the soil, and a huge breadth of foliage overshadowing the whole front of the edifice. One was an oak, and the other a linden-tree. Their boughs — it was strange and beautiful to see — were intertwined together, and embraced one another, so that each tree seemed to live in the other tree's bosom much more than in its own.

While the guests were marveling how these trees, that must have required at least a century to grow, could have come to be so tall and venerable in a single night, a breeze sprang up, and set their intermingled boughs astir. And then there was a deep, broad murmur in the air, as if the two mysterious trees were speaking.

"I am old Philemon!" murmured the oak.

"I am old Baucis!" murmured the linden-tree.

But, as the breeze grew stronger, the trees both spoke at once, — "Philemon! Baucis! Baucis! Philemon!" — as if one were both and both were one, and talking together in the depths of their mutual heart. It was plain enough to perceive that the good old couple had renewed their age, and were now to spend a quiet and delightful hundred years or so, Philemon as an oak, and Baucis as a linden-tree. And oh, what a hospitable shade did they fling around them! Whenever a wayfarer paused beneath it, he heard a pleasant whisper of the leaves above his head, and wondered how the sound should so much resemble words like these: —

"Welcome, welcome, dear traveler, welcome!"

And some kind soul, that knew what would have pleased old Baucis and old Philemon best, built a circular seat around both their trunks, where, for a great

THE MIRACULOUS PITCHER

while afterwards, the weary, and the hungry, and the thirsty used to repose themselves, and quaff milk abundantly from the miraculous pitcher.

And I wish, for all our sakes, that we had the pitcher here now

THE GOLDEN TOUCH

By *Nathaniel Hawthorne*

ONCE upon a time, there lived a very rich man,
and a king besides, whose name was Midas; and
he had a little daughter, whom nobody but myself ever
heard of, and whose name I either never knew or have
entirely forgotten. So, because I love odd names for
little girls, I choose to call her Marygold.

This King Midas was fonder of gold than of anything else in the world. He valued his royal crown
chiefly because it was composed of that precious metal.
If he loved anything better, or half so well, it was
the one little maiden who played so merrily around
her father's footstool. But the more Midas loved his
daughter, the more did he desire and seek for wealth.
He thought, foolish man! that the best thing he could
possibly do for this dear child would be to bequeath
her the immensest pile of yellow, glistening coin, that
had ever been heaped together since the world was
made. Thus, he gave all his thoughts and all his time
to this one purpose. If ever he happened to gaze for
an instant at the gold-tinted clouds of sunset, he wished
that they were real gold, and that they could be squeezed
safely into his strong box. When little Marygold ran
to meet him with a bunch of buttercups and dandelions,
he used to say, "Poh, poh, child! If these flowers were

as golden as they look, they would be worth the plucking!"

And yet, in his earlier days, before he was so entirely possessed of this insane desire for riches, King
Midas had shown a great taste for flowers. He had
planted a garden, in which grew the biggest and beau-
tifulest and sweetest roses that any mortal ever saw
or smelt. These roses were still growing in the garden, as large, as lovely, and as fragrant as when Midas
used to pass whole hours in gazing at them and in-
haling their perfume. But now, if he looked at them
at all, it was only to calculate how much the garden
would be worth if each of the innumerable rose-petals
were a thin plate of gold. And though he once was
fond of music (in spite of an idle story about his ears,
which were said to resemble those of an ass), the
only music for poor Midas, now, was the chink of one
coin against another.

At length (as people always grow more and more
foolish, unless they take care to grow wiser and wiser),
Midas had got to be so exceedingly unreasonable, that
he could scarcely bear to see or touch any object that
was not gold. He made it his custom, therefore, to
pass a large portion of every day in a dark and dreary
apartment, under ground, at the basement of his palace. It was here that he kept his wealth. To this
dismal hole — for it was little better than a dungeon
— Midas betook himself, whenever he wanted to be
particularly happy. Here, after carefully locking the
door, he would take a bag of gold coin, or a gold cup
as big as a washbowl, or a heavy golden bar, or a peck-

measure of gold-dust, and bring them from the obscure corners of the room into the one bright and narrow sunbeam that fell from the dungeon-like window. He valued the sunbeam for no other reason but that his treasure would not shine without its help. And then would he reckon over the coins in the bag; toss up the bar, and catch it as it came down; sift the gold-dust through his fingers; look at the funny image of his own face, as reflected in the burnished circumference of the cup; and whisper to himself, "O Midas, rich King Midas, what a happy man art thou!" But it was laughable to see how the image of his face kept grinning at him, out of the polished surface of the cup. It seemed to be aware of his foolish behavior, and to have a naughty inclination to make fun of him.

Midas called himself a happy man, but felt that he was not yet quite so happy as he might be. The very tiptop of enjoyment would never be reached, unless the whole world were to become his treasure-room, and be filled with yellow metal which should be all his own.

Now, I need hardly remind such wise little people as you are, that in the old, old times, when King Midas was alive, a great many things came to pass, which we should consider wonderful if they were to happen in our own day and country. And, on the other hand, a great many things take place nowadays, which seem not only wonderful to us, but at which the people of old times would have stared their eyes out. On the whole, I regard our own times as the strangest of the two; but, however that may be, I must go on with my story.

Midas was enjoying himself in his treasure-room,

one day, as usual, when he perceived a shadow fall over the heaps of gold; and, looking suddenly up, what hould he behold but the figure of a stranger, standing n the bright and narrow sunbeam! It was a young man, with a cheerful and ruddy face. Whether it was that the imagination of King Midas threw a yellow tinge over everything, or whatever the cause might be, he could not help fancying that the smile with which the stranger regarded him had a kind of golden radiance in it. Certainly, although his figure intercepted the sunshine, there was now a brighter gleam upon all the piled-up treasures than before. Even the remotest corners had their share of it, and were lighted up, when the stranger smiled, as with tips of flame and sparkles of fire.

As Midas knew that he had carefully turned the key in the lock, and that no mortal strength could possibly break into his treasure-room, he, of course, concluded that his visitor must be something more than mortal. It is no matter about telling you who he was. In those days, when the earth was comparatively a new affair, it was supposed to be often the resort of beings endowed with supernatural power, and who used to interest themselves in the joys and sorrows of men, women, and children, half playfully and half seriously. Midas had met such beings before now, and was not sorry to meet one of them again. The stranger's aspect, indeed, was so good-humored and kindly, if not beneficent, that it would have been unreasonable to suspect him of intending any mischief. It was far more probable that he came to do Midas a favor. And what could that favor be, unless to multiply his heaps of treasure?

The stranger gazed about the room; and when his lustrous smile had glistened upon all the golden objects that were there, he turned again to Midas.

"You are a wealthy man, friend Midas!" he observed. "I doubt whether any other four walls, on earth, contain so much gold as you have contrived to pile up in this room."

"I have done pretty well, — pretty well," answered Midas, in a discontented tone. "But, after all, it is but a trifle, when you consider that it has taken me my whole life to get it together. If one could live a thousand years, he might have time to grow rich!"

"What!" exclaimed the stranger. "Then you are not satisfied?"

Midas shook his head.

"And pray what would satisfy you?" asked the stranger. "Merely for the curiosity of the thing, I should be glad to know."

Midas paused and meditated. He felt a presentiment that this stranger, with such a golden lustre in his good-humored smile, had come hither with both the power and the purpose of gratifying his utmost wishes. Now, therefore, was the fortunate moment, when he had but to speak, and obtain whatever possible, or seemingly impossible thing, it might come into his head to ask. So he thought, and thought, and thought, and heaped up one golden mountain upon another, in his imagination, without being able to imagine them big enough. At last, a bright idea occurred to King Midas. It seemed really as bright as the glistening metal which he loved so much.

Raising his head, he looked the lustrous stranger in the face.

"Well, Midas," observed his visitor, "I see that you have at length hit upon something that will satisfy you. Tell me your wish."

"It is only this," replied Midas. "I am weary of collecting my treasures with so much trouble, and beholding the heap so diminutive, after I have done my best. I wish everything that I touch to be changed to gold!"

The stranger's smile grew so very broad, that it seemed to fill the room like an outburst of the sun, gleaming into a shadowy dell where the yellow autumnal leaves — for so looked the lumps and particles of gold — lie strewn in the glow of light.

"The Golden Touch!" exclaimed he. "You certainly deserve credit, friend Midas, for striking out so brilliant a conception. But are you quite sure that this will satisfy you?"

"How could it fail?" said Midas.

"And will you never regret the possession of it?"

"What could induce me?" asked Midas. "I ask nothing else, to render me perfectly happy."

"Be it as you wish, then," replied the stranger, waving his hand in token of farewell. "To-morrow, at sunrise, you will find yourself gifted with the Golden Touch."

The figure of the stranger then became exceedingly bright, and Midas involuntarily closed his eyes. On opening them again, he beheld only one yellow sunbeam in the room, and, all around him, the glistening of the precious metal which he had spent his life in hoarding up.

Whether Midas slept as usual that night, the story does not say. Asleep or awake, however, his mind was probably in the state of a child's, to whom a beautiful new plaything has been promised in the morning. At any rate, day had hardly peeped over the hills, when King Midas was broad awake, and, stretching his arms out of bed, began to touch the objects that were within reach. He was anxious to prove whether the Golden Touch had really come, according to the stranger's promise. So he laid his finger on a chair by the bedside, and on various other things, but was grievously disappointed to perceive that they remained of exactly the same substance as before. Indeed, he felt very much afraid that he had only dreamed about the lustrous stranger, or else that the latter had been making game of him. And what a miserable affair would it be, if, after all his hopes, Midas must content himself with what little gold he could scrape together by ordinary means, instead of creating it by a touch!

All this while it was only the gray of the morning, with but a streak of brightness along the edge of the sky, where Midas could not see it. He lay in a very disconsolate mood, regretting the downfall of his hopes, and kept growing sadder and sadder, until the earliest sunbeam shone through the window, and gilded the ceiling over his head. It seemed to Midas that this bright yellow sunbeam was reflected in rather a singular way on the white covering of the bed. Looking more closely, what was his astonishment and delight, when he found that this linen fabric had been transmuted to what seemed a woven texture of the purest and brightest gold! The Golden Touch had come to him with the first sunbeam!

Midas started up, in a kind of joyful frenzy, and ran about the room, grasping at everything that happened to be in his way. He seized one of the bed-posts, and it became immediately a fluted golden pillar. He pulled aside a window-curtain, in order to admit a clear spectacle of the wonders which he was performing; and the tassel grew heavy in his hand, — a mass of gold. He took up a book from the table. At his first touch, it assumed the appearance of such a splendidly bound and gilt-edged volume as one often meets with, nowadays; but, on running his fingers through the leaves, behold! it was a bundle of thin golden plates, in which all the wisdom of the book had grown illegible. He hurriedly put on his clothes, and was enraptured to see himself in a magnificent suit of gold cloth, which retained its flexibility and softness, although it burdened him a little with its weight. He drew out his handkerchief, which little Marygold had hemmed for him. That was likewise gold, with the dear child's neat and pretty stitches running all along the border, in gold thread!

Somehow or other, this last transformation did not quite please King Midas. He would rather that his little daughter's handiwork should have remained just the same as when she climbed his knee and put it into his hand.

But it was not worth while to vex himself about a

trifle. Midas now took his spectacles from his pocket, and put them on his nose, in order that he might see more distinctly what he was about. In those days, spectacles for common people had not been invented, but were already worn by kings; else, how could Midas have had any? To his great perplexity, however, excellent as the glasses were, he discovered that he could not possibly see through them. But this was the most natural thing in the world; for on taking them off, the transparent crystals turned out to be plates of yellow metal, and, of course, were worthless as spectacles, though valuable as gold. It struck Midas as rather inconvenient that, with all his wealth, he could never again be rich enough to own a pair of serviceable spectacles.

"It is no great matter, nevertheless," said he to himself, very philosophically. "We cannot expect any great good, without its being accompanied with some small inconvenience. The Golden Touch is worth the sacrifice of a pair of spectacles, at least, if not of one's very eyesight. My own eyes will serve for ordinary purposes, and little Marygold will soon be old enough to read to me."

Wise King Midas was so exalted by his good fortune that the palace seemed not sufficiently spacious to contain him. He therefore went downstairs, and smiled, on observing that the balustrade of the staircase became a bar of burnished gold, as his hand passed over it in his descent. He lifted the door-latch (it was brass only a moment ago, but golden when his fingers quitted it), and emerged into the garden. Here, as it happened, he found a great number of beautiful roses in full bloom, and others in all the stages of lovely bud and blossom. Very delicious was their fragrance in the morning breeze. Their delicate blush was one of the fairest sights in the world; so gentle, so modest, and so full of sweet tranquillity did these roses seem to be.

But Midas knew a way to make them far more precious, according to his way of thinking, than roses had ever been before. So he took great pains in going from bush to bush, and exercised his magic touch most indefatigably; until every individual flower and bud, and even the worms at the heart of some of them, were changed to gold. By the time this good work was completed, King Midas was summoned to breakfast; and as the morning air had given him an excellent appetite, he made haste back to the palace.

What was usually a king's breakfast in the days of Midas, I really do not know, and cannot stop now to investigate. To the best of my belief, however, on this particular morning, the breakfast consisted of hot cakes, some nice little brook trout, roasted potatoes, fresh boiled eggs, and coffee, for King Midas himself, and a bowl of bread and milk for his daughter Marygold. At all events, this is a breakfast fit to set before a king; and, whether he had it or not, King Midas could not have had a better.

Little Marygold had not yet made her appearance. Her father ordered her to be called, and, seating himself at table, awaited the child's coming, in order to begin his own breakfast. To do Midas justice, he really loved his daughter, and loved her so much the more this morning, on account of the good fortune which had befallen him. It was not a great while before he heard her coming along the passage-way crying bitterly. This circumstance surprised him, because Marygold was one of the cheerfullest little people whom you would see in a summer's day, and hardly shed a thimbleful of tears in a twelvemonth. When Midas heard her sobs, he determined to put little Marygold into better spirits, by an agreeable surprise; so, leaning across the table, he touched his daughter's bowl (which was a China one, with pretty figures all around it), and transmuted it to gleaming gold.

Meanwhile, Marygold slowly and disconsolately opened the door, and showed herself with her apron at her eyes, still sobbing as if her heart would break.

"How now, my little lady!" cried Midas. "Pray what is the matter with you, this bright morning?"

Marygold, without taking the apron from her eyes, held out her hand, in which was one of the roses which Midas had so recently transmuted.

"Beautiful!" exclaimed her father. "And what is there in this magnificent golden rose to make you cry?"

"Ah, dear father!" answered the child, as well as her sobs would let her; "it is not beautiful, but the ugliest flower that ever grew! As soon as I was dressed I ran into the garden to gather some roses for you; because I know you like them, and like them the better when gathered by your little daughter. But, oh dear, dear me! What do you think has happened? Such a misfortune! All the beautiful roses, that smelled so sweet and had so many lovely blushes, are blighted and spoilt! They are grown quite yellow, as you see this one, and have no longer any fragrance! What can have been the matter with them?"

"Poh, my dear little girl, — pray don't cry about it!" said Midas, who was ashamed to confess that he himself had wrought the change which so greatly afflicted her. "Sit down and eat your bread and milk! You will find it easy enough to exchange a golden rose like that (which will last hundreds of years) for an ordinary one which would wither in a day."

"I don't care for such roses as this!" cried Marygold, tossing it contemptuously away. "It has no smell, and the hard petals prick my nose!"

The child now sat down to table, but was so occupied with her grief for the blighted roses that she did not even notice the wonderful transmutation of her China bowl. Perhaps this was all the better; for Marygold was accustomed to take pleasure in looking at the queer figures, and strange trees and houses, that were painted on the circumference of the bowl; and these ornaments were now entirely lost in the yellow hue of the metal.

Midas, meanwhile, had poured out a cup of coffee, and, as a matter of course, the coffee-pot, whatever metal it may have been when he took it up, was gold when he set it down. He thought to himself, that it was rather an extravagant style of splendor, in a king of his simple habits, to breakfast off a service of gold, and began to be puzzled with the difficulty of keeping his treasures safe. The cupboard and the kitchen would no longer be a secure place of deposit for articles so valuable as golden bowls and coffee-pots.

Amid these thoughts, he lifted a spoonful of coffee to his lips, and, sipping it, was astonished to perceive that the instant his lips touched the liquid, it became molten gold, and the next moment, hardened into a lump!

"Ha!" exclaimed Midas, rather aghast.

"What is the matter, father?" asked little Marygold, gazing at him, with the tears still standing in her eyes.

"Nothing, child, nothing!" said Midas. "Eat your milk, before it gets quite cold."

He took one of the nice little trouts on his plate, and, by way of experiment, touched its tail with his finger. To his horror, it was immediately transmuted from an admirably fried brook trout into a gold-fish, though not one of those gold-fishes which people often keep in glass globes, as ornaments for the parlor. No; but it was really a metallic fish, and looked as if it had been very cunningly made by the nicest goldsmith in the world. Its little bones were now golden wires; its fins and tail were thin plates of gold; and there were the marks of the fork in it, and all the delicate, frothy appearance of a nicely fried fish, exactly imitated in metal. A very pretty piece of work, as you may suppose; only King Midas, just at that moment, would much rather have had a real trout in his dish than this elaborate and valuable imitation of one.

"I don't quite see," thought he to himself, "how I am to get any breakfast!"

He took one of the smoking-hot cakes, and had

scarcely broken it, when, to his cruel mortification, though, a moment before, it had been of the whitest wheat, it assumed the yellow hue of Indian meal. To say the truth, if it had really been a hot Indian cake, Midas would have prized it a good deal more than he now did, when its solidity and increased weight made him too bitterly sensible that it was gold. Almost in despair, he helped himself to a boiled egg, which immediately underwent a change similar to those of the trout and the cake. The egg, indeed, might have been mistaken for one of those which the famous goose, in the story-book, was in the habit of laying; but King Midas was the only goose that had had anything to do with the matter.

"Well, this is a quandary!" thought he, leaning back in his chair, and looking quite enviously at little Marygold, who was now eating her bread and milk with great satisfaction. "Such a costly breakfast before me, and nothing that can be eaten!"

Hoping that, by dint of great dispatch, he might avoid what he now felt to be a considerable inconvenience, King Midas next snatched a hot potato, and attempted to cram it into his mouth, and swallow it in a hurry. But the Golden Touch was too nimble for him. He found his mouth full, not of mealy potato, but of solid metal, which so burnt his tongue that he roared aloud, and, jumping up from the table, began to dance and stamp about the room, both with pain and affright.

"Father, dear father!" cried little Marygold, who was a very affectionate child, " pray what is the matter? Have you burnt your mouth?"

"Ah, dear child," groaned Midas dolefully, "I don't know what is to become of your poor father!"

And, truly, my dear little folks, did you ever hear of such a pitiable case in all your lives? Here was literally the richest breakfast that could be set before a king, and its very richness made it absolutely good for nothing. The poorest laborer, sitting down to his crust of bread and cup of water, was far better off than King Midas, whose delicate food was really worth its weight in gold. And what was to be done? Already, at breakfast, Midas was excessively hungry. Would he be less so by dinner-time? And how ravenous would be his appetite for supper, which must undoubtedly consist of the same sort of indigestible dishes as those now before him! How many days, think you, would he survive a continuance of this rich fare?

These reflections so troubled wise King Midas, that he began to doubt whether, after all, riches are the one desirable thing in the world, or even the most desirable. But this was only a passing thought. So fascinated was Midas with the glitter of the yellow metal, that he would still have refused to give up the Golden Touch for so paltry a consideration as a breakfast. Just imagine what a price for one meal's victuals! It would have been the same as paying millions and millions of money (and as many millions more as would take forever to reckon up) for some fried trout, an egg, a potato, a hot cake, and a cup of coffee!

"It would be quite too dear," thought Midas.

Nevertheless, so great was his hunger, and the perplexity of his situation, that he again groaned aloud, and very grievously too. Our pretty Marygold could endure it no longer. She sat, a moment, gazing at her father, and trying with all the might of her little wits to find out what was the matter with him. Then, with a sweet and sorrowful impulse to comfort him, she started from her chair, and, running to Midas, threw her arms affectionately about his knees. He bent down and kissed her. He felt that his little daughter's love was worth a thousand times more than he had gained by the Golden Touch.

"My precious, precious Marygold!" cried he.

But Marygold made no answer.

Alas, what had he done? How fatal was the gift which the stranger bestowed! The moment the lips of Midas touched Marygold's forehead, a change had taken place. Her sweet, rosy face, so full of affection as it had been, assumed a glittering yellow color, with yellow teardrops congealing on her cheeks. Her beautiful brown ringlets took the same tint. Her soft and tender little form grew hard and inflexible within her father's encircling arms. Oh, terrible misfortune! The victim of his insatiable desire for wealth, little Marygold was a human child no longer, but a golden statue!

Yes, there she was, with the questioning look of love, grief, and pity, hardened into her face. It was the prettiest and most woeful sight that ever mortal saw. All the features and tokens of Marygold were there; even the beloved little dimple remained in her golden chin. But the more perfect was the resemblance, the greater was the father's agony at beholding this golden image, which was all that was left him of a daughter. It had been a favorite phrase of Midas, whenever he felt particularly fond of the child, to say that she was worth her weight in gold. And now the phrase had become literally true. And now, at last, when it was too late, he felt how infinitely a warm and tender heart, that loved him, exceeded in value all the wealth that could be piled up betwixt the earth and sky!

It would be too sad a story, if I were to tell you how Midas, in the fullness of all his gratified desires, began to wring his hands and bemoan himself; and how he could neither bear to look at Marygold, nor yet to look away from her. Except when his eyes were fixed on the image, he could not possibly believe that she was changed to gold. But stealing another glance, there was the precious little figure, with a yellow tear-drop on its yellow cheek, and a look so piteous and tender that it seemed as if that very expression must needs soften the gold, and make it flesh again. This, however, could not be. So Midas had only to wring his hands, and to wish that he were the poorest man in the wide world, if the loss of all his wealth might bring back the faintest rose-color to his dear child's face.

While he was in this tumult of despair, he suddenly beheld a stranger standing near the door. Midas bent down his head, without speaking; for he recognized the same figure which had appeared to him, the day before, in the treasure-room, and had bestowed on him this disastrous faculty of the Golden Touch. The stranger's countenance still wore a smile, which seemed to shed a yellow lustre all about the room, and gleamed on little Marygold's image, and on the other objects that had been transmuted by the touch of Midas.

"Well, friend Midas," said the stranger, "pray how do you succeed with the Golden Touch?"

Midas shook his head.

"I am very miserable," said he.

"Very miserable, indeed!" exclaimed the stranger. "And how happens that? Have I not faithfully kept my promise with you? Have you not everything that your heart desired?"

"Gold is not everything," answered Midas. "And I have lost all that my heart really cared for."

"Ah! So you have made a discovery, since yesterday?" observed the stranger. "Let us see, then. Which of these two things do you think is really worth the most, — the gift of the Golden Touch, or one cup of clear cold water?"

"O blessed water!" exclaimed Midas. "It will never moisten my parched throat again!"

"The Golden Touch," continued the stranger, "or a crust of bread?"

"A piece of bread," answered Midas, "is worth all the gold on earth!"

"The Golden Touch," asked the stranger, "or your own little Marygold, warm, soft, and loving as she was an hour ago?"

"Oh, my child, my dear child!" cried poor Midas, wringing his hands. "I would not have given that one small dimple in her chin for the power of changing this whole big earth into a solid lump of gold!"

"You are wiser than you were, King Midas!" said the stranger, looking seriously at him. "Your own heart, I perceive, has not been entirely changed from flesh to gold. Were it so, your case would indeed be desperate. But you appear to be still capable of understanding that the commonest things, such as lie within everybody's grasp, are more valuable than the riches which so many mortals sigh and struggle after. Tell me, now, do you sincerely desire to rid yourself of this Golden Touch?"

"It is hateful to me!" replied Midas.

A fly settled on his nose, but immediately fell to the floor; for it, too, had become gold. Midas shuddered.

"Go, then," said the stranger, "and plunge into the river that glides past the bottom of your garden. Take likewise a vase of the same water, and sprinkle it over any object that you may desire to change back again from gold into its former substance. If you do this in earnestness and sincerity, it may possibly repair the mischief which your avarice has occasioned."

King Midas bowed low; and when he lifted his head, the lustrous stranger had vanished.

You will easily believe that Midas lost no time in snatching up a great earthen pitcher (but, alas me! it was no longer earthen after he touched it), and hastening to the riverside. As he scampered along, and forced his way through the shrubbery, it was positively marvelous to see how the foliage turned yellow behind him, as if the autumn had been there, and nowhere else. On reaching the river's brink, he plunged headlong in, without waiting so much as to pull off his shoes.

THE GOLDEN TOUCH

"Poof! poof! poof!" snorted King Midas, as his head emerged out of the water. "Well; this is really a refreshing bath, and I think it must have quite washed away the Golden Touch. And now for filling my pitcher!"

As he dipped the pitcher into the water, it gladdened his very heart to see it change from gold into the same good, honest earthen vessel which it had been before he touched it. He was conscious, also, of a change within himself. A cold, hard, and heavy weight seemed to have gone out of his bosom. No doubt his heart had been gradually losing its human substance, and transmuting itself into insensible metal, but had now softened back again into flesh. Perceiving a violet, that grew on the bank of the river, Midas touched it with his finger, and was overjoyed to find that the delicate flower retained its purple hue, instead of undergoing a yellow blight. The curse of the Golden Touch had therefore really been removed from him.

King Midas hastened back to the palace; and I suppose the servants knew not what to make of it when they saw their royal master so carefully bringing home an earthen pitcher of water. But that water, which was to undo all the mischief that his folly had wrought, was more precious to Midas than an ocean of molten gold could have been. The first thing he did, as you need hardly be told, was to sprinkle it by handfuls over the golden figure of little Marygold.

No sooner did it fall on her than you would have laughed to see how the rosy color came back to the

111

dear child's cheek! and how she began to sneeze and sputter! — and how astonished she was to find herself dripping wet, and her father still throwing more water over her!

"Pray do not, dear father!" cried she. "See how you have wet my nice frock, which I put on only this morning!"

For Marygold did not know that she had been a little golden statue; nor could she remember anything that had happened since the moment when she ran with outstretched arms to comfort poor King Midas.

Her father did not think it necessary to tell his beloved child how very foolish he had been, but contented himself with showing how much wiser he had now grown. For this purpose he led little Marygold into the garden, where he sprinkled all the remainder of the water over the rose-bushes, and with such good effect that above five thousand roses recovered their beautiful bloom. There were two circumstances, however, which, as long as he lived, used to put King Midas in mind of the Golden Touch. One was, that the sands of the river sparkled like gold; the other, that little Marygold's hair had now a golden tinge, which he had never observed in it before she had been transmuted by the effect of his kiss. This change of hue was really an improvement, and made Marygold's hair richer than in her babyhood.

When King Midas had grown quite an old man, and used to trot Marygold's children on his knee, he was fond of telling them this marvelous story, pretty much as I have now told it to you. And then would he stroke their glossy ringlets, and tell them that their hair, likewise, had a rich shade of gold, which they had inherited from their mother.

"And to tell you the truth, my precious little folks," quoth King Midas, diligently trotting the children all the while, "ever since that morning, I have hated the very sight of all other gold, save this!"

THE POMEGRANATE SEEDS

By Nathaniel Hawthorne

MOTHER CERES was exceedingly fond of her daughter Proserpina, and seldom let her go alone into the fields. But, just at the time when my story begins, the good lady was very busy, because she had the care of the wheat, and the Indian corn, and the rye and barley, and, in short, of the crops of every kind, all over the earth; and as the season had thus far been uncommonly backward, it was necessary to make the harvest ripen more speedily than usual. So she put on her turban, made of poppies (a kind of flower which she was always noted for wearing), and got into her car drawn by a pair of winged dragons, and was just ready to set off.

"Dear mother," said Proserpina, "I shall be very lonely while you are away. May I not run down to the shore, and ask some of the sea-nymphs to come up out of the waves and play with me?"

"Yes, child," answered Mother Ceres. "The sea-nymphs are good creatures, and will never lead you into any harm. But you must take care not to stray away from them, nor go wandering about the fields by yourself. Young girls, without their mothers to take care of them, are very apt to get into mischief."

The child promised to be as prudent as if she were

114

a grown-up woman, and, by the time the winged drag-ons had whirled the car out of sight, she was already on the shore, calling to the sea-nymphs to come and play with her. They knew Proserpina's voice, and were not long in showing their glistening faces and sea-green hair above the water, at the bottom of which was their home. They brought along with them a great many beautiful shells; and, sitting down on the moist sand, where the surf wave broke over them, they busied themselves in making a necklace, which they hung round Proserpina's neck. By way of showing her gratitude, the child besought them to go with her a little way into the fields, so that they might gather abundance of flowers, with which she would make each of her kind playmates a wreath.

"Oh, no, dear Proserpina," cried the sea-nymphs; "we dare not go with you upon the dry land. We are apt to grow faint, unless at every breath we can snuff up the salt breeze of the ocean. And don't you see how careful we are to let the surf wave break over us every moment or two, so as to keep ourselves comfortably moist? If it were not for that, we should soon look like bunches of uprooted sea-weed dried in the sun."

"It is a great pity," said Proserpina, "but do you wait for me here, and I will run and gather my apron full of flowers, and be back again before the surf wave has broken ten times over you. I long to make you some wreaths that shall be as lovely as this necklace of many-colored shells."

"We will wait, then," answered the sea-nymphs.

"But while you are gone, we may as well lie down on a bank of soft sponge, under the water. The air to-day is a little too dry for our comfort. But we will pop up our heads every few minutes to see if you are coming."

The young Proserpina ran quickly to a spot where, only the day before, she had seen a great many flowers. These, however, were now a little past their bloom; and wishing to give her friends the freshest and loveliest blossoms, she strayed farther into the fields, and found some that made her scream with delight. Never had she met with such exquisite flowers before, — violets, so large and fragrant, — roses, with so rich and delicate a blush, — such superb hyacinths and such aromatic pinks, — and many others, some of which seemed to be of new shapes and colors. Two or three times, moreover, she could not help thinking that a tuft of most splendid flowers had suddenly sprouted out of the earth before her very eyes, as if on purpose to tempt her a few steps farther. Proserpina's apron was soon filled and brimming over with delightful blossoms. She was on the point of turning back in order to rejoin the sea-nymphs, and sit with them on the moist sands, all twining wreaths together. But, a little farther on, what should she behold? It was a large shrub, completely covered with the most magnificent flowers in the world.

"The darlings!" cried Proserpina; and then she thought to herself, "I was looking at that spot only a moment ago. How strange it is that I did not see the flowers!"

The nearer she approached the shrub, the more attractive it looked, until she came quite close to it; and then, although its beauty was richer than words can tell, she hardly knew whether to like it or not. It bore above a hundred flowers of the most brilliant hues, and each different from the others, but all having a kind of resemblance among themselves, which showed them to be sister blossoms. But there was a deep, glossy lustre on the leaves of the shrub, and on the petals of the flowers, that made Proserpina doubt whether they might not be poisonous. To tell you the truth, foolish as it may seem, she was half inclined to turn round and run away.

"What a silly child I am!" thought she, taking courage. "It is really the most beautiful shrub that ever sprang out of the earth. I will pull it up by the roots, and carry it home, and plant it in my mother's garden."

Holding up her apron full of flowers with her left hand, Proserpina seized the large shrub with the other, and pulled and pulled, but was hardly able to loosen the soil about its roots. What a deep-rooted plant it was! Again the girl pulled with all her might, and observed that the earth began to stir and crack to some distance around the stem. She gave another pull, but relaxed her hold, fancying that there was a rumbling sound right beneath her feet. Did the roots extend down into some enchanted cavern? Then, laughing at herself for so childish a notion, she made another effort; up came the shrub, and Proserpina staggered back, holding the stem triumphantly in her hand, and gazing at the deep hole which its roots had left in the soil.

Much to her astonishment this hole kept spreading wider and wider, and growing deeper and deeper, until it really seemed to have no bottom; and all the while, there came a rumbling noise out of its depths, louder and louder, and nearer and nearer, and sounding like the tramp of horses' hoofs and the rattling of wheels. Too much frightened to run away, she stood straining her eyes into this wonderful cavity, and soon saw a team of four sable horses, snorting smoke out of their nostrils, and tearing their way out of the earth with a splendid golden chariot whirling at their heels. They leaped out of the bottomless hole, chariot and all; and there they were, tossing their black manes, flourishing their black tails, and curvetting with every one of their hoofs off the ground at once, close by the spot where Proserpina stood. In the chariot sat the figure of a man, richly dressed, with a crown on his head, all flaming with diamonds. He was of a noble aspect, and rather handsome, but looked sullen and discontented; and he kept rubbing his eyes and shading them with his hand, as if he did not live enough in the sunshine to be very fond of its light.

As soon as this personage saw the affrighted Proserpina, he beckoned her to come a little nearer.

"Do not be afraid," said he, with as cheerful a smile as he knew how to put on. "Come! Will not you like to ride a little way with me, in my beautiful chariot?"

But Proserpina was so alarmed that she wished for

118

THEY LEAPED OUT OF THE BOTTOMLESS HOLE, CHARIOT AND
ALL; AND THERE THEY WERE TOSSING THEIR BLACK TAILS,
AND CURVETTING WITH EVERY ONE OF THEIR HOOFS OFF
THE GROUND AT ONCE, CLOSE BY THE SPOT WHERE PRO-
SERPINA STOOD. IN THE CHARIOT SAT THE FIGURE OF A MAN

nothing but to get out of his reach. And no wonder. The stranger did not look remarkably good-natured, in spite of his smile; and as for his voice, its tones were deep and stern, and sounded as much like the rumbling of an earthquake under ground as anything else. As is always the case with children in trouble, Proserpina's first thought was to call for her mother.

"Mother, Mother Ceres!" cried she, all in a tremble. "Come quickly and save me."

But her voice was too faint for her mother to hear. Indeed, it is most probable that Ceres was then a thousand miles off, making the corn grow in some far-distant country. Nor could it have availed her poor daughter, even had she been within hearing; for no sooner did Proserpina begin to cry out, than the stranger leaped to the ground, caught the child in his arms, and again mounting the chariot, shook the reins, and shouted to the four black horses to set off. They immediately broke into so swift a gallop that it seemed rather like flying through the air than running along the earth. In a moment, Proserpina lost sight of the pleasant vale of Enna, in which she had always dwelt. Another instant, and even the summit of Mount Ætna had become so blue in the distance that she could scarcely distinguish it from the smoke that gushed out of its crater. But still the poor child screamed, and scattered her apron full of flowers along the way, and left a long cry trailing behind the chariot; and many mothers, to whose ears it came, ran quickly to see if any mischief had befallen their children. But Mother Ceres was a great way off, and could not hear the cry.

As they rode on, the stranger did his best to soothe her.

"Why should you be so frightened, my pretty child?" said he, trying to soften his rough voice. "I promise not to do you any harm. What! You have been gathering flowers? Wait till we come to my palace, and I will give you a garden full of prettier flowers than those, all made of pearls, and diamonds, and rubies. Can you guess who I am? They call my name Pluto, and I am the king of diamonds and all other precious stones. Every atom of the gold and silver that lies under the earth belongs to me, to say nothing of the copper and iron, and of the coal-mines, which supply me with abundance of fuel. Do you see this splendid crown upon my head? You may have it for a plaything. Oh, we shall be very good friends, and you will find me more agreeable than you expect, when once we get out of this troublesome sunshine."

"Let me go home!" cried Proserpina. "Let me go home!"

"My home is better than your mother's," answered King Pluto "It is a palace, all made of gold, with crystal windows; and because there is little or no sunshine thereabouts, the apartments are illuminated with diamond lamps. You never saw anything half so magnificent as my throne. If you like, you may sit down on it, and be my little queen, and I will sit on the footstool."

"I don't care for golden palaces and thrones," sobbed Proserpina. "Oh, my mother, my mother! Carry me back to my mother!"

120

But King Pluto, as he called himself, only shouted to his steeds to go faster.

"Pray do not be foolish, Proserpina," said he, in rather a sullen tone. "I offer you my palace and my crown, and all the riches that are under the earth; and you treat me as if I were doing you an injury. The one thing which my palace needs is a merry little maid, to run upstairs and down, and cheer up the rooms with her smile. And this is what you must do for King Pluto."

"Never!" answered Proserpina, looking as miserable as she could. "I shall never smile again till you set me down at my mother's door."

But she might just as well have talked to the wind that whistled past them; for Pluto urged on his horses, and went faster than ever. Proserpina continued to cry out, and screamed so long and so loudly, that her poor little voice was almost screamed away; and when it was nothing but a whisper, she happened to cast her eyes over a great, broad field of waving grain — and whom do you think she saw? Who, but Mother Ceres, making the corn grow, and too busy to notice the golden chariot as it went rattling along. The child mustered all her strength, and gave one more scream, but was out of sight before Ceres had time to turn her head.

King Pluto had taken a road which now began to grow excessively gloomy. It was bordered on each side with rocks and precipices, between which the rumbling of the chariot-wheels was reverberated with a noise like rolling thunder. The trees and bushes that grew in the crevices of the rocks had very dismal foliage; and by and by, although it was hardly noon, the air became obscured with a gray twilight. The black horses had rushed along so swiftly, that they were already beyond the limits of the sunshine. But the duskier it grew, the more did Pluto's visage assume an air of satisfaction. After all, he was not an ill-looking person, especially when he left off twisting his features into a smile that did not belong to them. Proserpina peeped at his face through the gathering dusk, and hoped that he might not be so very wicked as she at first thought him.

"Ah, this twilight is truly refreshing," said King Pluto, "after being so tormented with that ugly and impertinent glare of the sun. How much more agreeable is lamplight or torchlight, more particularly when reflected from diamonds! It will be a magnificent sight when we get to my palace."

"Is it much farther?" asked Proserpina. "And will you carry me back when I have seen it?"

"We will talk of that by and by," answered Pluto. "We are just entering my dominions. Do you see that tall gateway before us? When we pass those gates, we are at home. And there lies my faithful mastiff at the threshold. Cerberus! Cerberus! Come hither, my good dog!"

So saying, Pluto pulled at the reins, and stopped the chariot right between the tall, massive pillars of the gateway. The mastiff of which he had spoken got up from the threshold, and stood on his hinder legs, so as to put his forepaws on the chariot-wheel. But, my stars, what a strange dog it was! Why, he was a big, rough, ugly-looking monster, with three separate heads, and each of them fiercer than the two others; but, fierce as they were, King Pluto patted them all. He seemed as fond of his three-headed dog as if it had been a sweet little spaniel, with silken ears and curly hair. Cerberus, on the other hand, was evidently rejoiced to see his master, and expressed his attachment, as other dogs do, by wagging his tail at a great rate. Proserpina's eyes being drawn to it by its brisk motion, she saw that this tail was neither more nor less than a live dragon, with fiery eyes, and fangs that had a very poisonous aspect. And while the three-headed Cerberus was fawning so lovingly on King Pluto, there was the dragon tail wagging against its will, and looking as cross and ill-natured as you can imagine, on its own separate account.

"Will the dog bite me?" asked Proserpina, shrinking closer to Pluto. "What an ugly creature he is!"

"Oh, never fear," answered her companion. "He never harms people unless they try to enter my dominions without being sent for, or to get away when I wish to keep them here. Down, Cerberus! Now, my pretty Proserpina, we will drive on."

On went the chariot, and King Pluto seemed greatly pleased to find himself once more in his own kingdom. He drew Proserpina's attention to the rich veins of gold that were to be seen among the rocks, and pointed to several places where one stroke of a pick-axe would loosen a bushel of diamonds. All along the road, indeed, there were sparkling gems, which would have been of inestimable value above ground, but which were here reckoned of the meaner sort, and hardly worth a beggar's stooping for.

Not far from the gateway, they came to a bridge, which seemed to be built of iron. Pluto stopped the chariot, and bade Proserpina look at the stream which was gliding so lazily beneath it. Never in her life had she beheld so torpid, so black, so muddy-looking a stream: its waters reflected no images of anything that was on the banks, and it moved as sluggishly as if it had quite forgotten which way it ought to flow, and had rather stagnate than flow either one way or the other.

"This is the river Lethe," observed King Pluto. "Is it not a very pleasant stream?"

"I think it a very dismal one," said Proserpina.

"It suits my taste, however," answered Pluto, who was apt to be sullen when anybody disagreed with him. "At all events, its water has one very excellent quality; for a single draught of it makes people forget every care and sorrow that has hitherto tormented them. Only sip a little of it, my dear Proserpina, and you will instantly cease to grieve for your mother, and will have nothing in your memory that can prevent your being perfectly happy in my palace. I will send for some, in a golden goblet, the moment we arrive."

"Oh, no, no, no!" cried Proserpina, weeping afresh. "I had a thousand times rather be miserable with remembering my mother than be happy in forgetting her. That dear, dear mother! I never, never will forget her."

"We shall see," said King Pluto. "You do not

124

know what fine times we will have in my palace. Here we are just at the portal. These pillars are solid gold, I assure you."

He alighted from the chariot, and taking Proserpina in his arms, carried her up a lofty flight of steps into the great hall of the palace. It was splendidly illuminated by means of large precious stones, of various hues, which seemed to burn like so many lamps, and glowed with a hundred-fold radiance all through the vast apartment. And yet there was a kind of gloom in the midst of this enchanted light; nor was there a single object in the hall that was really agreeable to behold, except the little Proserpina herself, a lovely child, with one earthly flower which she had not let fall from her hand. It is my opinion that even King Pluto had never been happy in his palace, and that this was the true reason why he had stolen away Proserpina, in order that he might have something to love, instead of cheating his heart any longer with this tiresome magnificence. And, though he pretended to dislike the sunshine of the upper world, yet the effect of the child's presence, bedimmed as she was by her tears, was as if a faint and watery sunbeam had somehow or other found its way into the enchanted hall.

Pluto now summoned his domestics, and bade them lose no time in preparing a most sumptuous banquet, and above all things, not to fail of setting a golden beaker of the water of Lethe by Proserpina's plate.

"I will neither drink that nor anything else," said Proserpina. "Nor will I taste a morsel of food, even if you keep me forever in your palace."

"I should be sorry for that," replied King Pluto, patting her cheek; for he really wished to be kind, if he had only known how. "You are a spoiled child, I perceive, my little Proserpina; but when you see the nice things which my cook will make for you, your appetite will quickly come again."

Then, sending for the head cook, he gave strict orders that all sorts of delicacies, such as young people are usually fond of, should be set before Proserpina. He had a secret motive in this; for, you are to understand, it is a fixed law that, when persons are carried off to the land of magic, if they once taste any food there, they can never get back to their friends. Now, if King Pluto had been cunning enough to offer Proserpina some fruit, or bread and milk (which was the simple fare to which the child had always been accustomed), it is very probable that she would soon have been tempted to eat it. But he left the matter entirely to his cook, who, like all other cooks, considered nothing fit to eat unless it were rich pastry, or highly seasoned meat, or spiced sweet cakes, — things which Proserpina's mother had never given her, and the smell of which quite took away her appetite, instead of sharpening it.

But my story must now clamber out of King Pluto's dominions, and see what Mother Ceres has been about, since she was bereft of her daughter. We had a glimpse of her, as you remember, half hidden among the waving grain, while the four black steeds were swiftly whirling along the chariot in which her beloved Proserpina was so unwillingly borne away. You recollect, too, the loud scream which Proserpina gave, just when the chariot was out of sight.

Of all the child's outcries, this last shriek was the only one that reached the ears of Mother Ceres. She had mistaken the rumbling of the chariot-wheels for a peal of thunder, and imagined that a shower was coming up, and that it would assist her in making the corn grow. But, at the sound of Proserpina's shriek, she started, and looked about in every direction, not knowing whence it came, but feeling almost certain that it was her daughter's voice. It seemed so unaccountable, however, that the girl should have strayed over so many lands and seas (which she herself could not have traversed without the aid of her winged dragons), that the good Ceres tried to believe that it must be the child of some other parent, and not her own darling Proserpina, who had uttered this lamentable cry. Nevertheless, it troubled her with a vast many tender fears, such as are ready to bestir themselves in every mother's heart, when she finds it necessary to go away from her dear children without leaving them under the care of some maiden aunt, or other such faithful guardian. So she quickly left the field in which she had been so busy; and, as her work was not half done, the grain looked, next day, as if it needed both sun and rain, and as if it were blighted in the ear, and had something the matter with its roots.

The pair of dragons must have had very nimble wings; for, in less than an hour, Mother Ceres had alighted at the door of her home, and found it empty. Knowing, however, that the child was fond of sporting on the seashore, she hastened thither as fast as she could, and there beheld the wet faces of the poor sea-nymphs peeping over a wave. All this while, the good creatures had been waiting on the bank of sponge, and once every half-minute or so, had popped up their four heads above water, to see if their playmate were yet coming back. When they saw Mother Ceres, they sat down on the crest of the surf wave, and let it toss them ashore at her feet.

"Where is Proserpina?" cried Ceres. "Where is my child? Tell me, you naughty sea-nymphs, have you enticed her under the sea?"

"Oh, no, good Mother Ceres," said the innocent sea-nymphs, tossing back their green ringlets, and looking her in the face. "We never should dream of such a thing. Proserpina has been at play with us, it is true; but she left us a long while ago, meaning only to run a little way upon the dry land, and gather some flowers for a wreath. This was early in the day, and we have seen nothing of her since."

Ceres scarcely waited to hear what the nymphs had to say, before she hurried off to make inquiries all through the neighborhood. But nobody told her anything that could enable the poor mother to guess what had become of Proserpina. A fisherman, it is true, had noticed her little footprints in the sand, as he went homeward along the beach with a basket of fish; a rustic had seen the child stooping to gather flowers; several persons had heard either the rattling of chariot-wheels or the rumbling of distant thunder; and one old woman, while plucking vervain and catnip, had heard a scream, but supposed it to be some childish nonsense, and therefore did not take the trouble to look up. The stupid people! It took them such a tedious while to tell the nothing that they knew, that it was dark night before Mother Ceres found out that she must seek her daughter elsewhere. So she lighted a torch, and set forth, resolving never to come back until Proserpina was discovered.

In her haste and trouble of mind, she quite forgot her car and the winged dragons; or, it may be, she thought that she could follow up the search more thoroughly on foot. At all events, this was the way in which she began her sorrowful journey, holding her torch before her, and looking carefully at every object along the path. And as it happened, she had not gone far before she found one of the magnificent flowers which grew on the shrub that Proserpina had pulled up.

"Ha!" thought Mother Ceres, examining it by torchlight. "Here is mischief in this flower! The earth did not produce it by any help of mine, nor of its own accord. It is the work of enchantment, and is therefore poisonous; and perhaps it has poisoned my poor child."

But she put the poisonous flower in her bosom, not knowing whether she might ever find any other memorial of Proserpina.

All night long, at the door of every cottage and farmhouse, Ceres knocked, and called up the weary laborers to inquire if they had seen her child; and they stood, gaping and half asleep, at the threshold, and answered her pityingly, and besought her to come in and rest. At the portal of every palace, too, she made so loud a summons that the menials hurried to throw open the gate, thinking that it must be some great king or queen, who would demand a banquet for supper and a stately chamber to repose in. And when they saw only a sad and anxious woman, with a torch in her hand and a wreath of withered poppies on her head, they spoke rudely, and sometimes threatened to set the dogs upon her. But nobody had seen Proserpina, nor could give Mother Ceres the least hint which way to seek her. Thus passed the night; and still she continued her search without sitting down to rest, or stopping to take food, or even remembering to put down the torch; although first the rosy dawn, and then the glad light of the morning sun, made its red flame look thin and pale. But I wonder what sort of stuff this torch was made of; for it burned dimly through the day, and at night was as bright as ever, and never was extinguished by the rain or wind, in all the weary days and nights while Ceres was seeking for Proserpina.

It was not merely of human beings that she asked tidings of her daughter. In the woods and by the streams, she met creatures of another nature, who used, in those old times, to haunt the pleasant and solitary places, and were very sociable with persons who understood their language and customs, as Mother Ceres did. Sometimes, for instance, she tapped with her finger against the knotted trunk of a majestic oak; and immediately its rude bark would cleave asunder,

130

and forth would step a beautiful maiden, who was the hamadryad of the oak, dwelling inside of it, and sharing its long life, and rejoicing when its green leaves sported with the breeze. But not one of these leafy damsels had seen Proserpina. Then, going a little farther, Ceres would, perhaps, come to a fountain, gushing out of a pebbly hollow in the earth, and would dabble with her hand in the water. Behold, up through its sandy and pebbly bed, along with the fountain's gush, a young woman with dripping hair would arise, and stand gazing at Mother Ceres, half out of the water, and undulating up and down with its ever-restless motion. But when the mother asked whether her poor lost child had stopped to drink out of the fountain, the naiad, with weeping eyes (for these water-nymphs had tears to spare for everybody's grief), would answer, "No!" in a murmuring voice, which was just like the murmur of the stream.

Often, likewise, she encountered fauns, who looked like sunburnt country people, except that they had hairy ears, and little horns upon their foreheads, and the hinder legs of goats, on which they gamboled merrily about the woods and fields. They were a frolicsome kind of creature, but grew as sad as their cheerful dispositions would allow when Ceres inquired for her daughter, and they had no good news to tell. But sometimes she came suddenly upon a rude gang of satyrs, who had faces like monkeys and horses' tails behind them, and who were generally dancing in a very boisterous manner, with shouts of noisy laughter. When she stopped to question them, they would only laugh the louder, and make new merriment out of the lone woman's distress. How unkind of those ugly satyrs! And once, while crossing a solitary sheep pasture, she saw a personage named Pan, seated at the foot of a tall rock, and making music on a shepherd's flute. He, too, had horns, and hairy ears, and goat's feet; but, being acquainted with Mother Ceres, he answered her question as civilly as he knew how, and invited her to taste some milk and honey out of a wooden bowl. But neither could Pan tell her what had become of Proserpina, any better than the rest of these wild people.

And thus Mother Ceres went wandering about for nine long days and nights, finding no trace of Proserpina, unless it were now and then a withered flower; and these she picked up and put in her bosom, because she fancied that they might have fallen from her poor child's hand. All day she traveled onward through the hot sun; and at night, again, the flame of the torch would redden and gleam along the pathway, and she continued her search by its light, without ever sitting down to rest.

On the tenth day, she chanced to espy the mouth of a cavern, within which (though it was bright noon everywhere else) there would have been only a dusky twilight; but it so happened that a torch was burning there. It flickered and struggled with the duskiness, but could not half light up the gloomy cavern with all its melancholy glimmer. Ceres was resolved to leave no spot without a search; so she peeped into the entrance of the cave, and lighted it up a little more by holding her own torch before her. In so doing, she caught a glimpse of what seemed to be a woman, sitting on the brown leaves of the last autumn, a great heap of which had been swept into the cave by the wind. This woman (if woman it were) was by no means so beautiful as many of her sex; for her head, they tell me, was shaped very much like a dog's, and, by way of ornament, she wore a wreath of snakes around it. But Mother Ceres, the moment she saw her, knew that this was an odd kind of a person, who put all her enjoyment in being miserable, and never would have a word to say to other people, unless they were as melancholy and wretched as she herself delighted to be.

"I am wretched enough now," thought poor Ceres, "to talk with this melancholy Hecate, were she ten times sadder than ever she was yet."

So she stepped into the cave, and sat down on the withered leaves by the dog-headed woman's side. In all the world, since her daughter's loss, she had found no other companion.

"O Hecate," said she, "if ever you lose a daughter, you will know what sorrow is. Tell me, for pity's sake, have you seen my poor child Proserpina pass by the mouth of your cavern?"

"No," answered Hecate, in a cracked voice, and sighing betwixt every word or two, — "no, Mother Ceres, I have seen nothing of your daughter. But my ears, you must know, are made in such a way that all cries of distress and affright, all over the world, are pretty sure to find their way to them; and nine days ago, as I sat in my cave, making myself very miserable, I heard the voice of a young girl, shrieking as if in great distress. Something terrible has happened to the child, you may rest assured. As well as I could judge, a dragon, or some other cruel monster, was carrying her away."

"You kill me by saying so," cried Ceres, almost ready to faint. "Where was the sound, and which way did it seem to go?"

"It passed very swiftly along," said Hecate, "and, at the same time, there was a heavy rumbling of wheels towards the eastward. I can tell you nothing more, except that, in my honest opinion, you will never see your daughter again. The best advice I can give you is to take up your abode in this cavern, where we will be the two most wretched women in the world."

"Not yet, dark Hecate," replied Ceres. "But do you first come with your torch, and help me to seek for my lost child. And when there shall be no more hope of finding her (if that black day is ordained to come), then, if you will give me room to fling myself down, either on these withered leaves or on the naked rock, I will show you what it is to be miserable. But until I know that she has perished from the face of the earth, I will not allow myself space even to grieve."

The dismal Hecate did not much like the idea of going abroad into the sunny world. But then she reflected that the sorrow of the disconsolate Ceres would be like a gloomy twilight round about them both, let the sun shine ever so brightly, and that therefore she might enjoy her bad spirits quite as well as if she were to stay in the cave. So she finally consented to go, and they set out together, both carrying torches, although it was broad daylight and clear sunshine. The torchlight seemed to make a gloom; so that the people whom they met along the road could not very distinctly see their figures; and, indeed, if they once caught a glimpse of Hecate, with the wreath of snakes round her forehead, they generally thought it prudent to run away, without waiting for a second glance.

As the pair traveled along in this woebegone manner, a thought struck Ceres.

"There is one person," she exclaimed, "who must have seen my poor child, and can doubtless tell what has become of her. Why did not I think of him before? It is Phœbus."

"What," said Hecate, "the young man that always sits in the sunshine? Oh, pray do not think of going near him. He is a gay, light, frivolous young fellow, and will only smile in your face. And besides, there is such a glare of the sun about him, that he will quite blind my poor eyes, which I have almost wept away already."

"You have promised to be my companion," answered Ceres. "Come, let us make haste, or the sunshine will be gone, and Phœbus along with it."

Accordingly, they went along in quest of Phœbus, both of them, sighing grievously, and Hecate, to say the truth, making a great deal worse lamentation than Ceres; for all the pleasure she had, you know, lay in being miserable, and therefore she made the most of it. By and by, after a pretty long journey, they arrived at the sunniest spot in the whole world. There they beheld a beautiful young man, with long, curl-

ing ringlets, which seemed to be made of golden sunbeams; his garments were like light summer clouds;
and the expression of his face was so exceedingly vivid,
that Hecate held her hands before her eyes, muttering
that he ought to wear a black veil. Phœbus (for this
was the very person whom they were seeking) had a
lyre in his hands, and was making its chords tremble
with sweet music; at the same time singing a most
exquisite song, which he had recently composed. For
besides a great many other accomplishments, this
young man was renowned for his admirable poetry.

As Ceres and her dismal companion approached
him, Phœbus smiled on them so cheerfully that Hecate's wreath of snakes gave a spiteful hiss, and Hecate heartily wished herself back in her cave. But as
for Ceres, she was too earnest in her grief either to
know or care whether Phœbus smiled or frowned.

"Phœbus!" exclaimed she, "I am in great trouble,
and have come to you for assistance. Can you tell me
what has become of my dear child Proserpina?"

"Proserpina! Proserpina, did you call her name?"
answered Phœbus, endeavoring to recollect; for there
was such a continual flow of pleasant ideas in his mind
that he was apt to forget what had happened no longer
ago than yesterday. "Ah, yes, I remember her now.
A very lovely child, indeed. I am happy to tell you,
my dear madam, that I did see the little Proserpina
not many days ago. You may make yourself perfectly
easy about her. She is safe, and in excellent hands."

"Oh, where is my dear child?" cried Ceres, clasp-
ing her hands and flinging herself at his feet.

THE POMEGRANATE SEEDS

"Why," said Phœbus, — and as he spoke, he kept touching his lyre so as to make a thread of music run in and out among his words, — "as the little damsel was gathering flowers (and she has really a very exquisite taste for flowers) she was suddenly snatched up by King Pluto, and carried off to his dominions. I have never been in that part of the universe; but the royal palace, I am told, is built in a very noble style of architecture, and of the most splendid and costly materials. Gold, diamonds, pearls, and all manner of precious stones will be your daughter's ordinary playthings. I recommend to you, my dear lady, to give yourself no uneasiness. Proserpina's sense of beauty will be duly gratified, and, even in spite of the lack of sunshine, she will lead a very enviable life."

"Hush! Say not such a word!" answered Ceres indignantly. "What is there to gratify her heart? What are all the splendors you speak of, without affection? I must have her back again. Will you go with me, Phœbus, to demand my daughter of this wicked Pluto?"

"Pray excuse me," replied Phœbus, with an elegant obeisance. "I certainly wish you success, and regret that my own affairs are so immediately pressing that I cannot have the pleasure of attending you. Besides, I am not upon the best of terms with King Pluto. To tell you the truth, his three-headed mastiff would never let me pass the gateway; for I should be compelled to take a sheaf of sunbeams along with me, and those, you know, are forbidden things in Pluto's kingdom."

"Ah, Phœbus," said Ceres, with bitter meaning in

her words, "you have a harp instead of a heart. Farewell."

"Will not you stay a moment," asked Phœbus, "and hear me turn the pretty and touching story of Proserpina into extemporary verses?"

But Ceres shook her head, and hastened away, along with Hecate. Phœbus (who, as I have told you, was an exquisite poet) forthwith began to make an ode about the poor mother's grief; and, if we were to judge of his sensibility by this beautiful production, he must have been endowed with a very tender heart. But when a poet gets into the habit of using his heartstrings to make chords for his lyre, he may thrum upon them as much as he will, without any great pain to himself. Accordingly, though Phœbus sang a very sad song, he was as merry all the while as were the sunbeams amid which he dwelt.

Poor Mother Ceres had now found out what had become of her daughter, but was not a whit happier than before. Her case, on the contrary, looked more desperate than ever. As long as Proserpina was above ground there might have been hopes of regaining her. But now that the poor child was shut up within the iron gates of the king of the mines, at the threshold of which lay the three-headed Cerberus, there seemed no possibility of her ever making her escape. The dismal Hecate, who loved to take the darkest view of things, told Ceres that she had better come with her to the cavern, and spend the rest of her life in being miserable. Ceres answered that Hecate was welcome to go back thither herself, but that, for her part, she would wander about the earth in quest of the entrance to King Pluto's dominions. And Hecate took her at her word, and hurried back to her beloved cave, frightening a great many little children with a glimpse of her dog's face, as she went.

Poor Mother Ceres! It is melancholy to think of her, pursuing her toilsome way all alone, and holding up that never-dying torch, the flame of which seemed an emblem of the grief and hope that burned together in her heart. So much did she suffer, that, though her aspect had been quite youthful when her troubles began, she grew to look like an elderly person in a very brief time. She cared not how she was dressed, nor had she ever thought of flinging away the wreath of withered poppies, which she put on the very morning of Proserpina's disappearance. She roamed about in so wild a way, and with her hair so dishevelled, that people took her for some distracted creature, and never dreamed that this was Mother Ceres, who had the oversight of every seed which the husbandman planted. Nowadays, however, she gave herself no trouble about seed-time nor harvest, but left the farmers to take care of their own affairs, and the crops to fade or flourish, as the case might be. There was nothing, now, in which Ceres seemed to feel an interest, unless when she saw children at play or gathering flowers along the wayside. Then, indeed, she would stand and gaze at them with tears in her eyes. The children, too, appeared to have a sympathy with her grief, and would cluster themselves in a little group about her knees, and look up wistfully in her face;

and Ceres, after giving them a kiss all around, would lead them to their homes, and advise their mothers never to let them stray out of sight.

"For if you do," said she, "it may happen to you, as it has to me, that the iron-hearted King Pluto will take a liking to your darlings, and snatch them up in his chariot, and carry them away."

One day, during her pilgrimage in quest of the entrance to Pluto's kingdom, she came to the palace of King Celeus, who reigned at Eleusis. Ascending a lofty flight of steps, she entered the portal, and found the royal household in very great alarm about the queen's baby. The infant, it seems, was sickly (being troubled with its teeth, I suppose), and would take no food, and was all the time moaning with pain. The queen — her name was Metanira — was desirous of finding a nurse; and when she beheld a woman of matronly aspect coming up the palace steps, she thought, in her own mind that here was the very person whom she needed. So Queen Metanira ran to the door, with the poor wailing baby in her arms, and besought Ceres to take charge of it, or, at least, to tell her what would do it good."

"Will you trust the child entirely to me?" asked Ceres.

"Yes, and gladly too," answered the queen, "if you will devote all your time to him. For I can see that you have been a mother."

"You are right," said Ceres. "I once had a child of my own. Well, I will be the nurse of this poor, sickly boy. But beware, I warn you, that you do not
140

interfere with any kind of treatment which I may judge proper for him. If you do so, the poor infant must suffer for his mother's folly."

Then she kissed the child, and it seemed to do him good, for he smiled and nestled closely into her bosom.

So Mother Ceres set her torch in a corner (where it kept burning all the while), and took up her abode in the palace of King Celeus, as nurse to the little Prince Demophöon. She treated him as if he were her own child, and allowed neither the king nor the queen to say whether he should be bathed in warm or cold water, or what he should eat, or how often he should take the air, or when he should be put to bed. You would hardly believe me, if I were to tell how quickly the baby prince got rid of his ailments, and grew fat, and rosy, and strong, and how he had two rows of ivory teeth in less time than any other little fellow, before or since. Instead of the palest, and wretchedest, and puniest imp in the world (as his own mother confessed him to be when Ceres first took him in charge), he was now a strapping baby, crowing, laughing, kicking up his heels, and rolling from one end of the room to the other. All the good women of the neighborhood crowded to the palace, and held up their hands, in unutterable amazement, at the beauty and wholesomeness of this darling little prince. Their wonder was the greater, because he was never seen to taste any food, — not even so much as a cup of milk.

"Pray, nurse," the queen kept saying, "how is it that you make the child thrive so?"

"I was a mother once," Ceres replied always; "and having nursed my own child, I know what other children need."

But Queen Metanira, as was very natural, had a great curiosity to know precisely what the nurse did to her child. One night, therefore, she hid herself in the chamber where Ceres and the little prince were accustomed to sleep. There was a fire in the chimney, and it had now crumbled into great coals and embers, which lay glowing on the hearth, with a blaze flickering up now and then, and flinging a warm and ruddy light upon the walls. Ceres sat before the hearth with the child in her lap, and the firelight making her shadow dance upon the ceiling overhead. She undressed the little prince, and bathed him all over with some fragrant liquid out of a vase. The next thing she did was to rake back the red embers, and make a hollow place among them, just where the backlog had been. At last, while the baby was crowing and clapping its fat little hands, and laughing in the nurse's face (just as you may have seen your little brother or sister do before going into its warm bath), Ceres suddenly laid him, all naked as he was, in the hollow, among the red-hot embers. She then raked the ashes over him, and turned quietly away.

You may imagine, if you can, how Queen Metanira shrieked, thinking nothing less than that her dear child would be burned to a cinder. She burst forth from her hiding-place, and running to the hearth, raked open the fire, and snatched up poor little Prince Demophoön out of his bed of live coals, one of which he was grip-

ing in each of his fists. He immediately set up a grievous cry, as babies are apt to do when rudely startled
out of a sound sleep. To the queen's astonishment
and joy, she could perceive no token of the child's being
injured by the hot fire in which he had lain. She now
turned to Mother Ceres, and asked her to explain the
mystery.

"Foolish woman," answered Ceres, "did you not
promise to intrust this poor infant entirely to me?
You little know the mischief you have done him. Had
you left him to my care, he would have grown up like
a child of celestial birth, endowed with superhuman
strength and intelligence, and would have lived forever. Do you imagine that earthly children are to become immortal without being tempered to it in the
fiercest heat of the fire? But you have ruined your
own son. For though he will be a strong man and a
hero in his day, yet, on account of your folly, he will
grow old, and finally die, like the sons of other women.
The weak tenderness of his mother has cost the poor
boy an immortality. Farewell."

Saying these words, she kissed the little prince Demophoön, and sighed to think what he had lost, and
took her departure without heeding Queen Metanira,
who entreated her to remain, and cover up the child
among the hot embers as often as she pleased. Poor
baby! He never slept so warmly again.

While she dwelt in the king's palace, Mother Ceres
had been so continually occupied with taking care of
the young prince, that her heart was a little lightened
of its grief for Proserpina. But now, having nothing

else to busy herself about, she became just as wretched as before. At length, in her despair, she came to the dreadful resolution that not a stalk of grain, nor a blade of grass, not a potato, nor a turnip, nor any other vegetable that was good for man or beast to eat, should be suffered to grow until her daughter were restored. She even forbade the flowers to bloom, lest somebody's heart should be cheered by their beauty.

Now, as not so much as a head of asparagus ever presumed to poke itself out of the ground, without the especial permission of Ceres, you may conceive what a terrible calamity had here fallen upon the earth. The husbandmen ploughed and planted as usual; but there lay the rich black furrows, all as barren as a desert of sand. The pastures looked as brown in the sweet month of June as ever they did in chill November. The rich man's broad acres and the cottager's small garden-patch were equally blighted. Every little girl's flower-bed showed nothing but dry stalks. The old people shook their white heads, and said that the earth had grown aged like themselves, and was no longer capable of wearing the warm smile of summer on its face. It was really piteous to see the poor starving cattle and sheep, how they followed behind Ceres, lowing and bleating, as if their instinct taught them to expect help from her; and everybody that was acquainted with her power besought her to have mercy on the human race, and, at all events, to let the grass grow. But Mother Ceres, though naturally of an affectionate disposition, was now inexorable.

"Never," said she. "If the earth is ever again to

see any verdure, it must first grow along the path which my daughter will tread in coming back to me."

Finally, as there seemed to be no other remedy, our old friend Quicksilver was sent post haste to King Pluto, in hopes that he might be persuaded to undo the mischief he had done, and to set everything right again, by giving up Proserpina. Quicksilver accordingly made the best of his way to the great gate, took a flying leap right over the three-headed mastiff, and stood at the door of the palace in an inconceivably short time. The servants knew him both by his face and garb; for his short cloak and his winged cap and shoes and his snaky staff had often been seen thereabouts in times gone by. He requested to be shown immediately into the king's presence; and Pluto, who heard his voice from the top of the stairs, and who loved to recreate himself with Quicksilver's merry talk, called out to him to come up. And while they settle their business together, we must inquire what Proserpina has been doing ever since we saw her last.

The child had declared, as you may remember, that she would not taste a mouthful of food as long as she should be compelled to remain in King Pluto's palace. How she contrived to maintain her resolution, and at the same time to keep herself tolerably plump and rosy, is more than I can explain; but some young ladies, I am given to understand, possess the faculty of living on air, and Proserpina seems to have possessed it too. At any rate, it was now six months since she left the outside of the earth; and not a morsel, so far as the attendants were able to testify, had yet passed between her teeth. This was the more creditable to Proserpina, inasmuch as King Pluto had caused her to be tempted day after day, with all manner of sweetmeats, and richly preserved fruits, and delicacies of every sort, such as young people are generally most fond of. But her good mother had often told her of the hurtfulness of these things; and for that reason alone, if there had been no other, she would have resolutely refused to taste them.

All this time, being of a cheerful and active disposition, the little damsel was not quite so unhappy as you may have supposed. The immense palace had a thousand rooms, and was full of beautiful and wonderful objects. There was a never-ceasing gloom, it is true, which half hid itself among the innumerable pillars, gliding before the child as she wandered among them, and treading stealthily behind her in the echo of her footsteps. Neither was all the dazzle of the precious stones, which flamed with their own light, worth one gleam of natural sunshine; nor could the most brilliant of the many-colored gems which Proserpina had for playthings vie with the simple beauty of the flowers she used to gather. But still, wherever the girl went, among those gilded halls and chambers, it seemed as if she carried nature and sunshine along with her, and as if she scattered dewy blossoms on her right hand and on her left. After Proserpina came, the palace was no longer the same abode of stately artifice and dismal magnificence that it had before been. The inhabitants all felt this, and King Pluto more than any of them.

146

"My own little Proserpina," he used to say, "I wish you could like me a little better. We gloomy and cloudy-natured persons have often as warm hearts at bottom as those of a more cheerful character. If you would only stay with me of your own accord, it would make me happier than the possession of a hundred such palaces as this."

"Ah," said Proserpina, "you should have tried to make me like you before carrying me off. And the best thing you can do now is to let me go again. Then I might remember you sometimes, and think that you were as kind as you knew how to be. Perhaps, too, one day or other, I might come back, and pay you a visit."

"No, no," answered Pluto, with his gloomy smile, "I will not trust you for that. You are too fond of living in the broad daylight, and gathering flowers. What an idle and childish taste that is! Are not these gems, which I have ordered to be dug for you, and which are richer than any in my crown, — are they not prettier than a violet?"

"Not half so pretty," said Proserpina, snatching the gems from Pluto's hand, and flinging them to the other end of the hall. "Oh, my sweet violets, shall I never see you again?"

And then she burst into tears. But young people's tears have very little saltness or acidity in them, and do not inflame the eyes so much as those of grown persons; so that it is not to be wondered at if, a few moments afterwards, Proserpina was sporting through the hall almost as merrily as she and the four sea-nymphs had sported along the edge of the surf wave. King Pluto gazed after her, and wished that he, too, was a child. And little Proserpina, when she turned about, and beheld this great king standing in his splendid hall, and looking so grand, and so melancholy, and so lonesome, was smitten with a kind of pity. She ran back to him, and, for the first time in all her life, put her small, soft hand in his.

"I love you a little," whispered she, looking up in his face.

"Do you, indeed, my dear child?" cried Pluto, bending his dark face down to kiss her; but Proserpina shrank away from the kiss, for though his features were noble, they were very dusky and grim. "Well, I have not deserved it of you, after keeping you a prisoner for so many months, and starving you, besides. Are you not terribly hungry? Is there nothing which I can get you to eat?"

In asking this question, the king of the mines had a very cunning purpose; for, you will recollect, if Proserpina tasted a morsel of food in his dominions, she would never afterwards be at liberty to quit them.

"No, indeed," said Proserpina. "Your head cook is always baking, and stewing, and roasting, and rolling out paste, and contriving one dish or another, which he imagines may be to my liking. But he might just as well save himself the trouble, poor, fat little man that he is. I have no appetite for anything in the world, unless it were a slice of bread of my mother's own baking, or a little fruit out of her garden."

When Pluto heard this, he began to see that he had

mistaken the best method of tempting Proserpina to eat. The cook's made dishes and artificial dainties were not half so delicious, in the good child's opinion, as the simple fare to which Mother Ceres had accustomed her. Wondering that he had never thought of it before, the king now sent one of his trusty attendants, with a large basket, to get some of the finest and juicest pears, peaches, and plums which could anywhere be found in the upper world. Unfortunately, however, this was during the time when Ceres had forbidden any fruits or vegetables to grow; and, after seeking all over the earth, King Pluto's servants found only a single pomegranate, and that so dried up as to be not worth eating. Nevertheless, since there was no better to be had, he brought this dry, old, withered pomegranate home to the palace, put it on a magnificent golden salver, and carried it up to Proserpina. Now it happened, curiously enough, that, just as the servant was bringing the pomegranate into the back door of the palace, our friend Quicksilver had gone up the front steps, on his errand to get Proserpina away from King Pluto.

As soon as Proserpina saw the pomegranate on the golden salver, she told the servant he had better take it away again.

"I shall not touch it, I assure you," said she. "If I were ever so hungry, I should never think of eating such a miserable, dry pomegranate as that."

"It is the only one in the world," said the servant.

He set down the golden salver, with the wizened pomegranate upon it, and left the room. When he was gone, Proserpina could not help coming close to the table, and looking at this poor specimen of dried fruit with a great deal of eagerness; for, to say the truth, on seeing something that suited her taste, she felt all the six months' appetite taking possession of her at once. To be sure, it was a very wretched-looking pomegranate, and seemed to have no more juice in it than an oyster-shell. But there was no choice of such things in King Pluto's palace. This was the first fruit she had seen there, and the last she was ever likely to see; and unless she ate it up immediately, it would grow drier than it already was, and be wholly unfit to eat.

"At least, I may smell it," thought Proserpina.

So she took up the pomegranate, and applied it to her nose; and, somehow or other, being in such close neighborhood to her mouth, the fruit found its way into that little red cave. Dear me! what an everlasting pity! Before Proserpina knew what she was about, her teeth had actually bitten it, of their own accord. Just as this fatal deed was done, the door of the apartment opened, and in came King Pluto, followed by Quicksilver, who had been urging him to let his little prisoner go. At the first noise of their entrance, Proserpina withdrew the pomegranate from her mouth. But Quicksilver (whose eyes were very keen, and his wits the sharpest that ever anybody had) perceived that the child was a little confused; and seeing the empty salver, he suspected that she had been taking a sly nibble of something or other. As for honest Pluto, he never guessed at the secret.

THE POMEGRANATE SEEDS

"My little Proserpina," said the king, sitting down, and affectionately drawing her between his knees, "here is Quicksilver, who tells me that a great many misfortunes have befallen innocent people on account of my detaining you in my dominions. To confess the truth, I myself had already reflected that it was an unjustifiable act to take you away from your good mother. But, then, you must consider, my dear child, that this vast palace is apt to be gloomy (although the precious stones certainly shine very bright), and that I am not of the most cheerful disposition, and that therefore it was a natural thing enough to seek for the society of some merrier creature than myself. I hoped you would take my crown for a plaything, and me — ah, you laugh, naughty Proserpina — me, grim as I am, for a playmate. It was a silly expectation."

"Not so extremely silly," whispered Proserpina. "You have really amused me very much, sometimes."

"Thank you," said King Pluto, rather dryly. "But I can see, plainly enough, that you think my palace a dusky prison, and me the iron-hearted keeper of it. And an iron heart I should surely have, if I could detain you here any longer, my poor child, when it is now six months since you tasted food. I give you your liberty. Go with Quicksilver. Hasten home to your dear mother."

Now, although you may not have supposed it, Proserpina found it impossible to take leave of poor King Pluto without some regrets, and a good deal of compunction for not telling him about the pomegranate. She even shed a tear or two, thinking how lonely and cheerless the great palace would seem to him, with all its ugly glare of artificial light, after she herself, — his one little ray of natural sunshine, whom he had stolen, to be sure, but only because he valued her so much, — after she should have departed. I know not how many kind things she might have said to the disconsolate king of the mines, had not Quicksilver hurried her away.

"Come along quickly," whispered he in her ear, "or his majesty may change his royal mind. And take care, above all things, that you say nothing of what was brought you on the golden salver."

In a very short time, they had passed the great gateway (leaving the three-headed Cerberus, barking and yelping, and growling, with threefold din, behind them), and emerged upon the surface of the earth. It was delightful to behold, as Proserpina hastened along, how the path grew verdant behind and on either side of her. Wherever she set her blessed foot, there was at once a dewy flower. The violets gushed up along the wayside. The grass and the grain began to sprout with tenfold vigor and luxuriance, to make up for the dreary months that had been wasted in barrenness. The starved cattle immediately set to work grazing, after their long fast, and ate enormously all day, and got up at midnight to eat more. But I can assure you it was a busy time of year with the farmers, when they found the summer coming upon them with such a rush. Nor must I forget to say that all the birds in the whole world hopped about upon the newly blossoming trees, and sang together in a prodigious ecstasy of joy.

THE POMEGRANATE SEEDS

Mother Ceres had returned to her deserted home, and was sitting disconsolately on the doorstep, with her torch burning in her hand. She had been idly watching the flame for some moments past, when, all at once, it flickered and went out.

"What does this mean?" thought she. "It was an enchanted torch, and should have kept burning till my child came back."

Lifting her eyes, she was surprised to see a sudden verdure flashing over the brown and barren fields, exactly as you may have observed a golden hue gleaming far and wide across the landscape, from the just risen sun.

"Does the earth disobey me?" exclaimed Mother Ceres indignantly. "Does it presume to be green, when I have bidden it be barren until my daughter shall be restored to my arms?"

"Then open your arms, dear mother," cried a well-known voice, "and take your little daughter into them."

And Proserpina came running, and flung herself upon her mother's bosom. Their mutual transport is not to be described. The grief of their separation had caused both of them to shed a great many tears; and now they shed a great many more, because their joy could not so well express itself in any other way.

When their hearts had grown a little more quiet, Mother Ceres looked anxiously at Proserpina.

"My child," said she, "did you taste any food while you were in King Pluto's palace?"

"Dearest mother," answered Proserpina, "I will

tell you the whole truth. Until this very morning, not a morsel of food had passed my lips. But to-day, they brought me a pomegranate (a very dry one it was, and all shriveled up, till there was little left of it but seeds and skin), and having seen no fruit for so long a time, and being faint with hunger, I was tempted just to bite it. The instant I tasted it, King Pluto and Quicksilver came into the room. I had not swallowed a morsel; but — dear mother, I hope it was no harm — but six of the pomegranate seeds, I am afraid, remained in my mouth."

"Ah, unfortunate child, and miserable me!" exclaimed Ceres. "For each of those six pomegranate seeds you must spend one month of each year in King Pluto's palace. You are but half restored to your mother. Only six months with me, and six with that good-for-nothing King of Darkness!"

"Do not speak so harshly of poor King Pluto," said Proserpina, kissing her mother. "He has some very good qualities, and I really think I can bear to spend six months in his palace, if he will only let me spend the other six with you. He certainly did very wrong to carry me off; but then, as he says, it was but a dismal sort of life for him, to live in that great gloomy place, all alone; and it has made a wonderful change in his spirits to have a little girl to run up stairs and down. There is some comfort in making him so happy; and so, upon the whole, dearest mother, let us be thankful that he is not to keep me the whole year round."

OLD GREEK FOLK–STORIES

ORPHEUS AND EURYDICE

By Josephine Preston Peabody

WHEN gods and shepherds piped and the stars sang, that was the day of musicians! But the triumph of Phœbus Apollo himself was not so wonderful as the triumph of a mortal man who lived on earth, though some say that he came of divine lineage. This was Orpheus, that best of harpers, who went with the Grecian heroes of the great ship Argo in search of the Golden Fleece.

After his return from the quest, he won Eurydice for his wife, and they were as happy as people can be who love each other and every one else. The very wild beasts loved them, and the trees clustered about their home as if they were watered with music. But even the gods themselves were not always free from sorrow, and one day misfortune came upon that harper Orpheus whom all men loved to honor.

Eurydice, his lovely wife, as she was wandering with the nymphs, unwittingly trod upon a serpent in the grass. Surely, if Orpheus had been with her, playing upon his lyre, no creature could have harmed her. But Orpheus came too late. She died of the sting, and was lost to him in the Underworld.

For days he wandered from his home, singing the story of his loss and his despair to the helpless pass-

157

ers-by. His grief moved the very stones in the wilderness, and roused a dumb distress in the hearts of savage beasts. Even the gods on Mount Olympus gave ear, but they held no power over the darkness of Hades.

Wherever Orpheus wandered with his lyre, no one had the will to forbid him entrance; and at length he found unguarded that very cave that leads to the Underworld, where Pluto rules the spirits of the dead. He went down without fear. The fire in his living heart found him a way through the gloom of that place. He crossed the Styx, the black river that the Gods name as their most sacred oath. Charon, the harsh old ferryman who takes the shades across, forgot to ask of him the coin that every soul must pay. For Orpheus sang. There in the Underworld the song of Apollo would not have moved the poor ghosts so much. It would have amazed them, like a star far off that no one understands. But here was a human singer, and he sang of things that grow in every human heart, youth and love and death, the sweetness of the Earth, and the bitterness of losing aught that is dear to us.

Now the dead, when they go to the Underworld, drink of the pool of Lethe; and forgetfulness of all that has passed comes upon them like a sleep, and they lose their longing for the world, they lose their memory of pain, and live content with that cool twilight. But not the pool of Lethe itself could withstand the song of Orpheus; and in the hearts of the shades all the old dreams awoke wondering. They remembered once more the life of men on earth, the glory of the sun and moon, the sweetness of new grass, the warmth of their homes, all the old joy and grief that they had known. And they wept.

Even the Furies were moved to pity. Those, too, who were suffering punishment for evil deeds ceased to be tormented for themselves, and grieved only for the innocent Orpheus who had lost Eurydice. Sisyphus, that fraudulent king (who is doomed to roll a monstrous boulder uphill forever), stopped to listen. The daughters of Danaus left off their task of drawing water in a sieve. Tantalus forgot hunger and thirst, though before his eyes hung magical fruits that were wont to vanish out of his grasp, and just beyond reach bubbled the water that was a torment to his ears; he did not hear it while Orpheus sang.

So, among a crowd of eager ghosts, Orpheus came, singing with all his heart, before the king and queen of Hades. And the queen Proserpina wept as she listened and grew homesick, remembering the fields of Enna and the growing of the wheat, and her own beautiful mother, Demeter. Then Pluto gave way.

They called Eurydice and she came, like a young guest unused to the darkness of the Underworld. She was to return with Orpheus, but on one condition. If he turned to look at her once before they reached the upper air, he must lose her again and go back to the world alone.

Rapt with joy, the happy Orpheus hastened on the way, thinking only of Eurydice, who was following him. Past Lethe, across the Styx they went, he and his lovely wife, still silent as a shade. But the place was full of gloom, the silence weighed upon him, he had not seen her for so long; her footsteps made no sound; and he could hardly believe the miracle, for Pluto seldom relents. When the first gleam of upper daylight broke through the cleft to the dismal world, he forgot all, save that he must know if she still followed. He turned to see her face, and the promise was broken!

She smiled at him forgivingly, but it was too late. He stretched out his arms to take her, but she faded from them, as the bright snow, that none may keep, melts in our very hands. A murmur of farewell came to his ears, — no more. She was gone.

He would have followed, but Charon, now on guard, drove him back. Seven days he lingered there between the worlds of life and death, but after the broken promise Hades would not listen to his song. Back to the earth he wandered, though it was sweet to him no longer. He died young, singing to the last, and round about the place where his body rested, nightingales nested in the trees. His lyre was set among the stars; and he himself went down to join Eurydice, unforbidden.

Those two had no need of Lethe, for their life on earth had been wholly fair, and now that they are together they no longer own a sorrow.

ICARUS AND DÆDALUS

By Josephine Preston Peabody

AMONG all those mortals who grew so wise that they learned the secrets of the gods, none was more cunning than Dædalus.

He once built, for King Minos of Crete, a wonderful Labyrinth of winding ways so cunningly tangled up and twisted around that, once inside, you could never find your way out again without a magic clue. But the king's favor veered with the wind, and one day he had his master architect imprisoned in a tower. Dædalus managed to escape from his cell; but it seemed impossible to leave the island, since every ship that came or went was well guarded by order of the king.

At length, watching the sea-gulls in the air, — the only creatures that were sure of liberty, — he thought of a plan for himself and his young son Icarus, who was captive with him.

Little by little, he gathered a store of feathers great and small. He fastened these together with thread, moulded them in with wax, and so fashioned two great wings like those of a bird. When they were done, Dædalus fitted them to his own shoulders, and after one or two efforts, he found that by waving his arms he could winnow the air and cleave it, as a swimmer does the sea. He held himself aloft, wavered this way and that, with the wind, and at last, like a great fledgling, he learned to fly.

Without delay, he fell to work on a pair of wings for the boy Icarus, and taught him carefully how to use them, bidding him beware of rash adventures among the stars. "Remember," said the father, "never to fly very low or very high, for the fogs about the earth would weigh you down, but the blaze of the sun will surely melt your feathers apart if you go too near."

For Icarus, these cautions went in at one ear and out by the other. Who could remember to be careful when he was to fly for the first time? Are birds careful? Not they! And not an idea remained in the boy's head but the one joy of escape.

The day came, and the fair wind that was to set them free. The father bird put on his wings, and, while the light urged them to be gone, he waited to see that all was well with Icarus, for the two could not fly hand in hand. Up they rose, the boy after his father. The hateful ground of Crete sank beneath them; and the country folk, who caught a glimpse of them when they were high above the tree-tops, took it for a vision of the gods, — Apollo, perhaps, with Cupid after him.

At first there was a terror in the joy. The wide vacancy of the air dazed them, — a glance downward made their brains reel. But when a great wind filled their wings, and Icarus felt himself sustained, like a halcyon-bird in the hollow of a wave, like a child uplifted by his mother, he forgot everything in the world but joy. He forgot Crete and the other islands that

162

he had passed over: he saw but vaguely that winged thing in the distance before him that was his father Dædalus. He longed for one draught of flight to quench the thirst of his captivity: he stretched out his arms to the sky and made towards the highest heavens.

Alas for him! Warmer and warmer grew the air. Those arms, that had seemed to uphold him, relaxed. His wings wavered, drooped. He fluttered his young hands vainly, — he was falling, — and in that terror he remembered. The heat of the sun had melted the wax from his wings; the feathers were falling, one by one, like snowflakes; and there was none to help.

He fell like a leaf tossed down the wind, down, down, with one cry that overtook Dædalus far away. When he returned, and sought high and low for the poor boy, he saw nothing but the bird-like feathers afloat on the water, and he knew that Icarus was drowned.

The nearest island he named Icaria, in memory of the child; but he, in heavy grief, went to the temple of Apollo in Sicily, and there hung up his wings as an offering. Never again did he attempt to fly.

PHAETHON

By Josephine Preston Peabody

ONCE upon a time, the reckless whim of a lad came near to destroying the Earth and robbing the spheres of their wits.

There were two playmates, said to be of heavenly parentage. One was Epaphus, who claimed Zeus as a father; and one was Phaethon, the earthly child of Phœbus Apollo (or Helios, as some name the sun-god). One day they were boasting together, each of his own father, and Epaphus, angry at the other's fine story, dared him to go prove his kinship with the Sun.

Full of rage and humiliation, Phaethon went to his mother, Clymene, where she sat with his young sisters, the Heliades.

"It is true, my child," she said, "I swear it in the light of yonder Sun. If you have any doubt, go to the land whence he rises at morning and ask of him any gift you will; he is your father, and he cannot refuse you."

As soon as might be, Phaethon set out for the country of sunrise. He journeyed by day and by night far into the east, till he came to the palace of the Sun. It towered high as the clouds, glorious with gold and all manner of gems that looked like frozen fire, if that might be. The mighty walls were wrought with images

164

of earth and sea and sky. Vulcan, the smith of the Gods, had made them in his workshop (for Mount Ætna is one of his forges, and he has the central fires of the earth to help him fashion gold and iron, as men do glass). On the doors blazed the twelve signs of the Zodiac, in silver that shone like snow in the sunlight. Phaethon was dazzled with the sight, but when he entered the palace hall he could hardly bear the radiance.

In one glimpse through his half-shut eyes, he beheld a glorious being, none other than Phœbus himself, seated upon a throne. He was clothed in purple raiment, and round his head there shone a blinding light, that enveloped even his courtiers upon the right and upon the left, — the Seasons with their emblems, Day, Month, Year, and the beautiful young Hours in a row. In one glance of those all-seeing eyes, the sun-god knew his child; but in order to try him he asked the boy his errand.

"O my father," stammered Phaethon, "if you are my father indeed" — and then he took courage; for the god came down from his throne, put off the glorious halo that hurt mortal eyes, and embraced him tenderly.

"Indeed, thou art my son," said he. "Ask any gift of me, and it shall be thine; I call the Styx to witness."

"Ah!" cried Phaethon rapturously. "Let me drive thy chariot for one day!"

For an instant the Sun's looks clouded. "Choose again, my child," said he. "Thou art only a mortal, and this task is mine alone of all the Gods. Not

Zeus himself dare drive the chariot of the Sun. The way is full of terrors, both for the horses and for all the stars along the roadside, and for the Earth, who has all blessings from me. Listen, and choose again." And therewith he warned Phaethon of all the dangers that beset the way, — the great steep that the steeds must climb, the numbing dizziness of the height, the fierce constellations that breathe out fire, and that descent in the west where the Sun seems to go headlong.

But these counsels only made the reckless boy more eager to win honor of such a high enterprise.

"I will take care; only let me go," he begged.

Now Phœbus had sworn by the black river Styx, an oath that none of the Gods dare break, and he was forced to keep his promise.

Already Aurora, goddess of dawn, had thrown open the gates of the east, and the stars were beginning to wane. The Hours came forth to harness the four horses, and Phaethon looked with exultation at the splendid creatures, whose lord he was for a day. Wild, immortal steeds they were, fed with ambrosia, untamed as the winds; their very pet names signified flame, and all that flame can do, — Pyrois, Eoüs, Æthon, Phlegon.

As the lad stood by, watching, Phœbus anointed his face with a philter that should make him strong to endure the terrible heat and light, then set the halo upon his head, with a last word of counsel.

"Follow the road," said he, "and never turn aside. Go not too high or too low, for the sake of heavens and earth; else men and Gods will suffer. The Fates

alone know whether evil is to come of this. Yet if
your heart fails you, as I hope, abide here and I will
make the journey, as I am wont to do."

But Phaethon held to his choice and bade his father
farewell. He took his place in the chariot, gathered
up the reins, and the horses sprang away, eager for
the road.

As they went, they bent their splendid necks to
see the meaning of the strange hand upon the reins,
— the slender weight in the chariot. They turned
their wild eyes upon Phaethon, to his secret forebod-
ing, and neighed one to another. This was no master
charioteer, but a mere lad, a feather riding the wind.
It was holiday for the horses of the Sun, and away
they went.

Grasping the reins that dragged him after, like an
enemy, Phaethon looked down from the fearful ascent
and saw the Earth far beneath him, dim and fair.
He was blind with dizziness and bewilderment. His
hold slackened and the horses redoubled their speed,
wild with new liberty. They left the old tracks. Before he knew where he was, they had startled the constellations and well-nigh grazed the Serpent, so that
it woke from its torpor and hissed.

The steeds took fright. This way and that they
went, terrified by the monsters they had never encountered before, shaking out of their silver quiet the cool
stars towards the north, then fleeing as far to the south
among new wonders. The heavens were full of terror.

Up, far above the clouds, they went, and down
again, towards the defenseless Earth, that could not

flee from the chariot of the Sun. Great rivers hid themselves in the ground, and mountains were consumed. Harvests perished like a moth that is singed in a candle-flame.

In vain did Phaethon call to the horses and pull upon the reins. As in a hideous dream, he saw his own Earth, his beautiful home and the home of all men, his kindred, parched by the fires of this mad chariot, and blackening beneath him. The ground cracked open and the sea shrank. Heedless water-nymphs, who had lingered in the shallows, were left gasping like bright fishes. The dryads shrank, and tried to cover themselves from the scorching heat. The poor Earth lifted her withered face in a last prayer to Zeus to save her if he might.

Then Zeus, calling all the Gods to witness that there was no other means of safety, hurled his thunderbolt; and Phaethon knew no more.

His body fell through the heavens, aflame like a shooting star; and the horses of the Sun dashed homeward with the empty chariot.

Poor Clymene grieved sore over the boy's death; but the young Heliades, daughters of the Sun, refused all comfort. Day and night they wept together about their brother's grave by the river, until the Gods took pity and changed them all into poplar-trees. And ever after that they wept sweet tears of amber, clear as sunlight.

NIOBE

By Josephine Preston Peabody

THERE are so many tales of the vanity of kings and queens that the half of them cannot be told.

There was Cassiopæia, queen of Æthiopia, who boasted that her beauty outshone the beauty of all the sea-nymphs, so that in anger they sent a horrible sea-serpent to ravage the coast. The king prayed of an oracle to know how the monster might be appeased, and learned that he must offer up his own daughter, Andromeda. The maiden was therefore chained to a rock by the sea-side, and left to her fate. But who should come to rescue her but a certain young hero, Perseus, who was hastening homeward after a perilous adventure with the snaky-haired Gorgons. Filled with pity at the story of Andromeda, he waited for the dragon, met and slew him, and set the maiden free. As for the boastful queen, the Gods forgave her, and at her death she was set among the stars. That story ended well.

But there was once a queen of Thebes, Niobe, fortunate above all women, and yet arrogant in the face of the gods. Very beautiful she was, and nobly born, but above all things she boasted of her children, for she had seven sons and seven daughters.

Now there came the day when the people were wont to celebrate the feast of Latona, mother of Apollo and

Diana; and Niobe, as she stood looking upon the worshipers on their way to the temple, was filled with overweening pride.

"Why do you worship Latona before me?" she cried out. "What does she possess that I have not in greater abundance? She has but two children, while I have seven sons and as many daughters. Nay, if she robbed me out of envy, I should still be rich. Go back to your houses; you have not eyes to know the rightful goddess."

Such impiety was enough to frighten any one, and her subjects returned to their daily work, awestruck and silent.

But Apollo and Diana were filled with wrath at this insult to their divine mother. Not only was she a great goddess and a power in the heavens, but during her life on earth she had suffered many hardships for their sake. The serpent Python had been sent to torment her; and, driven from land to land, under an evil spell, beset with dangers, she had found no resting-place but the island of Delos, held sacred ever after to her and her children. Once she had even been refused water by some churlish peasants, who could not believe in a goddess if she appeared in humble guise and travel-worn. But these men were all changed into frogs.

It needed no word from Latona herself to rouse her children to vengeance. Swift as a thought, the two immortal archers, brother and sister, stood in Thebes, upon the towers of the citadel. Near by, the youth were pursuing their sports, while the feast of Latona went neglected. The sons of Queen Niobe were there, and against them Apollo bent his golden bow. An arrow crossed the air like a sunbeam, and without a word the eldest prince fell from his horse. One by one his brothers died by the same hand, so swiftly that they knew not what had befallen them, till all the sons of the royal house lay slain. Only the people of Thebes, stricken with terror, bore the news to Queen Niobe, where she sat with her seven daughters. She would not believe in such a sorrow.

"Savage Latona," she cried, lifting her arms against the heavens, "never think that you have conquered. I am still the greater."

At that moment one of her daughters sank beside her. Diana had sped an arrow from her bow that is like the crescent moon. Without a cry, nay, even as they murmured words of comfort, the sisters died, one by one. It was all as swift and soundless as snowfall.

Only the guilty mother was left, transfixed with grief. Tears flowed from her eyes, but she spoke not a word, her heart never softened; and at last she turned to stone, and the tears flowed down her cold face forever.

PYRAMUS AND THISBE

By Josephine Preston Peabody

VENUS did not always befriend true lovers, as she had befriended Hippomenes, with her three golden apples. Sometimes, in the enchanted island of Cyprus, she forgot her worshipers far away, and they called on her in vain.

So it was in the sad story of Hero and Leander, who lived on opposite borders of the Hellespont. Hero dwelt at Sestos, where she served as a priestess, in the very temple of Venus; and Leander's home was in Abydos, a town on the opposite shore. But every night this lover would swim across the water to see Hero, guided by the light which she was wont to set in her tower. Even such loyalty could not conquer fate. There came a great storm, one night, that put out the beacon, and washed Leander's body up with the waves to Hero, and she sprang into the water to rejoin him, and so perished.

Not wholly unlike this was the fate of Halcyone, a queen of Thessaly, who dreamed that her husband Ceyx had been drowned, and on waking hastened to the shore to look for him. There she saw her dream come true, — his lifeless body floating towards her on the tide; and as she flung herself after him, mad with grief, the air upheld her and she seemed to fly.

Husband and wife were changed into birds; and there on the very water, at certain seasons, they build a nest that floats unhurt, — a portent of calm for many days and safe voyage for the ships. So it is that seamen love these birds and look for halcyon weather.

But there once lived in Babylonia two lovers named Pyramus and Thisbe, who were parted by a strange mischance. For they lived in adjoining houses; and although their parents had forbidden them to marry, these two had found a means of talking together through a crevice in the wall.

Here, again and again, Pyramus on his side of the wall and Thisbe on hers, they would meet to tell each other all that had happened during the day, and to complain of their cruel parents. At length they decided that they would endure it no longer, but that they would leave their homes and be married, come what might. They planned to meet, on a certain evening, by a mulberry-tree near the tomb of King Ninus, outside the city gates. Once safely met, they were resolved to brave fortune together.

So far all went well. At the appointed time, Thisbe, heavily veiled, managed to escape from home unnoticed, and after a stealthy journey through the streets of Babylon, she came to the grove of mulberries near the tomb of Ninus. The place was deserted, and once there she put off the veil from her face to see if Pyramus waited anywhere among the shadows. She heard the sound of a footfall and turned to behold — not Pyramus, but a creature unwelcome to any tryst — none other than a lioness crouching to drink from the pool hard by.

Without a cry, Thisbe fled, dropping her veil as she ran. She found a hiding-place among the rocks at some distance, and there she waited, not knowing what else to do.

The lioness, having quenched her thirst (after some ferocious meal), turned from the spring and, coming upon the veil, sniffed at it curiously, tore and tossed it with her reddened jaws,— as she would have done with Thisbe herself, — then dropped the plaything and crept away to the forest once more.

It was but a little after this that Pyramus came hurrying to the meeting-place, breathless with eagerness to find Thisbe and tell her what had delayed him. He found no Thisbe there. For a moment he was confounded. Then he looked about for some signs of her, some footprint by the pool. There was the trail of a wild beast in the grass, and near by a woman's veil, torn and stained with blood; he caught it up and knew it for Thisbe's.

So she had come at the appointed hour, true to her word; she had waited there for him alone and defenseless, and she had fallen a prey to some beast from the jungle! As these thoughts rushed upon the young man's mind, he could endure no more.

"Was it to meet me, Thisbe, that you came to such a death!" cried he. "And I followed all too late. But I will atone. Even now I come lagging, but by no will of mine!"

So saying, the poor youth drew his sword and fell upon it, there at the foot of that mulberry-tree which he had named as the trysting-place, and his life-blood ran about the roots.

During these very moments, Thisbe, hearing no sound and a little reassured, had stolen from her hiding-place and was come to the edge of the grove. She saw that the lioness had left the spring, and, eager to show her lover that she had dared all things to keep faith, she came slowly, little by little, back to the mulberry-tree.

She found Pyramus there, according to his promise. His own sword was in his heart, the empty scabbard by his side, and in his hand he held her veil still clasped. Thisbe saw these things as in a dream, and suddenly the truth awoke her. She saw the piteous mischance of all; and when the dying Pyramus opened his eyes and fixed them upon her, her heart broke. With the same sword she stabbed herself, and the lovers died together.

There the parents found them, after a weary search, and they were buried together in the same tomb. But the berries of the mulberry-tree turned red that day, and red they have remained ever since.

STORIES OF THE TROJAN WAR

THE APPLE OF DISCORD

By Josephine Preston Peabody

THERE was once a war so great that the sound
of it has come ringing down the centuries from
singer to singer, and will never die.

The rivalries of men and gods brought about many
calamities, but none so heavy as this; and it would
never have come to pass, they say, if it had not been
for jealousy among the immortals, — all because of a
golden apple! But Destiny has nurtured ominous
plants from little seeds; and this is how one evil grew
great enough to overshadow heaven and earth.

The sea-nymph Thetis (whom Zeus himself had
once desired for his wife) was given in marriage to a
mortal, Peleus, and there was a great wedding-feast
in heaven. Thither all the immortals were bidden,
save one, Eris, the goddess of Discord, ever an unwelcome guest. But she came unbidden. While the wed-
ding-guests sat at feast, she broke in upon their mirth,
flung among them a golden apple, and departed with
looks that boded ill. Some one picked up the strange
missile and read its inscription, " For the Fairest;" and
at once discussion arose among the goddesses. They
were all eager to claim the prize, but only three persisted.

Venus, the very goddess of beauty, said that it was
hers by right; but Juno could not endure to own her-

self less fair than another, and even Athene coveted
the palm of beauty as well as of wisdom, and would
not give it up! Discord had indeed come to the wedding-feast. Not one of the Gods dared to decide so
dangerous a question, — not Zeus himself, — and the
three rivals were forced to choose a judge among
mortals.

Now there lived on Mount Ida, near the city of
Troy, a certain young shepherd by the name of Paris.
He was as comely as Ganymede himself, — that Trojan
youth whom Zeus, in the shape of an eagle, seized
and bore away to Olympus, to be a cup-bearer to the
gods. Paris, too, was a Trojan of royal birth, but like
Œdipus, he had been left on the mountain in his in-
fancy, because the oracle had foretold that he would
be the death of his kindred and the ruin of his country.
Destiny saved and nurtured him to fulfill that prophecy. He grew up as a shepherd and tended his
flocks on the mountain, but his beauty held the favor
of all the wood-folk there and won the heart of the
nymph Œnone.

To him, at last, the three goddesses intrusted the
judgment and the golden apple. Juno first stood before him in all her glory as queen of Gods and men,
and attended by her favorite peacocks as gorgeous to
see as royal fan-bearers.

"Use but the judgment of a prince, Paris," she
said, "and I will give thee wealth and kingly power."

Such majesty and such promises would have moved
the heart of any man; but the eager Paris had at
least to hear the claims of the other rivals. Athene

TO HIM, AT LAST, THE THREE GODDESSES INTRUSTED THE JUDGMENT AND THE GOLDEN APPLE

rose before him, a vision welcome as daylight, with her sea-gray eyes and golden hair beneath a golden helmet.

"Be wise in honoring me, Paris," she said, "and I will give thee wisdom that shall last forever, great glory among men, and renown in war."

Last of all, Venus shone upon him, beautiful as none can ever hope to be. If she had come, unnamed, as any country maid, her loveliness would have dazzled him like sea-foam in the sun; but she was girt with her magical Cestus, a spell of beauty that no one can resist.

Without a bribe she might have conquered, and she smiled upon his dumb amazement, saying, "Paris, thou shalt yet have for wife the fairest woman in the world."

At these words, the happy shepherd fell on his knees and offered her the golden apple. He took no heed of the slighted goddesses, who vanished in a cloud that boded storm.

From that hour he sought only the counsel of Venus, and only cared to find the highway to his new fortunes. From her he learned that he was the son of King Priam of Troy, and with her assistance he deserted the nymph Œnone, whom he had married, and went in search of his royal kindred.

For it chanced at that time that Priam proclaimed a contest of strength between his sons and certain other princes, and promised as prize the most splendid bull that could be found among the herds of Mount Ida. Thither came the herdsmen to choose, and when they led away the pride of Paris's heart, he followed to Troy, thinking that he would try his fortune and perhaps win back his own.

The games took place before Priam and Hecuba and all their children, including those noble princes Hector and Helenus, and the young Cassandra, their sister. This poor maiden had a sad story, in spite of her royalty; for, because she had once disdained Apollo, she was fated to foresee all things, and ever to have her prophecies disbelieved. On this fateful day, she alone was oppressed with strange forebodings.

But if he who was to be the ruin of his country had returned, he had come victoriously. Paris won the contest. At the very moment of his honor, poor Cassandra saw him with her prophetic eyes; and seeing as well all the guilt and misery that he was to bring upon them, she broke into bitter lamentations, and would have warned her kindred against the evil to come. But the Trojans gave little heed; they were wont to look upon her visions as spells of madness. Paris had come back to them a glorious youth and a victor; and when he made known the secret of his birth, they cast the words of the oracle to the winds, and received the shepherd as a long-lost prince.

Thus far all went happily. But Venus, whose promise had not yet been fulfilled, bade Paris procure a ship and go in search of his destined bride. The prince said nothing of this quest, but urged his kindred to let him go; and giving out a rumor that he was to find his father's lost sister Hesione, he set sail for Greece, and finally landed at Sparta.

THE APPLE OF DISCORD

There he was kindly received by Menelaus, the king, and his wife, Fair Helen.

This queen had been reared as the daughter of Tyndarus and Queen Leda, but some say that she was the child of an enchanted swan, and there was indeed a strange spell about her. All the greatest heroes of Greece had wooed her before she left her father's palace to be the wife of King Menelaus, and Tyndarus, fearing for her peace, had bound her many suitors by an oath. According to this pledge, they were to respect her choice, and to go to the aid of her husband if ever she should be stolen away from him. For in all Greece there was nothing so beautiful as the beauty of Helen. She was the fairest woman in the world.

Now thus did Venus fulfill her promise and the shepherd win his reward with dishonor. Paris dwelt at the court of Menelaus for a long time, treated with a royal courtesy which he ill repaid. For at length, while the king was absent on a journey to Crete, his guest won the heart of Fair Helen, and persuaded her to forsake her husband and sail away to Troy, or Ilium.

King Menelaus returned to find the nest empty of the swan. Paris and the fairest woman in the world were well across the sea.

When this treachery came to light, all Greece took fire with indignation. The heroes remembered their pledge, and wrath came upon them at the wrong done to Menelaus. But they were less angered with Fair Helen than with Paris, for they felt assured that the queen had been lured from her country and out of her own senses by some spell of enchantment. So they took counsel how they might bring back Fair Helen to her home and husband.

Years had come and gone since that wedding-feast when Eris had flung the apple of discord, like a fire-brand, among the guests. But the spark of dissension that had smouldered so long burst into flame now, and, fanned by the enmities of men and the rivalries of the Gods, it seemed like to fire heaven and earth.

A few of the heroes answered the call to arms un-willingly. Time had reconciled them to the loss of Fair Helen, and they were loath to leave home and happiness for war, even in her cause.

One of these was Odysseus, or Ulysses, king of Ithaca, who had married Penelope, and was quite content with his kingdom and his little son Telemachus. Indeed, he was so unwilling to leave them that he feigned madness in order to escape service, appeared to forget his own kindred, and went ploughing the seashore and sowing salt in the furrows. But a messenger, Palamedes, who came with the summons to war, sus-pected that this sudden madness might be a stratagem, for the king was far famed as a man of many devices. He therefore stood by, one day (while Ulysses, pre-tending to take no heed of him, went ploughing the sand) and he laid the baby Telemachus directly in the way of the ploughshare. For once the wise man's craft deserted him. Ulysses turned the plough sharply, caught up the little prince, and there his fatherly wits were manifest! After this he could no longer play madman. He had to take leave of his beloved wife Penelope and set out to join the heroes, little dreaming that he was not to return for twenty years. Once embarked, however, he set himself to work in the common cause of the heroes, and was soon as ingenious as Palamedes in rousing laggard warriors.

There remained one who was destined to be the greatest warrior of all. This was Achilles, the son of Thetis, — foretold in the day of Prometheus as a man who should far outstrip his own father in glory and greatness. Years had passed since the marriage of Thetis to King Peleus, and their son Achilles was now grown to manhood, a wonder of strength indeed, and, moreover, invulnerable. For his mother, forewarned of his death in the Trojan War, had dipped him in the sacred river Styx when he was a baby, so that he could take no hurt from any weapon. From head to foot she had plunged him in, only forgetting the little heel that she held him by, and this alone could be wounded by any chance. But even with such precautions Thetis was not content. Fearful at the rumors of war to be, she had her son brought up, in woman's dress, among the daughters of King Lycomedes of Scyros, that he might escape the notice of men and cheat his destiny.

To this very palace, however, came Ulysses in the guise of a merchant, and he spread his wares before the royal household, — jewels and ivory, fine fabrics, and curiously wrought weapons. The king's daughters chose girdles and veils and such things as women delight in; but Achilles, heedless of the like, sought out the weapons, and handled them with such manly pleasure that his nature stood revealed. So he, too, yielded to his destiny and set out to join the heroes.

Everywhere men were banded together, building the ships and gathering supplies. The allied forces of Greece (the Achaians, as they called themselves) chose Agamemnon for their commander-in-chief. He was a mighty man, king of Mycenæ and Argos, and the brother of the wronged Menelaus. Second to Achilles in strength was the giant Ajax; after him Diomedes, then wise Ulysses, and Nestor, held in great reverence because of his experienced age and fame. These were the chief heroes. After two years of busy preparation, they reached the port of Aulis, whence they were to sail for Troy.

But here delay held them. Agamemnon had chanced to kill a stag which was sacred to Diana, and the army was visited by pestilence, while a great calm kept the ships imprisoned. At length the oracle made known the reason of this misfortune and demanded for atonement the maiden Iphigenia, Agamemnon's own daughter. In helpless grief the king consented to offer her up as a victim, and the maiden was brought, ready for sacrifice. But at the last moment Diana caught her away in a cloud, leaving a white hind in her place, and carried her to Tauris in Scythia, there to serve as a priestess in the temple. In the mean time, her kinsfolk, who were at a loss to understand how she had disappeared, mourned her as dead. But Diana had accepted their child as an offering, and healing came to the army, and the winds blew again. So the ships set sail.

Meanwhile, in Troy across the sea, the aged Priam

186

and Hecuba gave shelter to their son Paris and his stolen bride. They were not without misgivings as to these guests, but they made ready to defend their kindred and the citadel.

There were many heroes among the Trojans and their allies, brave and upright men, who little deserved that such reproach should be brought upon them by the guilt of Prince Paris. There were Æneas and Deïphobus, Glaucus and Sarpedon, and Priam's most noble son Hector, chief of all the forces, and the very bulwark of Troy. These and many more were bitterly to regret the day that had brought Paris back to his home. But he had taken refuge with his own people, and the Trojans had to take up his cause against the hostile fleet that was coming across the sea.

Even the Gods took sides. Juno and Athene, who had never forgiven the judgment of Paris, condemned all Troy with him and favored the Greeks, as did also Neptune, god of the sea. But Venus, true to her favorite, furthered the interests of the Trojans with all her power, and persuaded the warlike Mars to do likewise. Zeus and Apollo strove to be impartial, but they were yet to aid now one side, now another, according to the fortunes of the heroes whom they loved.

Over the sea came the great embassy of ships, sped hither safely by the god Neptune; and the heroes made their camp on the plain before Troy. First of all Ulysses and King Menelaus himself went into the city and demanded that Fair Helen should be given back to her rightful husband. This the Trojans refused, and so began the siege of Troy.

THE QUARREL BETWEEN AGA
MEMNON AND ACHILLES

By Alfred J. Church

THE Greeks sacked the city of Chryse, where was
a temple of Apollo, and a priest that served the
temple. And when they divided the spoil, they gave
to King Agamemnon with other gifts, the priest's
daughter, Chryseis. Thereupon there came to the
camp Chryses, the priest, wishing to ransom his daughter. Much gold he brought with him, and on his staff
of gold he carried the holy garland, that men might
reverence him the more. He went to all the chiefs,
and to the sons of Atreus first of all, saying, —

"Loose, I pray you, my dear daughter, and take
the ransom for her; so may the gods that dwell in
Olympus grant you to take the city of Troy, and to
have safe return to your homes."

Then all the others spake him fair, and would have
done what he wished. Only Agamemnon would not
have it so.

"Get thee out, graybeard!" he cried in great wrath.
"Let me not find thee lingering now by the ships,
neither coming hither again, or it shall be the worse
for thee, for all thy priesthood. And as for thy daughter, I shall carry her away to Argos, when I shall have
taken this city of Troy."

Then the old man went out hastily in great fear and trouble. And he walked in his sorrow by the shore of the sounding sea, and prayed to his god Apollo.

"Hear me, god of the silver bow! If I have built thee a temple, and offered thee fat of many bullocks and rams, hear me, and avenge my tears on the Greeks with thine arrows!"

And Apollo heard him. Wroth was he that men had so dishonored his priest, and he came down from the top of Olympus, where he dwelt. Dreadful was the rattle of his arrows as he went, and his coming was as the night when it cometh over the sky. Then he shot the arrows of death, first on the dogs and the mules, and then on the men; and soon all along the shore rolled the black smoke from the piles of wood on which they burnt the bodies of the dead.

For nine days the shafts of the god went throughout the host; but on the tenth day Achilles called the people to an assembly. So Juno bade him, for she loved the Greeks, and grieved to see them die. When they were gathered together he stood up among them, and spake to Agamemnon: —

"Surely it were better to return home, than that we should all perish here by war or plague. But come, let us ask some prophet or priest or dreamer of dreams why it is that Apollo is so wroth with us."

Then stood up Calchas, best of seers, who knew what had been, and what was, and what was to come, and spake: —

"Achilles, thou biddest me tell the people why Apollo is wroth with them. Lo! I will tell thee, but thou must first swear to stand by me, for I know that what I shall say will anger King Agamemnon, and it goes ill with common men when kings are angry."

"Speak out, thou wise man!" cried Achilles; "for I swear by Apollo that while I live no one shall lay hands on thee, no, not Agamemnon's self, though he be sovereign lord of the Greeks."

Then the blameless seer took heart, and spake: "It is not for vow or offering that Apollo is wroth; it is for his servant the priest, for he came to ransom his daughter, but Agamemnon scorned him, and would not let the maiden go. Now, then, ye must send her back to Chryse without ransom, and with her a hundred beasts for sacrifice, so that the plague may be stayed."

Then Agamemnon stood up in a fury, his eyes blazing like fire.

"Never," he cried, "hast thou spoken good concerning me, ill prophet that thou art, and now thou tellest me to give up this maiden! I will do it, for I would not that the people should perish. Only take care, ye Greeks, that there be a share of the spoil for me, for it would ill beseem the lord of all the host that he alone should be without his share."

"Nay, my lord Agamemnon," cried Achilles, "thou art too eager for gain. We have no treasures out of which we may make up thy loss, for what we got out of the towns we have either sold or divided; nor would it be fitting that the people should give back what has been given to them. Give up the maiden, then, without conditions, and when we shall have taken this city of Troy, we will repay thee three and four fold."

QUARREL OF AGAMEMNON AND ACHILLES

"Nay, great Achilles," said Agamemnon, "thou shalt not cheat me thus. If the Greeks will give me such a share as I should have, well and good. But if not, I will take one for myself, whether it be from thee or from Ajax or from Ulysses; for my share I will have. But of this hereafter. Now let us see that this maiden be sent back. Let them get ready a ship, and put her herein, and with her a hundred victims, and let some chief go with the ship, and see that all things be rightly done."

Then cried Achilles, and his face was as black as a thunder-storm: "Surely thou art altogether shameless and greedy, and, in truth, an ill ruler of men. No quarrel have I with the Trojans. They never harried oxen or sheep of mine in fertile Phthia, for many murky mountains lie between, and a great breadth of roaring sea. But I have been fighting in thy cause, and that of thy brother Menelaus. Naught carest thou for that. Thou leavest me to fight, and sittest in thy tent at ease. But when the spoil is divided, thine is always the lion's share. Small, indeed, is my part, — 'a little thing, but dear.' And this, forsooth, thou wilt take away! Now am I resolved to go home. I have no mind to heap up goods and gold for thee, and be myself dishonored."

And King Agamemnon answered, "Go, and thy Myrmidons with thee! I have other chieftains as good as thou art, and ready, as thou art not, to pay me due respect; and Zeus, the god of council, is with me. I hate thee, for thou always lovest war and strife. And as for the matter of the spoil, know that I will take thy share, the girl Briseïs, and fetch her myself, if need be, that all may know that I am sovereign lord here in the host of the Greeks."

Then Achilles was mad with anger, and he thought in his heart, "Shall I arise and slay this caitiff, or shall I keep down the wrath in my breast?" And as he thought he laid his hand on his sword-hilt, and had half-drawn his sword from the scabbard, when lo! the goddess Athene stood behind him (for Juno, who loved both this chieftain and that, had sent her), and caught him by the long locks of his yellow hair. But Achilles marveled much to feel the mighty grasp, and turned and looked, and knew the goddess, but no one else in the assembly might see her. Terrible was the flash of his eyes as he cried, "Art thou come, child of Zeus, to see the insolence of Agamemnon? Of a truth, I think that he will perish for his folly."

But Athene said, "Nay, but I am come from heaven to abate thy wrath, if thou wilt hear me; white-armed Juno sent me, for she loveth and cherisheth you both alike. Draw not thy sword; but use bitter words, even as thou wilt. Of a truth, I tell thee that for this insolence of to-day he will bring thee hereafter splendid gifts, threefold and fourfold for all that he may take away. Only refrain thyself and do my bidding."

Then Achilles answered, "I will abide by thy command for all my wrath, for the man who hearkens to the immortal gods is also heard of them." And as he spake he laid his heavy hand upon the hilt, and thrust back the sword into the scabbard, and Athene went her way to Olympus.

Then he turned him to King Agamemnon, and spake

again, for his anger was not spent. "Drunkard, with
the eyes of a dog and the heart of a deer! never fighting in the front of the battle, nor daring to lie in the
ambush! 'T is a race of dastards that thou rulest,
or this had been thy last wrong. But this I tell thee,
and confirm my words with a mighty oath — by this
sceptre do I swear. Once it was the branch of a tree,
but now the sons of the Greeks bear it in their hands,
even they who maintain the laws of Zeus; as surely
as it shall never again have bark, or leaves, or shoot,
so surely shall the Greeks one day miss Achilles, when
they fall in heaps before the dreadful Hector; and
thou shalt eat thy heart for rage, to think that thou
hast wronged the bravest of thy host."

And as he spake he dashed the sceptre, all embossed
with studs of gold, upon the ground, and sat down.
And on the other side Agamemnon sat in furious
anger. Then Nestor rose, an old man of a hundred
years and more, and counseled peace. Let them listen,
he said, to his counsel. Great chiefs in the old days,
with whom no man now alive would dare to fight, had
listened. Let not Agamemnon take away from the
bravest of the Greeks the prize of war; let not Achilles,
though he was mightier in battle than all other men, contend with Agamemnon, who was sovereign lord of all
the hosts of Greece. But he spake in vain. For Agamemnon answered, —

"Nestor, thou speakest well, and peace is good.
But this fellow would lord it over all; yet there are
some, methinks, who will not obey him. For if the immortal Gods have made him a great warrior, do they

therefore grant him leave to speak lawless words?
Verily he must be taught that there is one here, at least,
who is better than he."

And Achilles said, "I were a slave and a coward
if I owned thee as my lord. Not so; play the master
over others, but think not to master me. As for the
prize which the Greeks gave me, let them do as they will.
They gave it; let them take it away.' But if thou darest
to touch aught that is mine own, that hour thy life-
blood shall redden on my spear."

Then the assembly was dismissed. Chryseïs was
sent to her home with due offerings to the god, the wise
Ulysses going with her. And all the people purified
themselves, and offered offerings to the Gods; and the
sweet savor went up to heaven in the wreathing smoke.

But King Agamemnon would not go back from his
purpose. So he called to him the heralds, Talthybius
and Eurybates, and said, —

"Heralds, go to the tents of Achilles, and fetch the
maiden Briseïs. But if he will not let her go, say that
I will come myself with many others to fetch her; so
will it be the worse for him."

Sorely against their will the heralds went. Along
the seashore they walked, till they came to where,
amidst the Myrmidons, were the tents of Achilles.
There they found him, sitting between his tent and
his ship. He did not rejoice to see them, and they stood
in great terror and shame. But he knew in his heart
wherefore they had come, and cried aloud, "Come near,
ye heralds, messengers of Gods and men. 'T is no fault
of yours that ye are come on such an errand."

Then he turned to Patroclus (now Patroclus was his dearest friend) and said, —

"Bring the maiden from her tent, and let the heralds lead her away. But let them be witnesses, before gods and men, and before this evil-minded king, against the day when he shall have sore need of me to save his hosts from destruction. Fool that he is, who knoweth not to look back and to look forward, that his people may be safe!"

Then Patroclus brought forth the maiden from her tent, and gave her to the heralds. And they led her away; but it was sorely against her will that she went. But Achilles went apart from his comrades, and sat upon the seashore, falling into a great passion of tears, and stretching out his hands with loud prayer to his mother, Thetis, daughter of the sea. She heard him where she sat in the depths by her father, the old god of the sea, and rose from the gray sea, as a vapor rises, and came to where he was weeping, and stroked him with her hand, and called him by his name.

"What ails thee, my son?" she said.

Then he told her the story of his wrong, and when he had ended he said, —

"Go, I pray thee, to the top of Olympus, to the palace of Zeus. Often have I heard thee in my father's hall boast how, long ago, thou didst help him when the other gods would have bound him, fetching Briareus of the hundred hands, who sat by him in his strength, so that the Gods feared to touch him. Go now, and call these things to his mind, and pray him that he help the sons of Troy, and give them victory in the battle, so

195

that the Greeks, as they flee before them, may have joy of this king of theirs, who has done such wrong to the bravest of his host."

And his mother answered him, "Surely thine is an evil lot, my son. This life is short, and it should of right be without tears and full of joy; but now it seems to me to be both short and sad. But I will go as thou sayest to Olympus, to the palace of Zeus; but not now, for he has gone, and the other Gods with him, to a twelve days' feast with the pious Ethiopians. But when he cometh back I will entreat and persuade him. And do thou sit still, nor go forth to battle."

Meanwhile Ulysses drew near to Chryse with the holy offerings. And when they were come within the haven, they furled the sail, and laid it in the ship, and lowered the mast, and rowed the ship to her moorings. They cast out the anchor stones, and made fast the cables from the stern. After that they landed, taking with them the offerings and the maid Chryseïs. To the altar they brought the maid, and gave her into the arms of her father, and the wise Ulysses said, "See now; Agamemnon, King of men, sends back thy daughter, and with her a hundred beasts for sacrifice, that we may appease the god who hath smitten the Greeks in his wrath."

Then the priest received his daughter right gladly, and when they had ranged the beasts about the altar, and poured out the water of purification, and taken up handfuls of bruised barley, then the priest prayed, "Hear me, God of the silver bow! If before thou didst hearken to my prayer, and grievously afflict the Greeks, so hear me now, and stay this plague which is come upon them."

So prayed he, and the god gave ear.

Then they cast the barley on the heads of the cattle, and slew them, and flayed them, and they cut out the thigh-bones and wrapped them up in folds of fat, and laid raw morsels on them. These the priest burned on fagots, pouring on sparkling wine; and the young men stood by, having the five-pronged forks in their hands. And when the thighs were consumed, then they cut up the rest, and broiled the pieces carefully on spits. This being done, they made their meal, nor did any one lack his share. And when the meal was ended, then they poured a little wine into the cups to serve for libations to the Gods. After that they sat till sunset, singing a hymn to the Archer God, and making merry; and he heard their voice and was pleased.

When the sun went down, they slept beside the stern-cables; and when the dawn appeared, then they embarked, raising the mast and spreading the sail; and Apollo sent them a favoring wind, and the dark blue wave hissed about the stem of the ship as she went: so they came to the camp of the Greeks.

But all the time Achilles sat in wrath beside his ships; he went not to the war, nor yet to the assembly, but sat fretting in his heart, because he longed for the cry of the battle.

THE FIGHT BETWEEN PARIS AND MENELAUS

By Walter C. Perry

IN obedience to the summons of their leaders, the great host of the Achaians assembled on the plain of the flowing river Scamander, innumerable as the leaves and flowers in the season of spring. And in the midst of them stood the great ruler, Agamemnon: his head and eyes like those of Loud-thundering Zeus; his waist like that of the Man-slaying Mars; and with a breast like that of Neptune, the Ruler of the Sea. As the mail-clad Argives marched on, and rushed across the plain, the earth groaned beneath them.

Now Ægis-bearing Zeus sent his messenger, Iris, to the assembly of the Trojans, with the voice of Polites, son of Priam, their sentinel at Priam's gate, and spake thus to Hector: "This is no time for idle words, for stern war is already upon you. But to thee, O Hector, do I especially speak; and do thou obey my voice! As thou hast many allies, of diverse nations and tongues, let each chief marshal and command his own people, and lead them forth to war."

And the glorious Hector knew the voice of the messenger, and hastened to obey. He straightway dissolved the assembly. The gates of Troy were then thrown open, and the Trojan host rushed forth, with a mighty din. The blameless Hector, with his glancing helmet, was foremost of all, and led the bravest and strongest of the men; Æneas, son of the goddess Aphrodite, or Venus, born amidst the peaks of Ida, led the Dardans; and of the other leaders of the allies, the most famous were Sarpedon, son of Zeus, and blameless Glaucus, who led the Lycians, from distant Lycia, by the swift-eddying Xanthus.

And, as the countless hosts advanced, to meet each other in deadly conflict, the Trojans marched with noisy shouts, like the clamor of the cranes, when they fly to the streams of Oceanus, in the early morning, screaming, and bringing death and destruction to the Pigmy men; but the Achaians came on in silence, breathing dauntless courage.

But when they came near to each other, the goodly Paris went before the front rank of the Trojans, and brandished his spear, and challenged all the Argive chiefs to single combat. When the warlike Menelaus, whom Paris had so deeply wronged by carrying off his wife, the beautiful Helen, saw Paris there, he was glad, thinking that he should now punish the false traitor for his wickedness. So he leaped from his chariot, in his clanging armor, and advanced to meet the challenger. And Paris saw him; and pale fear got hold of him, like to a man who has trodden on a serpent, in a wooded valley among the mountains; and he shrank back among the lordly Trojans.

His brother Hector saw him, and reproached him with scornful words. "Base deceiver of women, beautiful in appearance and favor, but coward at heart! would that thou hadst never been born, or that thou hadst died unwedded! Now thou seest what kind of man is he, whose lovely wife thou hast carried off by stealth. Of no avail will be thy sounding lyre, thy beauteous face and curling hair, or all the gifts of golden Venus, when thou liest groveling in the dust."

And the goodly Paris answered him, "Hector, thou rightly chidest me, and not more than I deserve. *Thy* heart is ever undaunted, and keen as the axe, which cutteth the strong oak, in the hands of a skillful shipwright. But reproach me not for the lovely gifts of golden Aphrodite; for no man can obtain them by wishing for them, for they are among the precious gifts of the blessed Gods. But if thou desirest that I should do battle with the valiant Menelaus, make the Trojans and the Achaians sit down; and set me and Menelaus in the midst, to fight for Helen and for all the treasures which were taken away with her. And whichever of us twain shall be the victor, let him bear away the woman and the treasure, and take them home."

So spake he, and they all kept silence; but Menelaus of the loud war-cry stood forward amongst the Greeks and made harangue, "Hearken now to me, for my heart hath endured the greatest grief. Whosoever of us twain shall fall, there let him lie. But now bring a goodly sacrifice, a white ram and a black ewe, for the Earth and for the Sun; and another for Loud-thundering Zeus; and summon hither the great King Priam, that he may take the pledge; for his sons are reckless and faithless; young men's hearts are too frivolous and fickle, but an old man looketh to the future and the past."

FIGHT BETWEEN PARIS AND MENELAUS

And Hector sent heralds to the city, to fetch two lambs, and to summon Priam; while Agamemnon sent Talthybius for a ram. Now Iris, in Troy, came to Helen, in the semblance of Laodice, Paris's sister, fairest of Priam's daughters, wife of Helicaon, the son of Antenor. She found Helen weaving a great purple web, on which she was embroidering the battles of the Argives and the Trojans. The swift-footed Iris came near her, and said, "Come hither, dear lady, come with me, to see the wondrous deeds of the horse-taming Trojans and the mail-clad Argives; for now the battle is suspended, while Paris, and Menelaus, dear to Mars, will fight alone with their spears, for *thee;* and thou wilt be the fair wife of the victor." So Iris spoke, and put into Helen's bosom a longing for her former husband, and for her darling daughter. Then Helen veiled her face, and went straightway to the Scæan Gate, letting fall a tear; and her two handmaidens, Æthre and Clymene, followed her.

On the tower above the Scæan Gate, she found the Trojan elders. These, on account of their age, had ceased from war, but were still good orators, with voices like the grasshoppers which sit upon a tree, and send forth their lily-like voice; so sat the elders of the Trojans on the Tower. When those ancient sages saw the fair Helen coming to them, they were astounded, and whispered one to another, "No wonder that the Trojans and the Achaians have suffered so many things for such a glorious woman! But, fair as she is, let her sail away, and not stay here to trouble us and our children after us."

But the aged King Priam addressed her kindly. "Dear Daughter! come hither, and see thy former husband and kinsmen! I do not blame *thee*, but the Gods, and especially Venus, by whom this sad war has been brought upon us. But tell me who is that huge Achaian warrior? Many are taller than he, but I have never seen a man so stately and royal." And the fair Helen, the daughter of Zeus, replied, "O venerable Father of my lord! would that death had been my lot, when I followed thy son to Troy, and left my home and husband, and my dear young daughter, and all the loved companions of my girlhood! But that was not to be, and therefore I mourn and weep. The man of whom thou speakest is Atreides, the wide-ruling monarch Agamemnon, who is both a stately king and a doughty warrior; he is the brother of Menelaus my husband — shameless thing that I am!"

Then the aged Priam asked her about the other Achaian chiefs, — Ulysses, and the gigantic Ajax, the bulwark of the host, and the godlike Idomeneus; and the lovely Helen told him all, and said, "I see all the other bright-eyed Achaians, and could tell their names; but two I see not, even mine own brothers, horse-taming Castor and the boxer Pollux; peradventure they came not with the Achaians; or if they came, they fight not, for fear of the revilings which men heap on me — shameless that I am!" She knew not that the earth already covered them, in Lacedæmon, their dear native land. Now the aged Priam drove out through the Scæan Gate, with Antenor by his side; and, when he had come to the Achaians and the Tro-

202

jans, he descended from his chariot, and stood on the Earth, the bounteous grain-giver. Then Agamemnon, the king of men, and Ulysses, the man of many devices, rose up; and the stately heralds brought the holy oath-offerings to the gods, and mixed the ruddy wine in the mixing-bowl, from which they gave portions to the Achaian and the Trojan chiefs. Agamemnon raised his hands to heaven and prayed, "O Father Zeus, most great and glorious! O Sun, who seest and hearest all things! O ye Rivers, and thou, Mother Earth! be ye all witnesses to our oaths! If Paris shall kill Menelaus, then let him keep Helen and all her possessions; but if the yellow-haired Menelaus slay Paris, then let the Trojans give back Helen and her treasures!"

Then the lordly Agamemnon slew the lambs, and prayed again to Zeus. But Priam spake unto the Achaians and the Trojans. "I verily will return to breezy Ilium; for I cannot bear to see my own son engaged in deadly conflict with the war-loving Menelaus."

Then the goodly Paris, lord of the fair-haired Helen, put on his beautiful armor. First he set the splendid greaves upon his legs, fastened round the ankles with silver clasps; then he donned the corslet, which he had borrowed from his brother Lycaon; and he threw over his shoulders the silver-studded sword-belt with his sword, and took up his mighty shield; and upon his beauteous head he placed the helmet, with a horse-hair crest, and the plume nodded terribly; and he took a strong spear in his hand.

Then he and Menelaus stood face to face, on the ground which Hector and Ulysses had meted out; and they brandished their spears, with wrath against each other. Paris drew the lot to be the first to cast his long-shafted spear; he threw it, and it struck the round shield of Atreides Menelaus, but did not pierce it; for the point of the spear was turned.

Then Menelaus, poising his lance, prayed to Zeus, "O Father Zeus! grant me to take vengeance on goodly Paris, who did me such foul wrong — *me*, who had shown him so much kindness!" He said, and hurled his strong spear, which struck the bright shield of the son of Priam; and the sharp point passed through it, and through his breastplate, and rent the tunic, close to the side of his body; but Paris swerved from it, and shunned the black fate of death. Then Menelaus drew his sword from the silver-studded sheath, and smote on the helmet of Paris, but the sword was shattered, and fell in pieces from his hand. Then he looked up to heaven, and exclaimed, "O Father Zeus! thou art the most cruel of all the Gods!"

So saying, he caught Paris by his horse-hair crest, and dragged him towards the well-greaved Achaians, and the embroidered strap of the helmet went nigh to strangle him. But Venus, daughter of great Zeus, who loved the beauteous Paris, drew near him, and tore the strap of leather; and the helmet came away, empty, in the strong hand of the son of Atreus. Full of wrath, he hurled it towards his trusty companions, and they took it up. He then rushed back again, to slay his enemy; but golden-haired Venus, being a goddess, easily caught up Paris, and hid him in thick darkness, and carried him into Troy, to his high and fragrant chamber.

Venus, the golden Goddess of Love, then went to summon Helen, in the likeness of an old woman, a wool-comber, who had worked for Helen in Lacedæmon, and whom she greatly loved. She found the white-armed Helen on the high tower, and spake: " Come hither to Paris, who sends for thee; he is there in the fragrant chamber, shining in beauty —

> " Not like a warrior parted from the foe,
> But some fair dancer from the public show."
>
> (Pope's Translation of the *Iliad*.)

But Helen's heart was greatly moved; she knew the golden Venus, saw her fair neck and sparkling eyes, and called her by her name. " O thou strange Goddess! wouldst thou again deceive me? Now Menelaus hath conquered Paris, and will carry me home — accursed as I am! And now do *thou* no more return to Olympus, but leave the dwelling of the Gods, and go and sit by Paris, till he make *thee* his wife — or perchance, his slave. But *I* will not go to him; for all the Trojan women would justly blame me hereafter; I have innumerable griefs within my heart."

Then was the bright goddess sore displeased, and spake harshly to her. " Beware! thou foolish woman! lest in my wrath I leave thee, and henceforth hate thee, as I have loved thee until now!" Venus spake, and Helen, daughter of great Zeus, trembled and obeyed, wrapping her beautiful garments about her; and the goddess led her to the fragrant chamber in the palace, and set her on a chair before the goodly Paris.

But Helen looked askance at her lord, and chode him with bitter words. "Would that thou hadst never come back from the fight, but hadst perished by the arm of the warrior who was once my husband! Thou didst boast thyself to be a better man than Menelaus! Go then, and challenge him again, to meet thee face to face once more!"

Yet Helen, though she could not but despise Paris, soon became reconciled to him, partly from a remnant of her former love for him, and partly from her fear of Venus.

In the meantime, Menelaus was raging through the field in search of him. Nor could any of the Trojans find him, or they would have given him up; for they hated him like death, as the cause of all their sufferings.

And King Agamemnon said to the Trojans, "Now that the Mars-loving Menelaus hath conquered Paris do ye give back to us Helen and all her treasures!" But this was not to be.

THE DUEL BETWEEN HECTOR AND AJAX

By Walter C. Perry

AND now we must speak of Hector, the noble Trojan prince, who, after Achilles, was the most famous warrior of the two hostile armies. Achilles, indeed, was the son of a goddess, even silver-footed Thetis; while Hector's mother, Hecuba, was a mortal woman.

Well knowing the dangers to which he was exposed, and how soon he might fall in battle, Hector now bethought him of his lovely wife, Andromache, and his little boy Astyanax. When he came to the Scæan Gate, the Trojan women came running to him, with eager questions about their husbands, sons, and brothers; and sorrow filled their hearts. Among them came his fond and generous mother, Hecuba, leading by the hand the fairest of her daughters, Laodice, and she called him by his name, and spoke: "Dear Son! why hast thou left the field? Do the Achaians press thee hard? Dost thou come to make prayers to Father Zeus, from the Citadel? But come, I will bring thee honey-sweet wine, that thou mayest pour out a libation to Almighty Zeus, the Son of Cronos, and refresh thyself with a draught."

But Hector answered her, "Bring me no luscious wine, dear mother! lest thou rob me of my strength and courage. Nor dare I make a libation to Zeus, with hands unwashen and soiled with blood. But go thou to the Temple of Athene, driver of the spoil; and lay the finest robe, the most precious to thyself, upon her knees; and vow to sacrifice twelve fat kine to her; and beg her to have mercy on the Trojans, and on their wives and little children! So, perhaps, she will hold back the terrible warrior, Tydides, from sacred Ilium. And I will go and seek out Paris; would that the earth would swallow him up! for Zeus hath cherished him to be the bane of his country, and of his father Priam."

Then Hecuba went to her ambrosial chamber, and took the finest of her embroidered robes, the work of Sidonian women, which shone like a star; and went, with other aged women, to the temple of Athene. And the fair-cheeked Theano, daughter of Kisseus, the priestess, wife of Antenor, opened the temple gates, and took the shining robe, and laid it upon Athene's knees, and prayed to the great daughter of Zeus. But the goddess did not grant her prayer.

But Hector went his way to the fair palace of Paris, and found him in his chamber, polishing his beautiful armor, and proving his curved bow. Then, when Hector saw him, he reproached him with bitter words. "O thou strange man! thou dost not well to nurse thy spite against the Trojans, who are now perishing before the city, and all for thy sake! Rise, then, now, lest the city be burned with fire!"

And the goodly Paris answered, "It is not so much by reason of my wrath against the Trojans, but I would fain indulge my sorrow. My wife, too, hath urged me to the battle. Tarry then awhile, and I will don my armor; or go thou before, and I will follow."

Then the divine Helen, daughter of great Zeus, came and spoke gently to Hector, and said, "O brother! brother of vile *me*, who am a dog — would that, when my mother bare me, the storm-wind had snatched me away to a mountain, or a billow of the loud-roaring sea had swept me away, before all these evil things had befallen me! Would that I had been mated with a better man than Paris, whose heart is not sound, and never will be. But come, my brother, and sit by me; for thou verily hast suffered most for me, who am a dog, and for the grievous sin of Paris, upon whom, surely, Zeus is bringing evil days; he will be, hereafter, a song of scorn in the mouths of future men, through all time to come."

But noble Hector answered her, "If thou lovest me, dear Helen, bid me not stay; for I go to succor my friends, who long for me in my absence. But do thou try and rouse this husband of thine, and bid him overtake me. As for me, I shall first go to my home, and to my wife and my little son; for who knoweth whether I shall ever return to them again?"

So spake the glorious Hector, and went his way to his own well-furnished house; but he found not Andromache there; for she had gone to the tower, with her fair-robed nurse and with her boy, all bathed in tears. Hector asked the servants whither the white-armed Andromache was gone; and the busy matron of the house replied, "She is gone to the tower of holy Troy; for she heard that the Trojans were defeated, and the Achaians victorious." Then Hector returned, by the same way, down the wide streets, and came to the Scæan Gate.

And his peerless wife, even Andromache, daughter of the high-minded Eëtion, king of Cilicia — she whom he had won by countless gifts — came running to meet him. And with her came the handmaid, the nurse, bearing in her arms Hector's tender boy, Astyanax, beautiful as the morning star. And Hector smiled, and looked on his darling boy, while Andromache stood beside him weeping. And she clasped his hand, and called him by his name. "O my dear lord, thy dauntless courage will destroy thee! Hast thou no pity for thy infant child, and for thy hapless wife, who soon will be a widow? It were far better for me to die, if I lose *thee;* for nevermore can I know comfort, but only pain and sorrow. For I shall be utterly alone. I have neither father nor mother; for Eëtion, my royal sire, was slain by great Achilles. And all my seven brothers went down to Hades on the selfsame day! they too were slain by swift-footed Pelides. But my mother was smitten in her father's halls, by the gentle arrows of the archer Artemis. Lo! now, *thou* art all in all to me, father, mother, brother, and dearly loved husband! Come, then, take pity on us, and abide in the tower, and make not thy boy an orphan, and thy wife a widow!"

And the glorious Hector of the glancing helm answered her, and said, "Dear Wife! I too think of all these things. But how can I shun the battle, like a coward, to be the mock of the Trojans, and of the Trojan dames with trailing robes? I, who have always fought in the van of battle, and won glory for my father and myself? I know that the day will come, when sacred Ilium shall be leveled with the ground, and Priam and the people of Priam shall perish. But it is not so much the fate of Priam, and of my mother, Hecuba, and of my brethren, which fills my soul with anguish; but it is *thy* misery, dear one, in the day when some Achaian warrior shall bear thee away, weeping, and rob thee of thy freedom. Thou, alas! wilt abide in Argos, and ply the loom, the slave of another woman; or bear water from the Hypereian fount, being harshly treated! And one will say, as he looketh upon thee, 'This was the wife of Hector, the foremost of the horse-taming Trojans in the war round Ilium.' But may the deep earth cover *me*, ere I hear thee crying in the day of thy captivity."

So spake he, and held out his arms to take his darling boy. But the child shrank crying, and nestled in the bosom of his well-girdled nurse; for he feared the horse-hair crest, nodding terribly from the brazen helmet. Then the fond parents laughed; and Hector doffed his helmet, and laid it on the ground. And he kissed his dear child, and fondled him, and prayed thus to Zeus:—

"O Zeus! and all ye Gods! grant that this, my son, may like me be foremost to fight among the Trojans, and rule as a king in Ilium; so that men may say, 'He is far better than his father'!"

Thus speaking, he laid the child in the fragrant bosom of his dear wife Andromache; and he pitied her, and caressed her with his hand, and called her by her name. "Dear one! be not thus utterly cast down. No man can slay me till my hour of destiny is come. But no man, when once he hath been born, can escape his fate, be he a brave man or a coward. Go thou to thy house, to the distaff and the loom, and make thy maidens ply their labors. But *men* shall engage in war, and I the first of all in Troy."

So spake Hector of the glancing helmet, and went his way. And his dear wife went to her home, looking back at him as she went, shedding bitter tears. And she found her maidens there, and with them she bewailed her lord, while yet he lived; for they feared that he would never again return from battle.

And the goodly Paris donned his beautiful armor, and hastened after his brother, whom he overtook, and he made excuse for his long tarrying. And Hector answered him, "No man can justly speak lightly of thy deeds, for thou art strong; but thou art slack and careless, and I am grieved when I hear shameful things said of thee by the Trojans, who for thee bear so much toil. But let us be going."

So the twain brothers, the glorious Hector and the goodly Paris, went forth to the battle. And Paris slew Menesthius, of Arne, son of Areïthous; and Hector smote noble Eïoneus in the neck, and relaxed his limbs in death. And Glaucus, captain of the Lycian allies, cast his spear at Iphinous, and pierced his shoulder; and he fell from his chariot, and his limbs were loosened.

But when the fierce-eyed Athene saw the Trojans making havoc of the Achaians, she rushed down from the peaks of Olympus, to sacred Ilium. And Apollo, who favored the Trojans, saw her from Pergamus, and hastened to meet her; and they met by the beech-tree, and Apollo of the Silver Bow addressed her: "Why dost thou come, O Daughter of the Loud-Thunderer? Is it to bring victory to the Greeks? for thou hast no pity on the Trojans. But hearken unto me, and let us stop the battle for this day — hereafter they shall fight again."

And the fierce-eyed goddess answered him, "Be it so, Far-Darter! for this was my purpose when I came from high Olympus. But how thinkest thou to make the war to cease?"

Then King Apollo spake. "Let us rouse the valiant spirit of horse-taming Hector, to challenge one of the Greeks to deadly single combat." And the fierce-eyed Maid assented to his words.

And the dear son of royal Priam, Helenus, the wise augur, who knew the counsel of the Gods, drew near to Hector, and spake thus to him: "Dear brother, who art peer of Zeus in counsel, wouldst thou listen to me? Make the Trojans and the Achaians sit down; and do thou challenge the bravest of the Achaians to meet thee in single combat. I hear the voice of the deathless Gods, that it is not yet thy lot to die."

And the great Hector rejoiced at his words; and going into the throng, he held back the companies of the Trojans with his spear, holding it in the middle, and made them all sit down. And Agamemnon made the well-greaved Achaians sit down. And Athene and Apollo, in the form of vultures, sat on a lofty tree, and watched the hosts. And Hector stood between the two armies, and spake: "Hear me, ye Trojans and Achaians! Amongst you are the great chiefs of the Achaians. Now let one of these be your champion, to fight with me, Hector: and I call Zeus to witness, that if he slay me, you shall let him carry off my armor, but give my body to the Trojans, that they may render to me the honor of the funeral pyre. But if the Far-Darter shall grant me glory, that I may slay *him*, then will I strip him of his armor, and hang it in the Temple of Apollo; but his lifeless body I will give back to the long-haired Achaians, that they may bury him, and build him a barrow by the Hellespont."

Thus spake the glorious Hector; but all were silent; for they were afraid to meet him. Then, at last, Menelaus, groaning deeply, reproached the Achaians, and said, "O ye women of Achaia, no longer *men!* surely this will be an everlasting shame to us, if none of the Greeks dare to fight with the noble Hector! But I myself will arm me; for the issues of victory are with the Gods."

And he began to put on his dazzling armor. And now wouldst thou, Menelaus, have yielded up thy life at the hands of Hector; but the great ruler, Agamemnon, rose up and stayed thee. "Art thou mad, O foster-son of Zeus? Draw back, though with grief and pain; and think not to fight with Hector, the man-slaying son of Priam; for he is a far better man than thou; even godlike Achilles feareth to meet this man in battle. Go then and sit down; and we will choose another champion."

DUEL BETWEEN HECTOR AND AJAX

And the fair-haired Menelaus obeyed his brother's words, and his henchmen gladly took off his bright armor. And the wise Nestor arose, and upbraided all the Achaian chiefs: "Fie on us! Shame and lamentation have come upon us all. Surely the aged Peleus, the goodly king of the Myrmidons, would deeply groan, if he heard that we are all cowering before great Hector; he would pray that his soul might leave his body and go down to Hades. Would to Zeus, and to Athene and Apollo, that I were young, as when the Pylians met the Arcadians in battle, and Ereuthalion, the squire of King Lycurgus of Arcadia, wearing the divine armor of Areïthous, of the iron mace, before the walls of Pheia, by the waters of Iardanus, challenged all our host; and they were afraid and trembled. Then I, the youngest of all, stood up and fought with him, and Athene gave me great glory; for he was the tallest man, and of the greatest bulk, that I have ever slain. Would that I were still so young and strong! But of you, leaders of the Achaians, not one has heart enough to meet great Hector."

The wise old man's reproaches filled the Achaian chiefs with shame; and nine of them rose up, ready to fight; namely, Agamemnon, king of men; and the stalwart Diomedes; and Idomeneus, and his brother in arms, Meriones, equal in fight to murderous Mars; and Eurypylus, and Thaus, and the wily Ulysses, and two others. Then Nestor spake again. "Now cast lots for him that shall be champion." Then each man marked his lot, and threw it into Agamemnon's helmet; and all men prayed that the lot might fall on Ajax or

Diomedes, or the king of rich Mycenæ. Then Nestor shook the helmet, and the lot of Ajax leapt out; and the herald placed it in the hand of mighty Ajax, and he was glad; for he said, "I think that I shall vanquish goodly Hector." And they all prayed to the Son of Cronos, to give victory to Ajax, or to grant unto each of them equal glory and renown.

Then huge Ajax donned his bright armor of bronze, and came forth like the war-god Mars when he goeth to battle. The Achaians were glad, but the Trojans trembled; and even the brave Hector felt his heart beat quicker in his breast. But he would not shrink from the combat, seeing that he had himself challenged all the Achaians. And Ajax came on, bearing a mighty shield, like a tower, which Tychius, the cunning leather-worker, had made for him, of sevenfold hides of lusty bulls, all overlaid with bronze. And he stood near god-like Hector, and spake: "Now shalt thou see what manner of men the Greeks have among them, even now when Achilles, the lion-hearted, hath left us in his wrath. But do thou begin the fight!"

And Hector answered him, "Great Ajax, son of Telamon, sprung from Zeus! speak not to me as if I were a poor weak boy, or a woman! for I too have knowledge of war and slaughter. I know how to charge into the midst of the chariots, or, at close quarters, to join in the wild dance of Mars." He said, and hurled his long-shafted spear, and struck the sevenfold shield of Ajax; it passed through six folds, but was stopped by the seventh.

Then Ajax, sprung from Zeus, threw his ponderous

lance at the shield of mighty Priam's son. It passed
right through the bright shield, and through the well-
wrought corselet, and rent his tunic; but he swerved
aside, and escaped gloomy death. Then the two fell
upon each other, like ravening lions or wild boars;
and Hector smote the shield of Ajax with his spear,
but the sharp point was turned by the stout buckler.
Then Ajax leapt upon him, and drove his spear at
Hector's neck, making a wound from which the dark
blood flowed.

But Hector, undismayed, took up a great stone from
the ground, and with it smote the boss of Ajax's shield.
And Ajax heaved up a far bigger stone and threw it on
the buckler of Hector, and it fell on him like a huge
millstone, and stretched him on his back! But Apollo
raised him, and set him on his legs again.

Then they would have furiously attacked each other
with their swords, had not the Achaian herald, Talthybius, and the Trojan herald, Idaius, intervened
and stopped the fight, holding their staves of office between the godlike warriors; and Idaius spake to them:
"Fight no longer, brave youths; for Zeus loveth you
both; and we know well what gallant warriors ye are.
Night is upon us, whose commands it behooveth us to
obey."

And the Telamonian Ajax answered, "Let Hector
say those words; for it was he who challenged us."

And Hector of the shining helmet said, "Ajax,
since thou hast received strength and wisdom from
the Gods, and dost excel all the Achaians in the fight,
let us now cease from battle for the day, and hereafter

we will fight again, until the Gods shall give victory to one of us. Go now, and rejoice thy friends and kinsmen by the ships, and I will gladden the hearts of Trojan men and long-robed dames in the holy city of King Priam. But now let us exchange costly gifts, that Trojans and Achaians may say of us that we, having met in this heart-gnawing strife, have parted like good friends." He spake, and gave to Ajax a silver-studded sword; and Ajax gave him a purple belt. So they parted, and went their way; the one to the ships of the Achaians, and the other to the holy city of Troy. And the Trojans rejoiced that Hector had escaped unhurt from the unapproachable hands of mighty Ajax.

THE DEATH OF PATROCLUS AND THE BATTLE OF THE RIVER

By Alfred J. Church

PATROCLUS came and stood by the side of Achilles weeping. Then said Achilles, "What ails thee, Patroclus, that thou weepest like a girl-child that runs along by her mother's side, and would be taken up, holding her gown, and looking at her with tearful eyes till she lift her in her arms? Hast thou heard evil news from Phthia? Menœtius yet lives, they say, and Peleus. Or art thou weeping for the Greeks, because they perish for their folly?"

Then said Patroclus, "Be not wroth with me, great Achilles, for indeed the Greeks are in grievous straits, and all their bravest are wounded, and still thou cherishest thy wrath. Surely Peleus was not thy father, nor Thetis thy mother; but the rocks begat thee, and the sea brought thee forth. Or if thou goest not to battle, fearing some warning from the Gods, yet let me go, and thy Myrmidons with me. And let me put thy armor on me; so shall the Greeks have breathing-space from the war."

So he spake, entreating, nor knew that for his own doom he entreated. And Achilles made reply, —

"It is no warning that I heed, that I keep back from the war. But these men took from me my prize, which I won with my own hands. But let the past be past. I said I would not rise up till the battle should come nigh to my own ships. But thou mayest put my armor upon thee, and lead my Myrmidons to the fight. For in truth the men of Troy are gathered as a dark cloud about the ships, and the Greeks have scarce standing-ground between them and the sea. For they see not the gleam of my helmet. And Diomed is not there with his spear; nor do I hear the voice of Agamemnon, but only the voice of Hector as he calls the men of Troy to the battle. Go, therefore, Patroclus, and drive the fire from the ships. And then come thou back, nor fight any more with the Trojans, lest thou take my glory from me. And go not near, in the delight of the battle, to the walls of Troy, lest one of the Gods meet thee to thy hurt; and, of a truth, the keen Archer Apollo loves the Trojans well."

But as they talked the one to the other, Ajax could hold out no longer. For swords and javelins came thick upon him, and clattered on his helmet, and his shoulder was weary with the great shield which he held; and he breathed heavily and hard, and the great drops of sweat fell upon the ground. Then at the last Hector came near and smote his spear with a great sword, so that the head fell off. Then was Ajax sore afraid, and gave way, and the men of Troy set torches to the ship's stem, and a great flame shot up to the sky. And Achilles saw it, and smote his thigh and spake: —

"Haste thee, Patroclus, for I see the fire rising up from the ships. Put thou on the armor, and I will call my people to the war."

THE DEATH OF PATROCLUS

So Patroclus put on the armor — corselet, and shield, and helmet — and bound upon his shoulder the silver-studded sword, and took a mighty spear in his hand. But the great Pelian spear he took not, for that no man but Achilles might wield. Then Automedon yoked the horses to the chariot, Bayard and Piebald, and with them in the side harness, Pedasus; and they two were deathless steeds, but he was mortal.

Meanwhile Achilles had called the Myrmidons to battle. Fifty ships had he brought to Troy, and in each there were fifty men. Five leaders they had, and the bravest of the five was Pisander.

Then Achilles said, "Forget not, ye Myrmidons, the bold words that ye spake against the men of Troy during the days of my wrath, making complaint that I kept you from the battle against your will. Now, therefore, ye have that which you desired."

So the Myrmidons went to the battle in close array, helmet to helmet, and shield to shield, close as the stones with which a builder builds a wall. And in front went Patroclus, and Automedon in the chariot beside him. Then Achilles went to his tent and took a great cup from the chest, which Thetis his mother had given him. Now no man drank of that cup but he only, nor did he pour out of it libations to any of the Gods, but only to Zeus. This first he cleansed with sulphur, and then with water from the spring. And after this he washed his hands, and stood in the midst of the space before his tent, and poured out of it to Zeus, saying, "O Zeus, I send my comrade to this battle; make him strong and bold, and give him glory,

221

and bring him home safe to the ships, and my people with him."

So he prayed, and Father Zeus heard him, and part he granted and part denied.

But now Patroclus with the Myrmidons had come to where the battle was raging about the ship of Protesilaus, and when the men of Troy beheld him they thought that Achilles had forgotten his wrath and was come forth to the war. And first Patroclus slew Pyræchmes, who was the chief of the Pæonians who live on the banks of the broad Axius. Then the men of Troy turned to flee, and many chiefs of fame fell by the spears of the Greeks. So the battle rolled back to the trench, and in the trench many chariots of the Trojans were broken, but the horses of Achilles went across it at a stride, so nimble were they and strong. And the heart of Patroclus was set to slay Hector; but he could not overtake him, so swift were his horses. Then did Patroclus turn his chariot, and keep back those that fled, that they should not go to the city, and rushed hither and thither, still slaying as he went.

But Sarpedon, when he saw the Lycians dismayed and scattered, called to them that they should be of good courage, saying that he would himself make trial of this great warrior. So he leapt down from his chariot, and Patroclus also leapt down, and they rushed at each other as two eagles rush together. Then first Patroclus struck down Thrasymelus, who was the comrade of Sarpedon; and Sarpedon, who had a spear in either hand, with the one struck the horse Pedasus, which was of mortal breed, on the right shoulder, and with the other missed his aim, sending it over the left shoulder of Patroclus. But Patroclus missed not his aim, driving his spear into Sarpedon's heart. Then fell the great Lycian chief, as an oak, or a poplar, or a pine falls upon the hills before the axe. But he called to Glaucus, his companion, saying, "Now must thou show thyself a good warrior, Glaucus. First call the men of Lycia to fight for me, and do thou fight thyself, for it would be foul shame to thee, all thy days, if the Greeks should spoil me of my arms."

Then he died. But Glaucus was sore troubled, for he could not help him, so grievous was the wound where Teucer had wounded him. Therefore he prayed to Apollo, and Apollo helped him and made him whole. Then he went first to the Lycians, bidding them fight for their king, and then to the chiefs of the Trojans, that they should save the body of Sarpedon. And to Hector he said, "Little carest thou for thy allies. Lo! Sarpedon is dead, slain by Patroclus. Suffer not the Myrmidons to carry him off and do dishonor to his body."

But Hector was troubled to hear such news, and so were all the sons of Troy, for Sarpedon was the bravest of the allies, and led most people to the battle. So with a great shout they charged, and drove the Greeks back a space from the body; and then again the Greeks did the like. And so the battle raged, till no one would have known the great Sarpedon, so covered was he with spears and blood and dust. But at the last the Greeks drave back the men of Troy from the body, and stripped the arms, but the body itself they harmed not.

For Apollo came down at the bidding of Zeus, and carried it out of the midst of the battle, and washed it with water, and anointed it with ambrosia, and wrapped it in garments of the Gods. And then he gave it to Sleep and Death, and these two carried it to Lycia, his fatherland.

Then did Patroclus forget the word which Achilles had spoken to him, that he should not go near to Troy, for he pursued the men of the city even to the wall. Thrice he mounted on the angle of the wall, and thrice Apollo himself drove him back, pushing his shining shield. But the fourth time the god said, " Go thou back, Patroclus. It is not for thee to take the city of Troy; no, nor for Achilles, who is far better than thou art."

So Patroclus went back, fearing the wrath of the archer god. Then Apollo stirred up the spirit of Hector, that he should go against Patroclus. Therefore he went, with his brother Cebriones for driver of his chariot. But when they came near, Patroclus cast a great stone which he had in his hand, and smote Cebriones on the forehead, crushing it in, so that he fell headlong from the chariot. And Patroclus mocked him, saying, —

"How nimble is this man! how lightly he dives! What spoil he would take of oysters, diving from a ship, even in a stormy sea! Who would have thought that there were such skillful divers in Troy!"

Then again the battle waxed hot about the body of Cebriones, and this too, at the last, the Greeks drew unto themselves, and spoiled it of the arms. And this being accomplished, Patroclus rushed against the men of Troy. Thrice he rushed, and each time he slew nine chiefs of fame. But the fourth time Apollo stood behind him and struck him on the head and shoulders, so that his eyes were darkened. And the helmet fell from off his head, so that the horse-hair plumes were soiled with dust. Never before had it touched the ground, for it was the helmet of Achilles. And also the god brake the spear in his hand, and struck the shield from his arms, and loosed his corselet. All amazed he stood, and then Euphorbus, son of Panthous, smote him on the back with his spear, but slew him not. Then Patroclus sought to flee to the ranks of his comrades. But Hector saw him, and thrust at him with his spear, smiting him in the groin, so that he fell. And when the Greeks saw nim fall, they sent up a terrible cry. Then Hector stood over him and cried, —

"Didst thou think to spoil our city, Patroclus, and to carry away our wives and daughters in the ships? But lo! I have slain thee, and the fowls of the air shall eat thy flesh; nor shall the great Achilles help thee at all, — Achilles, who bade thee, I trow, strip the tunic from my breast, and thou thoughtest in thy folly to do it."

But Patroclus answered, "Thou boasteth much, Hector. Yet *thou* didst not slay me, but Apollo, who took from me my arms, for had twenty such as thou met me, I had slain them all. And mark thou this: death and fate are close to thee by the hand of the great Achilles."

And Hector answered, but Patroclus was dead already, "Why dost thou prophesy death to me? Maybe the great Achilles himself shall fall by my hand."

Then he drew his spear from the wound, and went after Automedon, to slay him, but the swift horse of Achilles carried him away.

Fierce was the fight about the body of Patroclus, and many heroes fell, both on this side and on that.

Meanwhile Antilochus, son of Nestor, ran to Achilles and said, "I bring ill news; Patroclus lies low. The Greeks fight for his body, but Hector hath his arms."

Then Achilles took of the dust of the plain in his hand, and poured it on his head, and lay at his length upon the ground, and tare his hair. And all the women wailed. And Antilochus sat weeping; but ever he held the hands of Achilles, lest he should slay himself in his great grief.

Then came his mother, hearing his cry, from where she sat in the depths of the sea, and laid her hand on him and said, —

"Why weepest thou, my son? Hide not the matter from me, but tell me."

And Achilles answered, "All that Zeus promised thee for me he hath fulfilled. But what profit have I, for my friend Patroclus is dead, and Hector has the arms which I gave him to wear. And as for me, I care not to live, except I can avenge me upon him."

Then said Thetis, "Nay, my son, speak not thus. For when Hector dieth, thy doom also is near."

And Achilles spake in great wrath: "Would that I might die this hour, seeing that I could not help my friend, but am a burden on the earth, — I, who am better in battle than all the Greeks besides. Cursed be the wrath that sets men to strive the one with the

FIERCE WAS THE FIGHT ABOUT THE BODY OF PATROCLUS AND MANY HEROES FELL

other, even as it set me to strive with King Agamemnon! But let the past be past. And as for my fate—let it come when it may, so that I first avenge myself on Hector. Wherefore, seek not to keep me back from the battle."

Then Thetis said, "Be it so; only thou canst not go without thy arms which Hector hath. But to-morrow will I go to Vulcan, that he may furnish thee anew."

But while they talked the men of Troy pressed the Greeks more and more, and the two heroes, Ajax the Greater and Ajax the Less, could no longer keep Hector back, but that he should lay hold of the body of Patroclus. And indeed he would have taken it, but that Zeus sent Iris to Achilles, who said,—

"Rouse thee, son of Peleus, or Patroclus will be a prey for the dogs of Troy."

But Achilles said, "How shall I go?— for arms have I none, nor know I whose I might wear. Haply I could shift with the shield of Ajax, son of Telamon, but he, I know, is carrying it in the front of the battle."

Then answered Iris, "Go only to the trench and show thyself; so shall the men of Troy tremble and cease from the battle, and the Greeks shall have breathing-space."

So he went, and Athene put her ægis about his mighty shoulders, and a golden halo about his head, making it shine as a flame of fire, even as the watch-fires shine at night from some city that is besieged. Then went he to the trench; with the battle he mingled not, heeding his mother's commands, but he shouted aloud, and his voice was as the sound of a trumpet. And when the men of Troy heard, they were stricken with fear, and the horses backed with the chariots, and the drivers were astonished when they saw the flaming fire above his head which Athene had kindled. Thrice across the trench the great Achilles shouted, and thrice the men of Troy fell back. And that hour there perished twelve chiefs of fame, wounded by their own spears or trampled by their own steeds, so great was the terror among the men of Troy.

Right gladly did the Greeks take Patroclus out of the press. Then they laid him on a bier, and carried him to the tent, Achilles walking with many tears by his side.

But on the other side the men of Troy held an assembly. Standing they held it, for none dared to sit, lest Achilles should be upon them.

Then spake Polydamas: "Let us not wait here for the morning. It was well for us to fight at the ships while Achilles yet kept his wrath against Agamemnon. But now it is not so, for to-morrow he will come against us in his anger, and many will fall before him. Wherefore, let us go back to the city, for high are the walls and strong the gates, and he will perish before he pass them."

Then said Hector, "This is ill counsel, Polydamas. Shall we shut ourselves up in the city, where all our goods are wasted already, buying meat for the people? Nay, let us watch to-night, and to-morrow will we fight with the Greeks. And if Achilles be indeed come forth from his tent, be it so. I will not shun to meet him, for Mars gives the victory now to one man and now to another."

So he spake, and all the people applauded, not knowing what the morrow should bring forth.

Thus did it come to pass that Achilles went again into the battle, eager above all things to meet with Hector and to slay him.

But Apollo stood by Æneas, and spake to him: "Æneas, where are now thy boastings that thou wouldst meet Achilles face to face?"

Then Æneas answered, "Nay, I have stood up against him in the day when he took the town of Lyrnessus. But I fled before him, and only my nimble feet saved me from falling by his spear. Surely a god is ever with him, making his spear to fly aright."

Him Apollo answered again, "Thou, too, art the son of a goddess, and thy mother is greater than his, for she is but a daughter of the sea. Drive straight at him with thy spear, and let not his threats dismay thee."

Then Æneas stood out from the press to meet Achilles and Achilles said, "Fightest thou with me because thou hopest to reign over the men of Troy, or have they given thee a choice portion of ground, ploughland and orchard, to be thine when thou hast slain me? Thou wilt not find it easy. Dost thou not remember how thou fleddest before me in the day that I took Lyrnessus?"

Then Æneas answered, "Think not to terrify me with words, son of Peleus, for I, too, am the son of a goddess. Let us make a trial one of the other."

Then he cast his spear, and it struck the shield of

Achilles with so dreadful a sound that the hero feared lest it should pierce it through, knowing not that the gifts of the Gods are not easy for mortal man to vanquish. Two folds, indeed, it pierced, that were of bronze, but in the gold it was stayed, and there were yet two of tin within. Then Achilles cast his spear. Through the shield of Æneas it passed, and though it wounded him not, yet was he sore dismayed, so near it came. Then Achilles drew his sword, and rushed on Æneas, and Æneas caught up a great stone to cast at him. But it was not the will of the Gods that Æneas should perish, seeing that he and his sons after him should rule over the men of Troy in the ages to come. Therefore Neptune lifted him up, and bore him over the ranks of men to the left of the battle, but first he drew the spear out of the shield, and laid it at the feet of Achilles. Much the hero marveled to see it, crying, "This is a great wonder that I behold with mine eyes. For I see my spear before me, but the man whom I sought to slay, I see not. Of a truth Æneas spake truth, saying that he was dear to the immortal Gods."

Then he rushed into the battle, slaying as he went. And Hector would have met him, but Apollo stood by him and said, "Fight not with Achilles, lest he slay thee." Therefore he went back among the men of Troy. Many did Achilles slay, and among them Polydorus, son of Priam, who, because he was the youngest and very dear, his father suffered not to go to the battle. Yet he went, in his folly, and being very swift of foot, he trusted in his speed, running through the foremost of the fighters. But as he ran Achilles smote him and wounded him to the death. When Hector saw it, he could not bear any more to stand apart. Therefore he rushed at Achilles, and Achilles rejoiced to see him, saying, "This is the man who slew my comrade;" and to Hector he cried, "Come hither, and taste of death."

And Hector made answer, "Son of Peleus, seek not to make me afraid with words. For though I be weaker than thou, yet victory lieth on the knees of the Gods, and I, too, bear a spear."

Then he cast his spear, but Athene turned it aside with her breath, and laid it again at his feet. And when Achilles leapt upon Hector with a shout, Apollo snatched him away. Three times did Achilles leap upon him, and three times he struck only the mist. But the fourth time he cried with a terrible voice, "Dog, thou hast escaped from death, Apollo helping thee; but I shall meet thee again, and make an end of thee."

Then Achilles turned to the others, and slew multitudes of them, so that they fled, some across the plain, and some to the river, the eddying Xanthus. And these leapt into the water as locusts leap into a river when a fire which men light drives them from the fields. And all the river was full of horses and men. Then Achilles leapt into the stream, leaving his spear on the bank, resting on the tamarisk trees. Only his sword had he, and with this he slew many; and they were as fishes which fly from some great dolphin in the sea. In all the bays of a harbor they hide themselves, for the great beast devours them apace. So did the Trojans hide themselves under the banks of the river. And when Achilles was weary of slaying, he took twelve alive, whom he would slay on the tomb of Patroclus.

Yet there was one man who dared to stand up against him, while the others fled. This was Asteropæus, who was the grandson of the river-god Axius, and led the men of Pæonia. And Achilles wondered to see him, and said, "Who art thou that standest against me?"

And he said, "I am the grandson of the river-god Axius, fairest of all the streams on the earth, and I lead the men of Pæonia."

And as he spake he cast two spears, one with each hand, for he could use either alike; and the one struck the shield, nor pierced it through, for the gold staved it, and the other grazed the right hand of Achilles so that the blood spurted forth. Then did Achilles cast his spear, but missed his aim, and the great spear stood fast in the bank. And thrice Asteropæus strove to draw it forth. Thrice he strove in vain, and the fourth time he strove to break the spear. But as he strove Achilles smote him that he died. Yet had he some glory, for that he wounded the great Achilles.

When the River saw that Asteropæus was dead, and that Achilles was slaying many of the Pæonians — for these were troubled, their chief being dead — he took upon him the shape of a man, and spake to Achilles, saying, "Truly, Achilles, thou excellest all other men in might and deeds of blood, for the Gods themselves protect thee. It may be that Zeus hath given thee to slay all the sons of Troy; nevertheless, depart from me and work thy will upon the plain; for my stream is choked with the multitude of corpses, nor can I pass to the sea. Do thou, therefore, cease from troubling me."

To him Achilles made answer, "This shall be as thou wilt, O Scamander. But the Trojans I will not cease from slaying till I have driven them into their city and have made trial of Hector, whether I shall vanquish him or he shall vanquish me."

And as he spake he sped on, pursuing the Trojans. Then the River cried to Apollo, "Little thou doest the will of thy father, thou of the Silver Bow, who bade thee stand by the men of Troy and help them till darkness should cover the land." And he rushed on with a great wave, stirring together all his streams. The dead bodies he threw upon the shore, roaring as a bull roareth; and them that lived he hid in the depths of his eddies. And all about Achilles rose up the flood, beating full upon his shield, so that he could not stand fast upon his feet. Then Achilles laid hold of a lime-tree, fair and tall, that grew upon the bank; but the tree brake therefrom with all its roots, and tare down the bank, and lay across the River, staying its flood, for it had many branches. Thereupon Achilles leapt out of the water and sped across the plain, being sore afraid. But the River ceased not from pursuing him, that he might stay him from slaughter and save the sons of Troy. So far as a man may throw a spear, so far did Achilles leap; strong as an eagle was he, the hunting-bird that is the strongest and swiftest of all birds. And still as he fled the River pursued after him with a great roar. Even as it is with a man that would water his garden, bringing a stream from a fountain; he has a pick-axe in his hand to break down all that would stay the water; and the stream runs on, rolling the pebbles along with it, and overtakes him that guides it. Even so did the River overtake Achilles, for all that he was swift of foot, for indeed the Gods are mightier than men. And when Achilles would have stood against the River, seeking to know whether indeed all the Gods were against him, then the great wave smote upon his shoulders; and when he leapt into the air, it bowed his knees beneath him and devoured the ground from under his feet. Then Achilles looked up to heaven and groaned, crying out, "O Zeus, will none of the Gods pity me, and save me from the River? I care not what else may befall me. Truly my mother hath deceived me, saying that I should perish under the walls of Troy by the arrows of Apollo. Surely it had been better that Hector should slay me, for he is the bravest of the men of Troy, but now I shall perish miserably in the River, as some herd-boy perisheth whom a torrent sweeps away in a storm."

So he spake; but Poseidon and Athene stood by him, having taken upon them the shape of men, and took him by the hand and strengthened him with comforting words, for Poseidon spake, saying, "Son of Peleus, tremble not, neither be afraid. It is not thy fate to be mastered by the River. He shall soon cease from troubling thee. And do thou heed what we say. Stay not thy hands from the battle, till thou shalt have driven all the sons of Troy that escape thee within the walls of the city. And when thou shalt have slain

Hector, go back to the ships; for this day is the day of thy glory."

Then the two departed from him. Now all the plain was covered with water, wherein floated much fair armor and many dead bodies. But Achilles went on even against the stream, nor could the River hold him back; for Athene put great might into his heart. Yet did not Scamander cease from his wrath, but lifted his waves yet higher, and cried aloud to Simois, "Dear brother, let us two stay the fury of this man, or else of a surety he will destroy the city of Priam. Come now, fill all thy streams and rouse thy torrents against him, and lift up against him a mighty wave with a great concourse of tree-trunks and stones, that we may stay this wild man from his fighting. Very high thoughts hath he, even as a god; yet shall neither his might nor his beauty nor his fair form profit him; for they shall be covered with much mud; and over himself will I heap abundance of sand beyond all counting. Neither shall the Greeks be able to gather his bones together, with such a heap will I hide them. Surely a great tomb will I build for him; nor will his people have need to make a mound over him when they would bury him."

Then he rushed again upon Achilles, swelling high with foam and blood and dead bodies of men. Very dark was the wave as it rose, and was like to have overwhelmed the man, so that Juno greatly feared for him, lest the River should sweep him away. And she cried to Vulcan, her son, saying, "Rouse thee, Haltfoot, my son! I thought that thou wouldst have been a match for Scamander in battle. But come, help us, and bring much fire with thee; and I will call the west wind and the south wind from the sea, with such a storm as shall consume the sons of Troy, both them and their arms. And do thou burn the trees that are by the banks of Xanthus, yea, and the River himself. And let him not turn thee from thy purpose by fury or by craft; but burn till I shall bid thee cease."

Then Vulcan lit a great fire. First he burned the dead bodies that lay upon the plain, and it dried all the plain, as the north wind in the autumn time dries a field, to the joy of him that tills it. After this it laid hold of the River. The lime-trees and the willows and the tamarisks it burned; also the plants that grew in the streams. And the eels and the fishes were sore distressed, twisting hither and thither in the water, being troubled by the breath of Vulcan. So the might of the River was subdued, and he cried aloud, "O Vulcan, no one of the Gods can match himself with thee. Cease now from consuming me; and Achilles may drive the men of Troy from their city if he will. What have I to do with the strife and sorrow of men?"

So he spake, for all his streams were boiling — as a cauldron boils with a great fire beneath it, when a man would melt the fat of a great hog; nor could he flow any longer to the sea, so sorely did the breath of the Fire-god trouble him. Then he cried aloud to Juno, entreating her: "O Juno, why doth thy son torment me only among all? Why should I be blamed more than others that help the men of Troy? Verily, I will cease from helping them, if he also will cease. Nay, I will swear a great oath that I will keep no more the day of doom from the sons of Troy; no, not when all the city shall be consumed with fire."

And Queen Juno heard him, and called to Vulcan, saying, "Cease, my son; it doth not beseem thee to work such damage to a god for the sake of a mortal man."

So Vulcan quenched his fire, and the River flowed as he flowed before.

VULCAN MAKES ARMOR FOR ACHILLES

By Walter C. Perry

ON high Olympus, the Loud-thundering Zeus spake mockingly to his consort, Juno, and said, "At length, thou hast what thou desirest, and hast roused Achilles to fight against the Trojans. Surely, the long-haired Achaians must be thine own children, since thou lovest them so dearly!"

And the ox-eyed queen replied, "Dread son of Cronos! what words are these which have passed the barrier of thy teeth? Even a mortal man doth what he can to help another; and shall not I, the chief of goddesses by birth and as thy wife — O thou king of the deathless Gods! — shall not *I* avenge myself upon the men of Troy?"

Thus these two strove with one another.

Meantime, the silver-footed Thetis came to the splendid palace of Vulcan, bright and immortal, which shone like a star among the mansions of the Gods. She found him at his bellows, sweating from his mighty toil; for he was forging twenty tripods, to stand round the walls of his well-built mansion. Beneath each of them he placed wheels of gold; and they move, of themselves, into the assembly of the Gods, and so return.

While he was thus employed, the silver-footed Thetis

approached the house. And Charis, of the shining veil, the wedded wife of Vulcan (whose first wife had been Aphrodite or Venus), came forth to meet her, and took her by the hand, and called her by her name. "O long-robed Thetis! dear and honored as thou art! not oft, I ween, dost thou come to visit us. But follow me, that I may show thee due hospitality."

Then she led the way in, and seated Thetis on a lofty chair with silver studs, beautiful, and cunningly wrought, and placed a footstool beneath her shining feet. And she called to Vulcan, the divine artificer, "Come hither, Vulcan! for the silver-footed Thetis seeketh thine aid."

And the glorious lame god answered, "Revered and dear to me is she; for she saved me, when my shameless mother threw me down from heaven; and I should have suffered dire anguish had not Eurynome, daughter of Oceanos, and Thetis taken me to their hearts and comforted me. Nine years I spent with them, and fashioned all kinds of curious work of bronze clasps, and spiral bracelets, and ear-rings, like the calyx of a flower, and necklaces — in the hollow grot, while all around me roared the streams of great Oceanus. And none of the other Gods knew where I was, but only Thetis and Eurynome. And now that she is come, a welcome guest, to my house, I will repay the fair-haired nymph in every way, for saving my life."

So saying, he raised his mighty bulk from the block, and, limping on his slender legs, moved quickly; and he put away his bellows, and placed his tools in a silver chest, and sponged his face and hands, his strong neck and hairy breast; then he donned his tunic, and leaning on a staff, he limped along. And golden handmaids, in the form of living maidens, came to help their lord; these have intelligent minds, and human voices, and skill from the deathless Gods. And he went with halting gait, and seated himself on a shining throne, near the silver-footed Thetis; and he took her by the hand, and said to her, "O dear and honored Thetis of the flowing robes! why comest thou to our house, thou, an infrequent guest?"

Then the silver-footed goddess answered him, "O Vulcan! hath Zeus, the son of Cronos, laid on any other goddess in Olympus such grievous woes as on *me*, unhappy that I am? He chose out me, from all the sea nymphs, to endure marriage with a mortal. A son I bare, the greatest of heroes. I brought him up, like a young tree in a fruitful soil, and sent him in a high-peaked ship to war against the Trojans; but never again will he return to me, in the halls of his aged father Peleus. And even while I yet see him, and he beholdeth the light of the sun, he is full of grief, and I cannot help him. For King Agamemnon took away his prize, the dearly loved maiden Briseis. For the loss of her, he pined and wept; nor would he allow his Myrmidons to join in the battle, though the Achaians were hard pressed and driven to their ships. The chiefs of the Argives came to him with prayers and tears, and many costly gifts. And though he refused himself to rescue them, he suffered Patroclus to put on his divine armor, and sent many of the Myrmidons with him to the battle. And the son of Menœtius performed high deeds of valor, and went near to sack the city. But the Far-Darting Apollo and glorious Hector slew him, and gained immortal glory. And now, I come as a suppliant, to clasp thy knees, and to pray that thou wouldst give my short-lived son a shield, a helmet, a breastplate, and goodly greaves."

Then the lame god, the famous artificer, replied, "Be of good cheer, O silver-footed Queen, and be not troubled about these things! Would that I could as surely save him from mournful death, as that I will supply him with goodly armor, a wonder to behold!"

And he returned to his workshop, and bade his bellows — there were twenty of them — blow the blasts on the fire and prepare the earthen moulds; and as Vulcan willed, the work was done. He melted the tough bronze and tin, the gold and silver, with the fire; and placed an anvil and took a strong hammer in one hand, and tongs in the other, and with these he worked.

First, he made the shield, broad and strong, with many decorations. Around it he placed a triple bright rim, and a silver strap depended from it. The shield itself was formed with five zones, in each of which he fashioned many curious works.

Therein he fashioned the Earth, the Sky, the Sea, the unwearied Sun, the Moon at the full, and all the bright luminaries which crown the azure firmament: the Pleiades, daughters of Atlas, the Hyades, the mighty Orion, and, turning about to watch Orion, the Bear, which alone of all the stars bathes not in the streams of Oceanus.

Also, on the shield, he sculptured two fair cities of articulate-speaking men. In one of these were wedding-festivals; and, with a blaze of torchlight, the brides were conducted from their chambers along the streets; while the hymeneal song was loud, and the youths whirled round and round in the giddy dance, to the music of flute and harp; while the women stood at their doors, watching and admiring. In that city he also fashioned an assembly of the people, in which a contention had arisen, about the blood-fine or "were-geld" for a murdered man; the people, with noisy shouts, cheered, on either side; but the heralds stilled the tumult, holding their staves of office in their hands; and then the judges rose up, to pronounce their verdict.

Around the other city lay two armies besieging it, with flashing arms. Two plans were considered: either to destroy the town, or to divide the wealth thereof with its citizens. But the beleaguered garrison had not yet yielded, but armed themselves and set an ambush. Their dear wives and children, and the old men, stood on the walls to defend it, while the strong men went forth to fight. And they were led by Mars and Athene, whose forms were fashioned in gold, with golden raiment; and, as gods, he made them larger and more beautiful than the mortals around them.

The men in ambush set upon the herdsmen who were driving oxen to the watering-place of the army, and making music with their pipes. They carried off the cattle; but the besiegers, as they sat before the rostra, heard the lowing of the oxen and drove up, with their high-stepping horses, to repel the raid. Then a fierce conflict arose; and in it were seen Strife, and Uproar, and Dire Fate; like living warriors, they rushed on one another, and haled away the dead whom they slew.

In another part of the shield, he represented a rich, deep-soiled, fallow field, thrice ploughed; and when the ploughers came to the end of the furrow, a man would give to each of them a goblet of sweet wine. And the ploughed ground grew black behind them, like real soil, although it was of gold. Then there, too, was a rich field of corn, where reapers were cutting the harvest with their sickles and it fell in rows; and others were binding it with bands of straw; while the lord looked on, and was glad at heart. And under a spreading oak a feast was being made ready for the reapers.

And he fashioned therein a vineyard, rich with clusters of black grapes, which the youths and maidens, in their glee, carried in baskets; while a boy, in their midst, made sweet music on a clear-sounding harp; and he sang the "Song of Linos," and the rest kept time with their feet.

And there was a herd of straight-horned oxen, all of gold and tin, hurrying to the pasture beside the gently murmuring stream and the waving rushes. Four herdsmen, of gold, followed them, and nine fleet dogs. And two terrible lions seized a bellowing bull. The herdsmen followed, but they could not set on their dogs to bite the lions, for the dogs shrank back, barking and whining, and turned away.

And therein the glorious divine artist placed a wide

pasture full of white sheep, with folds and tents and huts. And he made a dancing-ground, like that which Dædalus wrought at Gnosos for lovely fair-haired Ariadne. There, lusty youths in shining tunics glistening with oil, danced with fair maidens of costly wooing. The maidens had wreaths of flowers upon their heads; and the youths wore daggers hanging from silver sword-belts. They whirled round, with lightly tripping feet, swift as the potter's wheel, holding each other by the wrist; and then they ran, in lines, to meet each other. A crowd of friends stood round and joyfully watched the dance, and a divine minstrel made sweet music with his harp, while a pair of tumblers diverted the crowd.

Lastly, around the margin of the shield, Vulcan made the stream of the mighty river Oceanus, which encircleth the earth.

And when he had finished this strong and splendid shield, he wrought the breastplate, glowing with blazing fire; and he made a heavy helmet for the head, beautiful, and adorned with curious art; upon it was a crest of gold. But the goodly greaves he made of flexile tin. When he had completed the whole suit of glorious armor, he laid it before the silver-footed Thetis, the mother of Achilles; and she darted, swift as a hawk, from snowy Olympus, bearing the brightly glittering arms to her dear son.

THE SLAYING OF HECTOR

By Walter C. Perry

MEANTIME, Achilles went on slaughtering the Trojans; and the aged Priam stood on the sacred tower, and saw the son of Peleus driving the Trojans before him. And he shouted aloud to the brave warders of the gates, "Open the gates, that the fugitives may enter!" And the Far-Darter went to the front, to save the Trojans who were fleeing to the sheltering walls, with Achilles behind them in hot pursuit.

Then would the Achaians have stormed the lofty gates of Troy, had not Phœbus Apollo roused Agenor, a brave and noble prince, son of Antenor. Apollo stood by this man's side, leaning on an oak, and shrouded in mist, and put courage into his heart, that he might ward off fate from the Trojans. And when Agenor saw Achilles, he stood irresolute, and said to his mighty heart, "If I too flee before Achilles, he will catch me and slay me as a coward. Or shall I fly by another way, and hide me in the spurs of Ida? How, then, if I go forth to meet him? for his flesh, too, may surely be pierced by the keen bronze, and he has but one life, like other mortals."

And his heart grew strong within him, to stay and fight. And he cried out aloud to Achilles, "Surely, thou thinkest this very day to sack the proud city of

Troy? Fool! many terrible things will happen before
that; for there are many of us — many and brave —
to protect our dear parents and wives and little children,
and to guard holy Ilium. Thou, too, perhaps, mighty
as thou art, mayest here meet death."

He spake and hurled a spear at Achilles with his
strong hand. And it smote him below the knee, and the
tin-wrought greave rang loudly; but the stout spear
bounded off, for it could not pierce the work of Vulcan.

Then Achilles rushed on godlike Agenor; but him
Apollo caught in a mist, and carried him safely out of
the fray. And the god took the form of Agenor, and ran
a little way before Achilles, towards the deep-flowing
Scamander. And while Apollo thus deceived the mighty
son of Peleus, the routed Trojans ran, well pleased, to
their stronghold, and the great city was filled with their
multitude.

Then as he ran before Achilles, the mighty Far-
Darter addressed him, and spake: "O son of Peleus!
why dost thou, being a mortal man, pursue *me* with
thy swift feet, who am a deathless god?" Then, in
wrath, the son of Peleus answered him: "Thou hast
blinded me, most mischievous of all the Gods! and lured
me away from the walls; else would many a Trojan
have fallen, or ever he had reached the city." He then
went towards the city, with a proud heart, like a war-
horse victorious in a chariot race; and the aged Priam
saw him, blazing like the star in autumn brightest of
all, which men call "Orion's Dog," that bringeth fever
upon wretched mortals.

And the old man cried aloud, in his agony, and beat

his head with his fists, and called in a piercing voice
to his dear son Hector. For the brave hero, when all
the others had escaped into the city, remained alone
at the Scæan Gate eager to fight with Achilles. And
his wretched father stretched forth his withered hands,
and pleaded piteously to his son: —

"Hector! dear Hector! do not meet this terrible man
alone, for he is far mightier than thou, and knoweth
no pity. Already hath he robbed me of many a brave
son; and now I no longer see two of my children,
Lycaon and the goodly Polydorus, whom Laothoë,
princess among women, bare to me. But the death of
others will cause us briefer grief, if thou, dear Hector,
art not slain. Come, then, within the walls, and save
the men and women of Troy! And have pity on me,
too, to whom the son of Cronos hath allotted a terrible
doom in my old age — to see my brave sons dragged
away, and my fair daughters carried off, as captives,
by the cruel hands of the Achaians. Last of all, I too
shall be torn, on my own threshold, by ravenous dogs
— even the dogs which I myself have reared with food
from my table, to guard my house. They will tear my
flesh and drink my blood! It may well become a *young*
man to lie slain on the field, for he is highly honored
in his death; but when dogs defile an old man's head
and beard, this is the most lamentable thing that be-
falleth wretched mortals."

And the old man tore his hair in his sore agony;
but even he prevailed not with the soul of Hector.
And then his dear mother, Hecuba, took up the plaint
and spake through her piteous tears.

"Hector! my child! have respect to the mother who bare thee and nursed thee on this bosom! Pity *me!* and fight the foe from this side of the wall! For if he slay thee, not on a funeral bed shall I, and thy dear wife, won by so many gifts, deplore thee; but the swift dogs shall devour thee, far away from us, by the black ships of the Argives."

Thus wailed they over their glorious son, beseeching him; but they could not prevail, for honor held him fast. Meanwhile, Achilles drew nigh, in strength like a giant; but Hector awaited him undismayed, leaning his shield against the tower. And he communed thus with his brave soul: "Alas, if I go through the gates, Polydamas will justly blame me; for he gave me good advice — that I should lead the host into the city on that fatal night, when the noble Achilles returned to the war. And I would not hearken to him, although he counseled well. And now that I have brought this evil on the city by my folly, I am ashamed to appear before the men, and the proud dames with trailing robes, lest some one should taunt me and say, 'Hector in his pride hath ruined us.' Better then would it be for me to meet Achilles, and either slay him or fall with glory before the city. Or how would it be if I should lay aside all my arms, and go to meet the son of Peleus, and offer to restore Argive Helen and all her possessions to Menelaus and Agamemnon, and to divide the wealth of Troy with the Achaians? But no! I might come to him unarmed, but he is merciless, and would slay me on the spot, as if I were a woman. But why do I hesitate? This is no time to hold dalliance with him, from oak or rock, like youths and maidens. Better to fight at once, and see to whom Olympian Zeus will give the victory!"

While he thus pondered, Achilles, peer of Mars, came on, poising his terrible spear of Pelian ash; and his divine armor, the work of a god, blazed like fire or the rising sun. And when Hector saw him he was seized with panic, and he fled from the gates in terror.

But Achilles, swift of foot, rushed after him. As a falcon, swiftest of all birds, swoops upon the trembling dove, and takes no heed of her piteous screaming, so Achilles flew straight at Hector. And pursuer and pursued passed by the guard and the wild fig-tree, the sport of the winds, and came to the two springs of water, which feed the deep-whirling Scamander. Brave was he who fled, but mightier far was he who chased him on his swift feet; and they were racing not for some prize in the games, but for the life of the noble horse-taming Hector. And like horses in the race for a great prize — a tripod or a woman — so the twain ran thrice round the sacred city of King Priam; and all the Gods were looking on.

And Zeus, the great father of Gods and men, spake first: "Alas! I see a man whom I love above all others chased round the walls of Troy. Come now, let us take some counsel, whether to save him or leave him to be slain by the son of Peleus."

And the fierce-eyed Athene answered him, "O thou great Lord of the Lightning, Cloud-girt King! what a word hast thou spoken! Wouldst thou indeed save a mortal long ago doomed by Fate? Do as thou pleasest; but we Gods shall not praise thee."

And her great father, the Cloud-Gatherer, answered with gentle words, "O Trito-born, my dear child! be of good cheer. I spake not in earnest, and would fain please thee. Do as seemeth good to thee." And Athene, full of joy, sped down from high Olympus.

Achilles, with all speed, was chasing the noble Hector, as the dogs hunt the fawn of a deer through dale and woodland; and though the fawn hideth behind a bush, they follow by the scent until they find it; so Hector could not escape from the swift-footed son of Peleus. Often did Hector rush along the strong walls, in hopes that the Trojans within might succor him from above with their arrows. But Achilles gained on him and turned him into the plain again.

And so, though Hector failed in his flight and Achilles in his pursuit, yet might Hector have escaped his doom, had not this been the last time that Apollo the Far-Darter came nigh to him, to nerve his heart and his swift knees. Achilles had made a sign to his comrades, and forbade them to launch their darts against the noble Hector, lest one of them should gain high honor, and he come only second. And when they had, for the fourth time, run round the walls and reached the springs, then Zeus, the Great Father, raised his golden scales, and placed in each the lot of gloomy death, — one for Hector, and the other for Achilles. And he held the scales by the middle, and poised them; and the noble Hector's scale sank down to Hades; and Phœbus Apollo left him.

THE SLAYING OF HECTOR

But the fierce-eyed goddess Athene came near to Achilles and spake winged words: "Now, at last, O godlike Achilles! shall we twain carry off great glory to the Achaian ships! He cannot now escape us, though the Far-Darter should grovel at the feet of Zeus with fruitless prayers. But do thou stay and recover thy breath; and I will go and persuade Hector to stand up against thee in fight." And he gladly obeyed her voice, and stood leaning on his ashen spear.

And she, Athene, came to noble Hector in the likeness of his brother Deïphobus, and spake to him: "Dear Lord and elder Brother, surely the fleet-footed son of Peleus hath done great violence against thee, chasing thee round the walls! But let us twain make a stand against him!"

And the great Hector answered, "Deïphobus, thou wert ever the dearest of my brothers; now I honor thee still more, because thou hast dared to come out from behind the walls to aid me, while others skulk within."

The fierce-eyed goddess, as Deïphobus, spake again: "It is true that my father, and my queenly mother, and all my comrades, besought me to stay with them, so greatly do they fear the mighty son of Peleus; but my heart was sore for thee, dear brother! But let us fight amain, and see whether he will carry our spoils to his ships, or fall beneath thy spear!" And so, with her cunning words, she led him on to death.

And when he and Achilles were come near to each other, the noble Hector spake: "O mighty Achilles, thrice did I flee before thee round the great city of

Priam, and dared not await thy onslaught. But now I will stand up against thee, to slay or to be slain. But come, let us make a covenant with one another, and call the Gods, the best guardians of oaths, to witness. If Zeus grant me to take thy life, and despoil thee of thy divine armor, then will I give back thy body to the warlike Achaians; and do thou the same by me!"

And Achilles, with a malignant scowl, replied, "Speak not to me of covenants! There is no covenant between men and lions, or between wolves and sheep, but only eternal war. And there can be no pledge of faith between us twain, until one of us hath sated the murderous Mars with his blood. Therefore, show thyself a good spearman and a brave man of war! There is no escape for thee; for Pallas Athene hath delivered thee into my hands."

He spake, and cast his long-shafted spear at Hector. But Hector stooped, and the strong bronze spear flew over his head; but Athene picked it up, unknown to Hector, and gave it back to Achilles. Then Hector, rejoicing, spake to the son of Peleus: "Thou hast missed! Nor dost thou surely know the day of my doom, as thou pretendest. Thou shalt not plant thy spear in my back, as I flee before thee; but in my breast, if the Gods allow it. But now, in thy turn, avoid *my* spear!" So spake he, and smote the middle of Achilles' shield with his long-shafted spear, but it bounded back from the shield. Then Hector was dismayed, for he had no second spear to throw. And he called aloud to his brother, Deïphobus; but no answer came, for *he* was far away. Then Hector knew that he was betrayed, and that Athene had deceived him, in the likeness of his brother. "Now," he cried, "is Death come near me, and there is no way of escape! This is the will of Zeus and of the Far-Darter, who once were wont to succor me. But I will not die ingloriously, but yet perform some notable deed of arms."

He said, and, with his sharp sword, swooped down upon Achilles. But Achilles rushed at him, wild with fury, brandishing his spear, with evil intent against noble Hector, and eyed him over, to see where he might pierce his flesh most easily. The rest of Hector's body was protected by the splendid armor which he had stripped from the body of Patroclus; but there was one chink, between the collar-bone and the throat, through which Achilles thrust his spear. Yet it cut not the windpipe; and Hector was able to speak faint words to his insulting foe, after he had fallen to the ground.

Achilles triumphed over him: "Ah, Hector! when thou wert stripping Patroclus of my goodly armor, thou caredst nothing for me, who was far away! I, his friend and avenger, was left among the black ships — even I, a mightier man than he! Thee shall the dogs and birds devour; but he shall have honorable burial."

Then, with his last breath, the noble Hector of the bright helm addressed his pitiless foe: "Achilles! I pray thee, by thy soul, and by thy parents' heads, let not Achaian dogs devour me by the ships! but accept great store of gold and bronze from my father and my queenly mother, and restore my body to them, that the Trojans may deck my funeral pyre with all due honor!"

And Achilles, with a grim scowl, replied, "Clasp not my knees, vile dog! nor speak to me of parents! Such evil hast thou done me, that I could devour thee raw! Not for thy weight in gold would I give thee to thy queenly mother, to mourn over thee; but dogs and birds shall batten on thy flesh!"

Then the dying Hector uttered his last words: "Thou iron-hearted man! now I know thee; nor did I think to prevail upon thee. But beware of the wrath of the Gods, when Paris and the Far-Darter slay thee, at the Scæan Gate, brave though thou art!"

He spake; and Death overshadowed him; and his soul went down to Hades, wailing to leave beauty, youth, and vigor.

And Achilles spake again to the dead Hector: "Lie thou there! And as for me, I will die when it seemeth good to the deathless Gods!"

And the Achaians ran up, and looked with wonder at the noble stature and beauty of the Trojan hero. And they all inflicted wounds upon him, as he lay, saying, "He is easier to deal with now than when he was burning our ships with flames of fire."

And when the son of Peleus had stripped him of his armor, he stood up, and spake to the Achaians:—

"Great chiefs and counselors of the Argives! at last the Gods have granted us to slay this man, whose single arm hath wrought more evil to us than all the rest together. Let us now approach the city, and learn the purpose of the Trojans; whether they will now surrender the citadel or go on fighting, though great Hector is no more. But why do I thus ponder in my mind? Patroclus is lying unburied and unwept by the ships. Never can I forget him, while I live; and even in the House of Hades, I will remember my dearest friend. Come, then! let us raise the chant of victory, and bear our deadliest foe to the black ships!"

Then he foully outraged the dead body of glorious Hector; slitting the sinews of both feet, from heel to ankle, he passed ox-hide straps through them, and fastened them to his chariot, leaving the goodly head to trail upon the ground. Then he laid the armor on the chariot; and mounting it, lashed his willing horses to full speed. And in the dust lay the once beautiful head, with its flowing hair; for Zeus had now given Hector up to his enemies, to be foully used in his own native land.

And when his dear mother, Hecuba, saw her much-loved son dragged along, begrimed with dust, she tore her hair, and shrieked aloud, and tossed far away her glistening veil. And his father, King Priam, wailed and mourned; and with him all the men and women in the city, as if the beetling towers of Ilium were already smouldering in fire. Hardly could they keep the aged father from rushing through the gates; for he threw himself in the dust and supplicated each man by name: "O friend, forbear! and if you love me, let me go to the ships of the Achaians, and pray to this arrogant, this fearful man!" Thus wailed old Priam; and the men wailed with him. And Queen Hecuba led the loud lamentations of the women. "Why," she cried, "should I yet live, when thou, my son, my boast, my glory, art dead? the pride and blessing of all, both men and women of the city, who honored thee as a god; for in thy life thou wert an honor to them all!" Thus mourned his unhappy mother.

But to his wife, the noble, beautiful, tender-hearted Andromache, no messenger had brought the fearful tidings that Hector had remained without the gates. All unconscious, she was sitting in the inner chamber of her lofty palace, weaving a purple web of double woof, and embroidering it with many flowers. And she was ordering her handmaids to prepare a warm bath for her dear husband, when he should return from the battle; poor child! little knowing that the fierce-eyed Athene had treacherously slain him, by the hand of Achilles! But when she heard shrieks and lamentations from the walls, she reeled, and the shuttle dropped from her hands. And she spake again to her fair-haired maidens: "Surely, that was the cry of Hector's noble mother! Some terrible thing must have befallen my godlike husband! Come, then, follow me, that I may learn what has happened; I greatly fear that he has been cut off from the city by Achilles; for he would never retreat among the throng, or yield to any man, in his high courage."

And she rushed, all frantic, through the house, followed by her maidens, and came to the walls, and saw Hector dragged through the dust, towards the black ships of the Achaians. Then darkness shrouded her fair eyes, and she fell backwards in a swoon. And when roused, she tore from her head the net, the fillet, and the nuptial veil which golden Venus had given her, when noble Hector of the shining helm led her forth, from King Eëtion's palace, as his bride. And the sisters-in-law of her dear husband gathered round her, and raised her from the ground, all distracted as she was and nigh unto death. When she had recovered from her swoon, she sobbed and wailed, crying, " O Hector! to the same evil fate were we twain born, thou in Troy, and I in Thebes, where my great father, Eëtion, reared me as a little child. Would that I had never been born, since thou leavest me a hapless widow! And our son, thine and mine, ill-fated one! is but a little child; and thou canst no more profit him, nor he be a joy to thee, since thou art dead! A helpless orphan, he is cut off from his playmates; and if he pluck the robe of his father's friends, one may, in pity, just hold the cup to his lips, but give him not to satisfy his hunger and his thirst; while other children, whose parents still live, will drive him from their feast, with taunts and blows, saying, 'Away with thee! thou hast no father at our table!' Then will he come back to me, his lonely mother; he, who so lately sat on his father's knee, and fed on the choicest of food! and when sleep fell upon him, tired with his childish play, he nestled in a soft bed in his nurse's arms. But now that his father is no more, he shall suffer untold griefs, even he whom the Trojans called 'Astyanax,' king of the city, because thou, O my beloved lord! wert the sole defense and glory of their lofty walls." Thus wailed the fair Andromache; and the women moaned around her.

THE FUNERAL GAMES IN HONOR
OF PATROCLUS

By Walter C. Perry

THE noble Achilles could not do enough in honor
of his lost friend, Patroclus, and he had determined to hold games, of every kind, in which the mail-
clad Achaians might compete for prizes; and to this
end he had brought goodly treasures from his ships,
— tripods, and caldrons, horses, mules, and oxen,
well-girdled women, and hoary iron. The first and
most important contest was a chariot race, for which
he offered a woman skilled in needlework, and a two-
handled tripod, holding two-and-twenty measures —
these, for the best man of all; the second prize was a
mare, six years old, with a mule foal; the third prize
was a fair new caldron, of four measures; the fourth
was two talents of bright gold; the fifth was a two-
handled vase, untarnished by the fire.

And Achilles addressed the chiefs, and said, " If
the race were in honor of some other warrior, then
should I enter the lists, and bear away the prize; for
ye know that my horses are immortal, and by far the
best; Neptune, the Earth-Girdler, gave them to my
father, and he to me. But I and they will stand aside;
for they have lost a noble and gentle driver, who oft-
times washed them with clear water and then poured

soft oil upon their goodly manes! And now they stand with sorrow in their breasts, and their full long manes are trailing on the earth. But now, let whoever of you trusteth in his horses and his strong chariot take his place in the lists!"

And first came forward Eumelus, son of Admetus; next came the mighty Diomedes, with the famous horses of Tros, which he had taken from Æneas; then arose Menelaus, — the fair-haired, godlike Menelaus, with Aithe, Agamemnon's mare, and his own horse, Podargus; and the fourth was Antilochus, son of the wise Nestor, who yoked swift Pylian horses to his chariot.

His father Nestor, son of Neleus, stood by Antilochus, and gave him good advice, although he himself was wise. "Antilochus, my son," he said, "though thou art young, yet Zeus and Neptune have loved thee, and made thee a perfect horseman; and there is little need for me to teach thee. But the other horses are better than thine; and I fear that much trouble is in store for thee. But skill and cunning are better than force, and so one charioteer defeats another. Look well to the posts at either end, and run closely by them. Now I will tell thee another thing. Some six feet above the ground, there stands the withered stump of a tree, with two white stones, on either side; this is the mark fixed by the swift-footed Achilles. Do thou drive thy horses hard by this, and lean slightly to the left, and lash the off horse and give him rein; but let the near horse so closely skirt the post that the nave of the wheel of thy car may seem to graze the stone; but beware of touching it!"

Next, Meriones made ready his chariot; and so did the others. Then they mounted their cars, and drew lots for their places. Great Diomedes drew the best. Achilles ranged them all side by side, and pointed to the turning-post, in the plain, near which he posted old Phœnix, as umpire.

Then, at a signal from the son of Peleus, they raised their long whips, together, standing upright, and lashed their horses, and encouraged them by hand and voice. And the chariots now ran evenly on the ground, and now bounded high in air. But when they entered the last part of the course, driving towards the sea, the fleet mares of Eumelus, grandson of Pheres, rushed to the front; and next came Diomedes, with the stallions of Tros, so near that they seemed to be mounting the car of Eumelus, and with their hot breath covered his back and shoulders. Then Tydides would either have gained a victory, or it would have been at least a dead heat; but Phœbus Apollo was angry with him, and dashed his shining whip from his hand. He shed hot tears of fury, when he saw that the mares of Eumelus were still at their utmost speed, while his own horses slackened their speed, no longer feeling the lash. But, luckily for Diomedes, his constant friend Athene marked the trick of Apollo; and, speeding after Diomedes, she gave him back the scourge, and put fresh mettle into his steeds. She then pursued Eumelus, and brake the yoke of his horses; they bolted from the course, and he was hurled off his car into the dust. Meanwhile, Tydides rushed on before the others, for Athene was shedding glory on his head.

Next to him ran the horses of Menelaus, son of Atreus. Then came Antilochus, son of Nestor, who spake thus to his father's Pylian horses: "I do not ask you to contend with Tydides, whose horses Athene herself is speeding; but I pray you to catch up the chariot of Atrides; and be not beaten by Aithe, lest she, who is only a mare, pour ridicule upon you." Thus spake Antilochus, and his horses were afraid, and sped on more swiftly. But Antilochus noted a narrow gully, where the rain had collected and had carried away a part of the course. There Menelaus was driving, when Antilochus turned his horses out of the way, and followed him at one side. Then Menelaus, fearing a collision, shouted loudly to the son of Nestor: "Antilochus, hold in thy horses! and drive not so recklessly! close ahead there is a wider space, where we can pass one another!" But Antilochus, as if he heard him not, drove on more madly than ever and plied the lash; and the golden-haired son of Atreus called again to him, reproving him: "Antilochus, there is no man more spiteful than thou; away with thee! wrongly have we called thee *wise!*" Then he called on his horses, and they increased their speed, fearing the anger of their lord, and quickly overtook the others.

Now the Argive chiefs sat together, watching the race as the chariots flew along the course. The first to see them coming was Idomeneus, the Cretan prince, the son of Deucalion; he was sitting apart from the rest on the highest place, and he could distinguish the voices of the drivers. He noticed a chestnut horse, with a white star on his forehead, round like the full moon; and he stood up and spake: "Friends and Counselors of the Argives! can ye see the horses as I do? To me, there appeareth a new chariot and horses; and the mares which led at the start I can no longer see."

Then the son of Oïleus, Ajax, rebuked him in boorish fashion: "Idomeneus, why chatterest thou before the time? Thou art not one of the youngest, nor are thine eyes of the sharpest. The same mares of Eumelus are still leading, and he is standing up in the chariot."

And the great chief, Idomeneus, answered in great wrath, "Ajax, ever ready to abuse, inconsiderate slanderer! thou art in all respects inferior to the other Argives, for thy mind is rude."

Thus spoke the Cretan hero. And the son of Oïleus rose again, to reply with scornful words; but Achilles himself stood forward and said, "No longer, Idomeneus and Ajax, bandy insulting words with one another; for it is not meet! Sit ye still, and watch; and soon will ye know which horses are leading." He spake; and straightway Tydides came driving up in his fair chariot, overlaid with gold and tin, which ran lightly behind the horses, and scarcely left a trace in the fine dust of the plain. Checking his horses in the middle of the crowd, he leapt to the ground and claimed the splendid prize; and the gallant Sthenelus made no delay, but gave to his victorious comrade the woman and the tripod to bear away.

Next to Diomedes came the son of Nestor, Antilochus, who had passed by Menelaus by a clever stratagem, though his horses were inferior; but even so,

Menelaus had pressed him hard, and was behind him only so far as a horse is from the wheel of the chariot which he draweth.

But Meriones, the brave charioteer of Idomeneus, came in about the cast of a lance behind Menelaus; for his horses were the slowest, and he was himself but a sluggish driver. Last of all came Eumelus, the son of Admetus, dragging his broken chariot. The swift-footed Achilles, son of Peleus, pitied him, and spake winged words to the chiefs: "Lo! the best man of all comes last; but let us give him a prize — the second! And let Tydides bear away the first!"

All the Achaians heard him, and shouted applause; and the noble Achilles would have given him the mare had not Antilochus, son of the wise and glorious Nestor, stood up in defense of his claim: "O Achilles!" he said, "justly shall I be wroth with thee, if thou takest away the prize which I have fairly won. Thou thinkest only of the unlucky chance which hath befallen Eumelus and his horses; but he ought to have made prayer to the deathless Gods, and then he would not have come in last of all. If thou pitiest him, there is much treasure in thy house, — gold, and bronze, and sheep, and handmaids, and horses. Give him, if it pleaseth thee and the Achaians, a still richer prize. But I will not give up the mare; for she is *mine*."

And Achilles smiled on his comrade Antilochus, whom he dearly loved, and answered him, "Antilochus, I will do as thou sayest: I will give him the bronze cuirass, edged with shining tin, which I took from Asteropæus."

But the great Menelaus arose, filled with insatiable wrath against Antilochus. The herald placed a sceptre in his hand, and called for silence. Then the godlike king made harangue, and said, "Antilochus! thou who wert once accounted wise — what is this that thou hast done? Thou hast disgraced my skill, and discomfited my horses, by thrusting thine, which are far worse, in front of them. Come then, great chiefs of the Argives! give judgment, without favor, between him and me! That no one may say hereafter, that ye favored me for my power and rank, I will myself set the issue before you; so that no one may reproach me. Stand forth, Antilochus, before thy chariot; and take thy whip, and lay thy hand upon thy horses, and swear by the great Girdler and Shaker of the Earth, that thou didst not, by set purpose and malice, hinder my chariot in the course!"

Then Antilochus made prudent answer, "Be patient with me, King Menelaus! for I am younger, and thou art in all respects my better. Bear with me, then; and I will myself give thee the mare, my prize, rather than lose my place in thy heart, O thou beloved of Zeus!" Thus spake the noble-minded son of Nestor; and he gave the mare to Menelaus, king of men.

And the heart of the son of Atreus rejoiced, as the ripe ears of corn, when the dew descendeth upon them, in the glistening cornfield. And he spake kindly to Antilochus, and said, "Lo! at once do I put away my anger; for of old thou wert never rash or light-minded; but now thy reason was overborne by the impetuosity of youth. Therefore I grant thy prayer, and will even

264

give thee the mare; for I am in no wise covetous or unforgiving."

He spake, and gave the mare to Noëmon, the comrade of Antilochus, to lead away; but he took the bright caldron to himself. And Meriones, who came in fourth, took the two talents of gold. But the fifth prize, a vase with two handles, was not obtained; and the noble Achilles gave this to Nestor, and, standing by him, uttered winged words: —

"Let this, O Father! be for thee an heirloom, and a memorial of Patroclus' funeral games — of him, whom thou wilt never see again! I give it to thee since thou mayest not contend in boxing, nor in wrestling, nor in throwing the lance, nor in the foot-race; for rueful old age weigheth heavily upon thee."

Nestor gladly received the splendid gift, and spake: "True and fitting are thy words, dear friend! My limbs are no longer sound, nor do my arms move easily from my shoulders; and I must make way for younger men. But I accept thy free gift with joy, and rejoice that thou dost remember our old friendship."

Then Pelides brought forward the prizes for the rough, fierce boxing-match: a six-year-old unbroken mule for the winner; and a two-handled goblet for the loser. Then quickly rose the famous boxer Epeius, and laid his hand on the stubborn mule, and boasted aloud: "Let who will bear away the goblet; but the mule is mine! for no one will beat me with his fists!" They all kept silence, and feared. Only one came forward, even Euryalus, the gallant son of King Mecistus. The famous warrior Tydides made him ready for the fight, and bade him God speed. The twain went into the ring, and fell to work; and terrible was the gnashing of their teeth, and the sweat ran down from their limbs. Epeius came on fiercely, and struck Euryalus on the cheek, and that was enough; for all his limbs were loosened. As a fish on a weedy beach, in the ripple caused by Boreas, leapeth high in air, so Euryalus leapt up in his anguish. But the generous Epeius raised him again to his feet, and his comrades led him away, with dragging feet and drooping head, and spitting out black blood.

Next came the terrible wrestling match; and for this the glorious Achilles brought out two costly prizes: for the winner, a fireproof tripod, worth twelve oxen; and for the loser, a woman skilled in handiwork, valued at four oxen. And he cried aloud to the Achaians, "Stand forward all ye who will enter into this contest!"

Then rose Telamonian Ajax and the crafty Ulysses, and faced each other. And they entered the ring, and grasped each other with their strong hands, like the rafters of a house, joined by some skillful builder to withstand the wind. Their backbones grated and creaked beneath the strain; the sweat poured down from their limbs, and bloody weals streaked their sides and shoulders, as they struggled for the well-wrought tripod. But neither could Ulysses throw the burly Ajax, nor Ajax him. And when the Achaians grew tired of the futile contest, Ajax spake to Ulysses: "O thou offspring of the Gods, Laertes' son! do thou lift me, or I will lift thee, and the issue will be on the lap of Zeus!"

FUNERAL GAMES FOR PATROCLUS

So saying, he raised Ulysses. But the Wily One did not forget his craft. From behind, he struck the hollow of Ajax's knee, and threw him on his back; and Ulysses fell upon him; and the people marveled. Then, in his turn, Ulysses tried to lift huge Ajax, but could not; so he thrust his crooked knee into the hollow of the other's; and they again both fell to the ground, covered with dust. When they rose for a third bout, Achilles restrained them. "No longer wear ye one another out, with toil and pain! Ye both have won and shall receive equal prizes!" And they cleansed themselves, and put on their doublets.

Then the noble son of Peleus offered prizes for the foot-race; the first, a silver krater holding six measures, curiously chased by Sidonian artists — by far the most beautiful mixing-cup in the whole world. For the second he offered a stalled ox; and for the third, half a talent of gold. The wondrous krater Phœnicians had brought by sea, and given it to Thoas, the ruler of Lemnos; and Euneus, son of Jason, inherited it from Jason, who received it from Thoas, his father-in-law; and Euneus gave it to the hero Patroclus, as a ransom for Lycaon, son of Priam; this splendid goblet was offered to the swiftest of foot.

Then three valiant heroes arose: Ajax, son of Oïleus; Ulysses, the wily one; and Antilochus, the best runner of the youths. Achilles ranged them side by side, and showed them the goal. All started at full speed; but Ajax soon took the lead; and Ulysses came close behind him, near as the shuttle to the breast of a fair-girdled woman when she is weaving,— so near that

267

his breath was warm on the back of Ajax. But as they neared the goal, the wily Ulysses prayed to the fierce-eyed Athene, "O goddess, come and help my feet!" And Athene heard her favorite, and strengthened all his limbs. But just as they were about to pounce upon the prize, Ajax slipped in the blood of the slaughtered oxen, and fell; his mouth and nostrils were filled with dirt and gore. So the patient Ulysses took the price-less krater, and Ajax the fatted ox. But Ajax, holding his prize by the horn, and spitting the filth from his mouth, spake to the Achaians: "O fie upon it! it was the goddess who betrayed me; she who is ever near to Ulysses, as a mother to her child." And the Achaians laughed merrily, to see him in such a sorry plight.

Antilochus, smiling, took the last prize, half a talent of gold; and he too spake winged words to the Argives: "My friends, ye too will agree with me that the deathless Gods show favor to the older men. Ajax is a little older than I; but Ulysses is of a former generation. It were not easy for any one, except Achilles, fleet of foot, to outrun *him*."

Achilles was pleased at the honor done to his swiftness. "Not unrewarded," he said, "shall the praise be which thou hast bestowed on me: I give thee another half-talent of gold." Antilochus received it gladly. Then the assembly was dissolved, and the Achaians dispersed, each to his own ship.

THE WOODEN HORSE AND THE FALL OF TROY

By Josephine Preston Peabody

NINE years the Greeks laid siege to Troy, and
Troy held out against every device. On both
sides the lives of many heroes were spent, and they
were forced to acknowledge each other enemies of
great valor.

Sometimes the chief warriors fought in single combat, while the armies looked on, and the old men of
Troy, with the women, came out to watch afar off
from the city walls. King Priam and Queen Hecuba
would come, and Cassandra, sad with foreknowledge of
their doom, and Andromache, the lovely young wife
of Hector, with her little son, whom the people called
the city's king. Sometimes fair Helen came to look
across the plain to the fellow-countrymen whom she
had forsaken; and although she was the cause of all
this war, the Trojans half forgave her when she passed
by, because her beauty was like a spell, and warmed
hard hearts as the sunshine mellows apples. So for
nine years the Greeks plundered the neighboring towns,
but the city Troy stood fast, and the Grecian ships
waited with folded wings.

In the tenth year of the war the Greeks, who could
not take the city by force, pondered how they might

take it by craft. At length, with the aid of Ulysses, they devised a plan.

A portion of the Grecian host broke up camp and set sail as if they were homeward bound; but, once out of sight, they anchored their ships behind a neighboring island. The rest of the army then fell to work upon a great image of a horse. They built it of wood, fitted and carved, and with a door so cunningly concealed that none might notice it. When it was finished the horse looked like a prodigious idol; but it was hollow, skillfully pierced here and there, and so spacious that a band of men could lie hidden within and take no harm. Into this hiding-place went Ulysses, Menelaus, and the other chiefs, fully armed, and when the door was shut upon them, the rest of the Grecian army broke camp and went away.

Meanwhile, in Troy, the people had seen the departure of the ships, and the news had spread like wildfire. The great enemy had lost heart, — after ten years of war! Part of the army had gone, — the rest were going. Already the last of the ships had set sail, and the camp was deserted. The tents that had whitened the plain were gone like a frost before the sun. The war was over!

The whole city went wild with joy. Like one who has been a prisoner for many years, it flung off all restraint, and the people rose as a single man to test the truth of new liberty. The gates were thrown wide, and the Trojans — men, women, and children — thronged over the plain and into the empty camp of the enemy. There stood the Wooden Horse.

A GREAT IMAGE OF A HORSE. THEY BUILT IT OF WOOD,
FITTED AND CARVED, AND WITH A DOOR SO CUNNINGLY
CONCEALED THAT NONE MIGHT NOTICE IT. WHEN IT WAS
FINISHED THE HORSE LOOKED LIKE A PRODIGIOUS IDOL, BUT
IT WAS HOLLOW, SKILLFULLY PIERCED HERE AND THERE

No one knew what it could be. Fearful at first, they gathered around it, as children gather around a live horse; they marveled at its wondrous height and girth, and were for moving it into the city as a trophy of war.

At this, one man interposed, — Laocoön, a priest of Neptune. "Take heed, citizens," said he. "Beware of all that comes from the Greeks. Have you fought them for ten years without learning their devices? This is some piece of treachery."

But there was another outcry in the crowd, and at that moment certain of the Trojans dragged forward a wretched man who wore the garments of a Greek. He seemed the sole remnant of the Grecian army, and as such they consented to spare his life, if he would tell them the truth.

Sinon, for this was the spy's name, said that he had been left behind by the malice of Ulysses, and he told them that the Greeks had built the Wooden Horse as an offering to Athene, and that they had made it so huge in order to keep it from being moved out of the camp, since it was destined to bring triumph to its possessors.

At this the joy of the Trojans was redoubled, and they set their wits to find out how they might soonest drag the great horse across the plain and into the city to insure victory. While they stood talking, two immense serpents rose out of the sea and made towards the camp. Some of the people took flight, others were transfixed with terror; but all, near and far, watched this new omen. Rearing their crests, the sea-serpents

crossed the shore, swift, shining, terrible as a risen
water-flood that descends upon a helpless little town.
Straight through the crowd they swept, and seized the
priest Laocoön where he stood, with his two sons,
and wrapped them all round and round in fearful
coils. There was no chance of escape. Father and
sons perished together; and when the monsters had
devoured the three men, into the sea they slipped again,
leaving no trace of the horror.

The terrified Trojans saw an omen in this. To
their minds punishment had come upon Laocoön for
his words against the Wooden Horse. Surely, it was
sacred to the Gods; he had spoken blasphemy, and
had perished before their eyes. They flung his warning to the winds. They wreathed the horse with garlands, amid great acclaim; and then, all lending a
hand, they dragged it, little by little, out of the camp
and into the city of Troy. With the close of that victorious day, they gave up every memory of danger and
made merry after ten years of privation.

That very night Sinon the spy opened the hidden
door of the Wooden Horse, and in the darkness, Ulysses, Menelaus, and the other chiefs who had lain
hidden there crept out and gave the signal to the
Grecian army. For, under cover of night, those ships
that had been moored behind the island had sailed
back again, and the Greeks were come upon Troy.

Not a Trojan was on guard. The whole city was
at feast when the enemy rose in its midst, and the
warning of Laocoön was fulfilled.

Priam and his warriors fell by the sword, and their

kingdom was plundered of all its fair possessions, women and children and treasure. Last of all, the city itself was burned to its very foundations.

Homeward sailed the Greeks, taking as royal captives poor Cassandra and Andromache and many another Trojan. And home at last went fair Helen, the cause of all this sorrow, eager to be forgiven by her husband, King Menelaus. For she had awakened from the enchantment of Venus, and even before the death of Paris she had secretly longed for her home and kindred. Home to Sparta she came with the king after a long and stormy voyage, and there she lived and died the fairest of women.

But the kingdom of Troy was fallen. Nothing remained of all its glory but the glory of its dead heroes and fair women, and the ruins of its citadel by the river Scamander. There even now, beneath the foundations of later homes that were built and burned, built and burned, in the wars of a thousand years after, the ruins of ancient Troy lie hidden, like mouldered leaves deep under the new grass. And there, to this very day, men who love the story are delving after the dead city as you might search for a buried treasure.

THE WANDERINGS OF ULYSSES

AN ADVENTURE WITH THE CYCLOPS

By Alfred J. Church

[After the fall of Troy the Greeks set out for home, but many of them had troubles and dangers to meet before they saw again the shores of their native land. The one who suffered most was Ulysses, and the following is his story of his adventure with the one-eyed giant, the Cyclops.]

THE wind that bore me from Troy brought me to Ismarus, a city of the Ciconians. This I sacked, slaying the people that dwelt therein. Much spoil did we take out of the city, dividing it among the people, so that each man had his share. And when we had done this, I commanded my men that they should depart with all speed; but they, in their folly, would not hear me. For there was much wine to drink, and sheep and kine to slay; therefore they sat on the shore and feasted. Meanwhile the people of the city fetched others, their kinsmen that dwelt in the mountains, and were more in number and more valiant than they, and skillful in all manner of fighting. In the early morning they assembled themselves together, thick as the flowers and the leaves that grow in the springtime, and set the battle in array. Then we fought with them; while the day waxed we prevailed over them, and beat them back, though they were more in number than we; but when the sun was descending in the heavens, then the Cicones overcame us, and drave us to our ships. Six from each ship perished, but the remnant of us escaped from death.

On the tenth day after this we came to the land where the lotus grows — a wondrous fruit of which whosoever eats cares not to see country or wife or children again. Now the Lotus-Eaters, for they so called the people of the land, were a kindly folk, and gave of the fruit to some of the sailors, not meaning them any harm, but thinking it to be the best that they had to give. These, when they had eaten, said that they would not sail any more over the sea; which, when I heard, I bade their comrades bind them and carry them, sadly complaining, to the ships.

Then, the wind having abated, we took to our oars, and rowed for many days till we came to the country where the Cyclops dwell. Now, a mile or so from the shore there was an island, very fair and fertile, but no man dwells there or tills the soil, and in the island a harbor where a ship may be safe from all winds, and at the head of the harbor a stream falling from a rock, and whispering alders all about it. Into this the ships passed safely, and were hauled up on the beach, and the crews slept by them, waiting for the morning.

When the dawn appeared, then we wandered through the island; and the nymphs of the land started the wild goats that my company might have food to eat. Thereupon we took our bows and our spears from the ships, and shot at the goats; and the Gods gave us plenty of prey. Twelve ships I had in my company, and each ship had nine goats for its share, and my own portion was ten.

Then all the day we sat and feasted, drinking the sweet wine which we had taken from the city of the Cicones, and eating the flesh of the goats; and as we sat we looked across to the land of the Cyclops, seeing the smoke and hearing the voices of the men and of the sheep and of the goats. And when the sun set and darkness came over the land, we lay down upon the seashore and slept.

The next day I gathered my men together, and said, "Abide ye here, dear friends; I with my own ship and my own company will go and make trial of the folk that dwell in yonder island, whether they are just or unjust."

So I climbed into my ship, and bade my company follow me; so we came to the land of the Cyclops. Close to the shore was a cave, with laurels round about the mouth. This was the dwelling of the Cyclops. Alone he dwelt, a creature without law. Nor was he like to mortal men, but rather to some wooded peak of the hills that stands out apart from all the rest.

Then I bade the rest of my comrades abide by the ship, and keep it, but I took twelve men, the bravest that there were in the crew, and went forth. I had with me a goat-skin full of the wine, dark red, and sweet, which the priest of Apollo at Ismarus had given me. Because we kept him and his wife and child from harm when we sacked the city, reverencing the god, there-

fore did he give it me. Three things did he give me,
— seven talents of gold, and a mixing-bowl of silver,
and of wine twelve jars. So precious was it that none
in his house knew of it saving himself and his wife and
one dame that kept the house. When they drank of
it they mixed twenty measures of water with one of wine,
and the smell that went up from it was wondrous sweet.
No man could easily refrain from drinking it. With
this wine I filled a great skin and bore it with me; also
I bare corn in a wallet, for my heart within me boded
that I should need it.

So we entered the cave, and judged that it was the
dwelling of some rich and skillful shepherd. For within
there were pens for the young of the sheep and of the
goats, divided all according to their age, and there
were baskets full of cheeses, and full milkpails ranged
along the wall. But the Cyclops himself was away
in the pastures. Then my companions besought me
that I would depart, taking with me, if I would, a store
of cheeses and sundry of the lambs and of the kids.
But I would not, for I wished to see, after my wont,
what manner of host this strange shepherd might be,
and, if it might be, to take a gift from his hand, such as
is the due of strangers. Verily, his coming was not to
be a joy to my company.

It was evening when the Cyclops came home, —
a mighty giant, very tall of stature, and when we saw
him we fled into the sacred place of the cave in great
fear. On his shoulder he bore a vast bundle of pine
logs for his fire, and threw them down outside the
cave with a great crash, and drove the flocks within,

and closed the entrance with a huge rock, which twenty wagons and more could not bear. Then he milked the ewes and all the she-goats, and half of the milk he curdled for cheese, and half he set ready for himself, when he should sup. Next he kindled a fire with the pine logs, and the flame lighted up all the cave, showing to him both me and my comrades.

"Who are ye?" cried Polyphemus, for that was the giant's name. "Are ye traders, or, haply, pirates?"

I shuddered at the dreadful voice and shape, but bare me bravely, and answered, "We are no pirates, mighty sir, but Greeks sailing back from Troy, and subjects of the great King Agamemnon, whose fame is spread from one end of heaven to the other. And we are come to beg hospitality of thee in the name of Zeus, who rewards or punishes hosts and guests, according as they be faithful the one to the other, or no."

"Nay," said the giant; "it is but idle talk to tell me of Zeus and the other Gods. We Cyclops take no account of gods, holding ourselves to be much better and stronger than they. But come, tell me, where have you left your ship?"

But I saw his thought when he asked about the ship, how he was minded to break it, and take from us all hope of flight. Therefore I answered him craftily, —

"Ship have we none, for that which was ours King Neptune brake, driving it on a jutting rock on this coast, and we whom thou seest are all that are escaped from the waves."

Polyphemus answered nothing, but without more ado caught up two of the men, as a man might catch up the whelps of a dog, and dashed them on the ground, and tare them limb from limb, and devoured them, with huge draughts of milk between, leaving not a morsel, not even the very bones. But we that were left, when we saw the dreadful deed, could only weep and pray to Zeus for help. And when the giant had filled his maw with human flesh and with the milk of the flocks, he lay down among his sheep and slept.

Then I questioned much in my heart whether I should slay the monster as he slept, for I doubted not that my good sword would pierce to the giant's heart, mighty as he was. But my second thought kept me back, for I remembered that, should I slay him, I and my comrades would yet perish miserably. For who should move away the great rock that lay against the door of the cave? So we waited till the morning, with grief in our hearts. And the monster woke, and milked his flocks, and afterwards, seizing two men, devoured them for his meal. Then he went to the pastures, but put the great rock on the mouth of the cave, just as a man puts down the lid upon his quiver.

All that day I was thinking what I might best do to save myself and my companions, and the end of my thinking was this: there was a mighty pole in the cave, green wood of an olive-tree, big as a ship's mast, which Polyphemus purposed to use, when the smoke should have dried it, as a walking-staff. Of this I cut off a fathom's length, and my comrades sharpened it and hardened it in the fire, and then hid it away. At evening the giant came back, and drove his sheep into the cave, nor left the rams outside, as he had been wont to do before, but shut them in. And having duly done his shepherd's work, he took, as before, two of my comrades, and devoured them. And when he had finished his supper, I came forward, holding the wine-skin in my hand, and said, —

"Drink, Cyclops, now that thou hast feasted. Drink, and see what precious things we had in our ship. But no one hereafter will come to thee with such like, if thou dealest with strangers as cruelly as thou hast dealt with us."

Then the Cyclops drank, and was mightily pleased, and said, "Give me again to drink, and tell me thy name, stranger, and I will give thee a gift such as a host should give. In good truth this is a rare liquor. We, too, have vines, but they bear not wine like this, which, indeed, must be such as the Gods drink in heaven."

Then I gave him the cup again, and he drank. Thrice I gave it to him, and thrice he drank, not knowing what it was, and how it would work within his brain.

Then I spake to him: "Thou didst ask my name, Cyclops. My name is No Man. And now that thou knowest my name, thou shouldst give me thy gift."

And he said, "My gift shall be that I will eat thee last of all thy company."

And as he spake, he fell back in a drunken sleep. Then I bade my comrades be of good courage, for the time was come when they should be delivered. And they thrust the stake of olive-wood into the fire till it was ready, green as it was, to burst into flame, and they thrust it into the monster's eye; for he had but one eye, and that in the midst of his forehead, with the eyebrow below it. And I, standing above, leant with all my force upon the stake, and turned it about, as a man bores the timber of a ship with a drill. And the burning wood hissed in the eye, just as the red-hot iron hisses in the water when a man seeks to temper steel for a sword.

Then the giant leapt up, and tore away the stake, and cried aloud, so that all the Cyclops who dwelt on the mountain-side heard him and came about his cave, asking him, "What aileth thee, Polyphemus, that thou makest this uproar in the peaceful night, driving away sleep? Is any one robbing thee of thy sheep, or seeking to slay thee by craft or force?"

And the giant answered, "No Man slays me by craft."

"Nay, but," they said, "if no man does thee wrong we cannot help thee. The sickness which great Zeus may send, who can avoid? Pray to our father, Neptune, for help."

So they spake, and I laughed in my heart when I saw how I had beguiled them by the name that I had given.

But the Cyclops rolled away the great stone from the door of the cave, and sat in the midst, stretching out his hands, to feel whether perchance the men within the cave would seek to go out among the sheep.

Long did I think how I and my comrades should best escape. At last I lighted upon a device that seemed better than all the rest, and much I thanked Zeus for that this once the giant had driven the rams with the other sheep into the cave. For, these being great and

AN ADVENTURE WITH THE CYCLOPS

strong, I fastened my comrades under the bellies of the
beasts, tying them with osier twigs, of which the giant
made his bed. One ram I took, and fastened a man
beneath it, and two rams I set, one on either side.
So I did with the six, for but six were left out of the
twelve who had ventured with me from the ship. And
there was one mighty ram far larger than all the others,
and to this I clung, grasping the fleece tight with both
my hands. So we all waited for the morning. And when
the morning came, the rams rushed forth to the pasture; but the giant sat in the door and felt the back
of each as it went by, nor thought to try what might
be underneath. Last of all went the great ram. And
the Cyclops knew him as he passed, and said,—

"How is this, thou who art the leader of the flock?
Thou art not wont thus to lag behind. Thou hast
always been the first to run to the pastures and streams
in the morning, and the first to come back to the fold
when evening fell; and now thou art last of all. Perhaps thou art troubled about thy master's eye, which
some wretch — No Man, they call him — has destroyed,
having first mastered me with wine. He has not escaped, I ween. I would that thou couldst speak, and
tell me where he is lurking. Of a truth, I would dash
out his brains upon the ground, and avenge me of
this No Man."

So speaking, he let the ram pass out of the cave.
But when we were now out of reach of the giant, I
loosed my hold of the ram, and then unbound my comrades. And we hastened to our ship, not forgetting
to drive the sheep before us, and often looking back

till we came to the seashore. Right glad were those that had abode by the ship to see us. Nor did they lament for those that had died, though we were fain to do so, for I forbade, fearing lest the noise of their weeping should betray us to the giant, where we were. Then we all climbed into the ship, and sitting well in order on the benches smote the sea with our oars, laying to right lustily, that we might the sooner get away from the accursed land. And when we had rowed a hundred yards or so, so that a man's voice could yet be heard by one who stood upon the shore, I stood up in the ship and shouted,—

"He was no coward, O Cyclops, whose comrades thou didst so foully slay in thy den. Justly art thou punished, monster, that devourest thy guests in thy dwelling. May the Gods make thee suffer worse things than these!"

Then the Cyclops in his wrath brake off the top of a great hill, a mighty rock, and hurled it where he had heard the voice. Right in front of the ship's bow it fell, and a great wave rose as it sank, and washed the ship back to the shore. But I seized a long pole with both hands, and pushed the ship from the land, and bade my comrades ply their oars, nodding with my head, for I would not speak, lest the Cyclops should know where we were. Then they rowed with all their might and main.

And when we had gotten twice as far as before I made as if I would speak again; but my comrades sought to hinder me, saying, "Nay, my lord, anger not the giant any more. Surely we thought we were lost

THE CYCLOPS IN HIS WRATH BRAKE OFF THE TOP OF A GREAT HILL

before, when he threw the great rock, and washed our ship back to the shore. And if he hear thee now, he may crush our ship and us, for the man throws a mighty bolt, and throws it far."

But I would not be persuaded, but stood up and said, "Hear, Cyclops! If any man ask who blinded thee, say that it was the warrior Ulysses, son of Laertes, dwelling in Ithaca."

CIRCE'S PALACE

By Nathaniel Hawthorne

A T one time in the course of Ulysses' weary voyage, he arrived at an island that looked very green and pleasant, but the name of which was unknown to him. For, only a little while before he came thither, he had met with a terrible hurricane, or rather a great many hurricanes at once, which drove his fleet of vessels into a strange part of the sea, where neither himself nor any of his mariners had ever sailed. This misfortune was entirely owing to the foolish curiosity of his shipmates, who, while Ulysses lay asleep, had untied some very bulky leathern bags, in which they supposed a valuable treasure to be concealed. But in each of these stout bags, King Æolus, the ruler of the winds, had tied up a tempest, and had given it to Ulysses to keep, in order that he might be sure of a favorable passage homeward to Ithaca; and when the strings were loosened, forth rushed the whistling blasts, like air out of a blown bladder, whitening the sea with foam, and scattering the vessels nobody could tell whither.

Immediately after escaping from this peril, a still greater one had befallen him. Scudding before the hurricane, he reached a place which, as he afterwards found, was called Læstrygonia, where some monstrous giants had eaten up many of his companions, and had sunk every one of his vessels, except that in which he himself sailed, by flinging great masses of rock at them, from the cliffs along the shore. After going through such troubles as these, you cannot wonder that King Ulysses was glad to moor his tempest-beaten bark in a quiet cove of the green island, which I began with telling you about. But he had encountered so many dangers from giants, and one-eyed Cyclops, and monsters of the sea and land, that he could not help dreading some mischief, even in this pleasant and seemingly solitary spot. For two days, therefore, the poor weather-worn voyagers kept quiet, and either stayed on board of their vessel or merely crept along under cliffs that bordered the shore; and to keep themselves alive, they dug shell-fish out of the sand, and sought for any little rill of fresh water that might be running towards the sea.

Before the two days were spent, they grew very weary of this kind of life; for the followers of King Ulysses, as you will find it important to remember, were terrible gormandizers, and pretty sure to grumble if they missed their regular meals, and their irregular ones besides. Their stock of provisions was quite exhausted, and even the shell-fish began to get scarce, so that they had now to choose between starving to death or venturing into the interior of the island, where, perhaps, some huge three-headed dragon or other horrible monster had his den. Such misshapen creatures were very numerous in those days; and nobody ever expected to make a voyage or take a journey without running more or less risk of being devoured by them.

But King Ulysses was a bold man as well as a prudent one; and on the third morning he determined to discover what sort of a place the island was, and whether it were possible to obtain a supply of food for the hungry mouths of his companions. So, taking a spear in his hand, he clambered to the summit of a cliff, and gazed round about him. At a distance, towards the centre of the island, he beheld the stately towers of what seemed to be a palace, built of snow-white marble, and rising in the midst of a grove of lofty trees. The thick branches of these trees stretched across the front of the edifice, and more than half concealed it, although, from the portion which he saw, Ulysses judged it to be spacious and exceedingly beautiful, and probably the residence of some great nobleman or prince. A blue smoke went curling up from the chimney, and was almost the pleasantest part of the spectacle to Ulysses. For, from the abundance of this smoke, it was reasonable to conclude that there was a good fire in the kitchen, and that, at dinner-time, a plentiful banquet would be served up to the inhabitants of the palace, and to whatever guests might happen to drop in.

With so agreeable a prospect before him, Ulysses fancied that he could not do better than to go straight to the palace gate, and tell the master of it that there was a crew of poor shipwrecked mariners, not far off, who had eaten nothing for a day or two save a few clams and oysters, and would therefore be thankful for a little food. And the prince or nobleman must be a very stingy curmudgeon, to be sure, if, at least, when his own dinner was over, he would not bid them welcome to the broken victuals from the table.

Pleasing himself with this idea, King Ulysses had made a few steps in the direction of the palace, when there was a great twittering and chirping from the branch of a neighboring tree. A moment afterwards, a bird came flying towards him, and hovered in the air, so as almost to brush his face with its wings. It was a very pretty little bird, with purple wings and body, and yellow legs, and a circle of golden feathers round its neck, and on its head a golden tuft, which looked like a king's crown in miniature. Ulysses tried to catch the bird. But it fluttered nimbly out of his reach, still chirping in a piteous tone, as if it could have told a lamentable story, had it only been gifted with human language. And when he attempted to drive it away, the bird flew no farther than the bough of the next tree, and again came fluttering about his head, with its doleful chirp, as soon as he showed a purpose of going forward.

"Have you anything to tell me, little bird?" asked Ulysses.

And he was ready to listen attentively to whatever the bird might communicate; for at the siege of Troy and elsewhere he had known such odd things to happen that he would not have considered it much out of the common run had this little feathered creature talked as plainly as himself.

"Peep!" said the bird. "Peep, peep, pe—weep!"

And nothing else would it say, but only, "Peep, peep, pe—weep!" in a melancholy cadence, and over and over and over again. As often as Ulysses moved forward, however, the bird showed the greatest alarm, and did its best to drive him back, with the anxious flutter of its purple wings. Its unaccountable behavior made him conclude, at last, that the bird knew of some danger that awaited him, and which must needs be very terrible, beyond all question, since it moved even a little fowl to feel compassion for a human being. So he resolved, for the present, to return to the vessel, and tell his companions what he had seen.

This appeared to satisfy the bird. As soon as Ulysses turned back, it ran up the trunk of a tree, and began to pick insects out of the bark with its long, sharp bill; for it was a kind of woodpecker, you must know, and had to get its living in the same manner as other birds of that species. But every little while, as it pecked at the bark of the tree, the purple bird bethought itself of some secret sorrow, and repeated its plaintive note of "Peep, peep, pe—weep!"

On his way to the shore, Ulysses had the good luck to kill a large stag by thrusting his spear into its back. Taking it on his shoulders (for he was a remarkably strong man), he lugged it along with him, and flung it down before his hungry companions. I have already hinted to you what gormandizers some of the comrades of King Ulysses were. From what is related of them, I reckon that their favorite diet was pork, and that they had lived upon it until a good part of their physical substance was swine's flesh, and their tempers and dispositions were very much akin to the hog. A dish of venison, however, was no unacceptable meal to them, especially after feeding so long on oysters and clams. So, beholding the dead stag, they fell of its ribs in a knowing way, and lost no time in kindling a fire, of drift-wood, to cook it. The rest of the day was spent in feasting; and if these enormous eaters got up from table at sunset, it was only because they could not scrape another morsel off the poor animal's bones.

The next morning their appetites were as sharp as ever. They looked at Ulysses, as if they expected him to clamber up the cliff again, and come back with another fat deer upon his shoulders. Instead of setting out, however, he summoned the whole crew together, and told them it was in vain to hope that he could kill a stag every day for their dinner, and therefore it was advisable to think of some other mode of satisfying their hunger.

"Now," said he, "when I was on the cliff yesterday, I discovered that this island is inhabited. At a considerable distance from the shore stood a marble palace, which appeared to be very spacious, and had a great deal of smoke curling out of one of its chimneys."

"Aha!" muttered some of his companions, smacking their lips. "That smoke must have come from the kitchen fire. There was a good dinner on the spit; and no doubt there will be as good a one to-day."

"But," continued the wise Ulysses, "you must remember, my good friends, our misadventure in the cavern of one-eyed Polyphemus, the Cyclops! Instead of his ordinary milk diet, did he not eat up two of our comrades for his supper, and a couple more for breakfast, and two at his supper again? Methinks I see him yet, the hideous monster, scanning us with that great red eye, in the middle of his forehead, to single out the fattest. And then again, only a few days ago, did we not fall into the hands of the king of the Læstrygons, and those other horrible giants, his subjects, who devoured a great many more of us than are now left? To tell you the truth, if we go to yonder palace, there can be no question that we shall make our appearance at the dinner-table; but whether seated as guests or served up as food, is a point to be seriously considered."

"Either way," murmured some of the hungriest of the crew, "it will be better than starvation; particularly if one could be sure of being well fattened beforehand and daintily cooked afterwards."

"That is a matter of taste," said King Ulysses, "and, for my own part, neither the most careful fattening nor the daintiest of cookery would reconcile me to being dished at last. My proposal is, therefore, that we divide ourselves into two equal parties, and ascertain, by drawing lots, which of the two shall go to the palace, and beg for food and assistance. If these can be obtained, all is well. If not, and if the inhabitants prove as inhospitable as Polyphemus or the Læstrygons, then there will but half of us perish, and the remainder may set sail and escape."

As nobody objected to this scheme, Ulysses proceeded to count the whole band, and found that there were forty-six men, including himself. He then numbered off twenty-two of them, and put Eurylochus (who was one of his chief officers, and second only to himself in sagacity) at their head. Ulysses took command of the remaining twenty-two men, in person. Then, taking off his helmet, he put two shells into it, on one of which was written, "Go," and on the other, "Stay." Another person now held the helmet, while Ulysses and Eurylochus drew out each a shell; and the word "Go" was found written on that which Eurylochus had drawn. In this manner it was decided that Ulysses and his twenty-two men were to remain at the seaside until the other party should have found out what sort of treatment they might expect at the mysterious palace. As there was no help for it, Eurylochus immediately set forth at the head of his twenty-two followers, who went off in a very melancholy state of mind, leaving their friends in hardly better spirits than themselves.

No sooner had they clambered up the cliff, than they discerned the tall marble towers of the palace, ascending, as white as snow, out of the lovely green shadow of the trees which surrounded it. A gush of smoke came from a chimney in the rear of the edifice. This vapor rose high in the air, and meeting with a breeze, was wafted seaward, and made to pass over the heads of the hungry mariners. When people's appetites are keen, they have a very quick scent for anything savory in the wind.

"That smoke comes from the kitchen!" cried one of them, turning up his nose as high as he could, and snuffing eagerly. "And, as sure as I'm a half-starved vagabond, I smell roast meat in it."

"Pig, roast pig!" said another. "Ah, the dainty little porker! My mouth waters for him."

"Let us make haste," cried the others, "or we shall be too late for the good cheer!"

But scarcely had they made half a dozen steps from the edge of the cliff, when a bird came fluttering to meet them. It was the same pretty little bird, with the purple wings and body, the yellow legs, the golden collar round its neck, and the crown-like tuft upon its head, whose behavior had so much surprised Ulysses. It hovered about Eurylochus, and almost brushed his face with its wings.

"Peep, peep, pe—weep!" chirped the bird.

So plaintively intelligent was the sound, that it seemed as if the little creature were going to break its heart with some mighty secret that it had to tell, and only this one poor note to tell it with.

"My pretty bird," said Eurylochus, — for he was a wary person, and let no token of harm escape his notice, — "my pretty bird, who sent you hither? And what is the message which you bring?"

"Peep, peep, pe—weep!" replied the bird, very sorrowfully.

Then it flew towards the edge of the cliff, and looked round at them, as if exceedingly anxious that they should return whence they came. Eurylochus and a few of the others were inclined to turn back. They could not help suspecting that the purple bird must be aware of something mischievous that would befall them at the palace, and the knowledge of which affected its airy spirit with a human sympathy and sorrow. But the rest of the voyagers, snuffing up the smoke from the palace kitchen, ridiculed the idea of returning to the vessel. One of them (more brutal than his fellows, and the most notorious gormandizer in the whole crew) said such a cruel and wicked thing, that I wonder the mere thought did not turn him into a wild beast in shape, as he already was in his nature.

"This troublesome and impertinent little fowl," said he, "would make a delicate titbit to begin dinner with. Just one plump morsel, melting away between the teeth. If he comes within my reach, I'll catch him, and give him to the palace cook to be roasted on a skewer."

The words were hardly out of his mouth, before the purple bird flew away, crying, "Peep, peep, pe—weep," more dolorously than ever.

"That bird," remarked Eurylochus, "knows more than we do about what awaits us at the palace."

"Come on, then," cried his comrades, "and we'll soon know as much as he does."

The party, accordingly, went onward through the green and pleasant wood. Every little while they caught new glimpses of the marble palace, which looked more and more beautiful the nearer they approached it. They soon entered a broad pathway, which seemed to be very neatly kept, and which went winding along with streaks of sunshine falling across it, and specks of light quivering among the deepest shadows that fell from the lofty trees. It was bordered, too, with a great many sweet-smelling flowers, such as the mariners had never seen before. So rich and beautiful they were that, if the shrubs grew wild here and were native in the soil, then this island was surely the flower-garden of the whole earth; or, if transplanted from some other clime, it must have been from the Happy Islands that lay towards the golden sunset.

"There has been a great deal of pains foolishly wasted on these flowers," observed one of the company; and I tell you what he said, that you may keep in mind what gormandizers they were. "For my part, if I were the owner of the palace, I would bid my gardener cultivate nothing but savory potherbs to make a stuffing for roast meat, or to flavor a stew with."

"Well said!" cried the others. "But I'll warrant you there's a kitchen garden in the rear of the palace."

At one place they came to a crystal spring, and paused to drink at it for want of liquor which they liked better. Looking into its bosom, they beheld their own faces dimly reflected, but so extravagantly distorted by the gush and motion of the water, that each one of them appeared to be laughing at himself and all his companions. So ridiculous were these images of themselves, indeed, that they did really laugh aloud, and could hardly be grave again as soon as they wished. And after they had drunk, they grew still merrier than before.

"It has a twang of the wine-cask in it," said one, smacking his lips.

"Make haste!" cried his fellows; "we'll find the wine-cask itself at the palace; and that will be better than a hundred crystal fountains."

Then they quickened their pace, and capered for joy at the thought of the savory banquet at which they hoped to be guests. But Eurylochus told them that he felt as if he were walking in a dream.

"If I am really awake," continued he, "then, in my opinion, we are on the point of meeting with some stranger adventure than any that befell us in the cave of Polyphemus, or among the gigantic man-eating Læstrygons, or in the windy palace of King Æolus, which stands on a brazen-walled island. This kind of dreamy feeling always comes over me before any wonderful occurrence. If you take my advice, you will turn back."

"No, no," answered his comrades, snuffing the air, in which the scent from the palace kitchen was now very perceptible. "We would not turn back, though we were certain that the king of the Læstrygons, as big as a mountain, would sit at the head of the table, and huge Polyphemus, the one-eyed Cyclops, at its foot."

At length they came within full sight of the palace, which proved to be very large and lofty, with a great number of airy pinnacles upon its roof. Though it was now midday, and the sun shone brightly over the marble front, yet its snowy whiteness and its fantastic style of architecture made it look unreal, like the frostwork on a window-pane, or like the shapes of castles which one sees among the clouds by moonlight. But just then a puff of wind brought down the smoke of the kitchen chimney among them, and caused each man to smell the odor of the dish that he liked best;

and, after scenting it, they thought everything else moonshine, and nothing real save this palace, and save the banquet that was evidently ready to be served up in it.

So they hastened their steps towards the portal, but had not got half-way across the wide lawn, when a pack of lions, tigers, and wolves came bounding to meet them. The terrified mariners started back, expecting no better fate than to be torn to pieces and devoured. To their surprise and joy, however, these wild beasts merely capered around them, wagging their tails, offering their heads to be stroked and patted, and behaving just like so many well-bred house-dogs, when they wish to express their delight at meeting their master or their master's friends. The biggest lion licked the feet of Eurylochus; and every other lion, and every wolf and tiger, singled out one of his two and twenty followers, whom the beast fondled as if he loved him better than a beef-bone.

But, for all that, Eurylochus imagined that he saw something fierce and savage in their eyes; nor would he have been surprised, at any moment, to feel the big lion's terrible claws, or to see each of the tigers make a deadly spring, or each wolf leap at the throat of the man whom he had fondled. Their mildness seemed unreal, and a mere freak; but their savage nature was as true as their teeth and claws.

Nevertheless, the men went safely across the lawn with the wild beasts frisking about them, and doing no manner of harm; although, as they mounted the steps of the palace, you might possibly have heard

300

a low growl, particularly from the wolves, as if they thought it a pity, after all, to let the strangers pass without so much as tasting what they were made of.

Eurylochus and his followers now passed under a lofty portal, and looked through the open doorway into the interior of the palace. The first thing that they saw was a spacious hall, and a fountain in the middle of it, gushing up towards the ceiling out of a marble basin, and falling back into it with a continual plash. The water of this fountain, as it spouted upward, was constantly taking new shapes, not very distinctly, but plainly enough for a nimble fancy to recognize what they were. Now it was the shape of a man in a long robe, the fleecy whiteness of which was made out of the fountain's spray; now it was a lion, or a tiger, or a wolf, or an ass, or, as often as anything else, a hog, wallowing in the marble basin as if it were his sty. It was either magic or some very curious machinery that caused the gushing waterspout to assume all these forms. But, before the strangers had time to look closely at this wonderful sight, their attention was drawn off by a very sweet and agreeable sound. A woman's voice was singing melodiously in another room of the palace, and with her voice was mingled the noise of a loom, at which she was probably seated, weaving a rich texture of cloth, and intertwining the high and low sweetness of her voice into a rich tissue of harmony.

By and by the song came to an end; and then, all at once, there were several feminine voices, talking airily and cheerfully, with now and then a merry burst of laughter, such as you may always hear when three or four young women sit at work together.

"What a sweet song that was!" exclaimed one of the voyagers.

"Too sweet, indeed," answered Eurylochus, shaking his head. "Yet it was not so sweet as the song of the Sirens, those birdlike damsels who wanted to tempt us on the rocks, so that our vessel might be wrecked, and our bones left whitening along the shore."

"But just listen to the pleasant voices of those maidens, and that buzz of the loom, as the shuttle passes to and fro," said another comrade. "What a domestic, household, homelike sound it is! Ah, before that weary siege of Troy, I used to hear the buzzing loom and the women's voices under my own roof. Shall I never hear them again? nor taste those nice little savory dishes which my dearest wife knew how to serve up?"

"Tush! we shall fare better here," said another. "But how innocently those women are babbling together, without guessing that we overhear them! And mark that richest voice of all, so pleasant and familiar, but which yet seems to have the authority of a mistress among them. Let us show ourselves at once. What harm can the lady of the palace and her maidens do to mariners and warriors like us?"

"Remember," said Eurylochus, "that it was a young maiden who beguiled three of our friends into the palace of the king of the Læstrygons, who ate up one of them in the twinkling of an eye."

No warning or persuasion, however, had any effect

on his companions. They went up to a pair of folding-doors at the farther end of the hall, and, throwing them wide open, passed into the next room. Eurylochus, meanwhile, had stepped behind a pillar. In the short moment while the folding-doors opened and closed again, he caught a glimpse of a very beautiful woman rising from the loom and coming to meet the poor weather-beaten wanderers, with a hospitable smile and her hand stretched out in welcome. There were four other young women, who joined their hands and danced merrily forward, making gestures of obeisance to the strangers. They were only less beautiful than the lady who seemed to be their mistress. Yet Eurylochus fancied that one of them had sea-green hair, and that the close-fitting bodice of a second looked like the bark of a tree, and that both the others had something odd in their aspect, although he could not quite determine what it was, in the little while that he had to examine them.

The folding-doors swung quickly back, and left him standing behind the pillar, in the solitude of the outer hall. There Eurylochus waited until he was quite weary, and listened eagerly to every sound, but without hearing anything that could help him to guess what had become of his friends. Footsteps, it is true, seemed to be passing and repassing in other parts of the palace. Then there was a clatter of silver dishes, or golden ones, which made him imagine a rich feast in a splendid banqueting-hall. But by and by he heard a tremendous grunting and squealing, and then a sudden scampering, like that of small, hard hoofs over a marble floor, while the voices of the mistress and her four handmaidens were screaming all together, in tones of anger and derision. Eurylochus could not conceive what had happened, unless a drove of swine had broken into the palace, attracted by the smell of the feast. Chancing to cast his eyes at the fountain, he saw that it did not shift its shape, as formerly, nor looked either like a long-robed man, or a lion, a tiger, a wolf, or an ass. It looked like nothing but a hog, which lay wallowing in the marble basin, and filled it from brim to brim.

But we must leave the prudent Eurylochus waiting in the outer hall, and follow his friends into the inner secrecy of the palace. As soon as the beautiful woman saw them, she arose from the loom, as I have told you, and came forward, smiling, and stretching out her hand. She took the hand of the foremost among them, and bade him and the whole party welcome.

"You have been long expected, my good friends," said she. "I and my maidens are well acquainted with you, although you do not appear to recognize us. Look at this piece of tapestry, and judge if your faces must not have been familiar to us."

So the voyagers examined the web of cloth which the beautiful woman had been weaving in her loom; and to their vast astonishment they saw their own figures perfectly represented in different colored threads. It was a lifelike picture of their recent adventures, showing them in the cave of Polyphemus, and how they had put out his one great moony eye; while in another part of the tapestry they were untying the leathern bags, puffed out with contrary winds; and farther on, they beheld themselves scampering away from the gigantic king of the Læstrygons, who had caught one of them by the leg. Lastly, there they were, sitting on the desolate shore of this very island, hungry and downcast, and looking ruefully at the bare bones of the stag which they devoured yesterday. This was as far as the work had yet proceeded; but when the beautiful woman should again sit down at her loom, she would probably make a picture of what had since happened to the strangers, and of what was now going to happen.

"You see," she said, "that I know all about your troubles; and you cannot doubt that I desire to make you happy for as long a time as you may remain with me. For this purpose, my honored guests, I have ordered a banquet to be prepared. Fish, fowl, and flesh, roasted, and in luscious stews, and seasoned, I trust, to all your tastes, are ready to be served up. If your appetites tell you it is dinner-time, then come with me to the festal saloon."

At this kind invitation, the hungry mariners were quite overjoyed; and one of them, taking upon himself to be spokesman, assured their hospitable hostess that any hour of the day was dinner-time with them, whenever they could get flesh to put in the pot, and fire to boil it with. So the beautiful woman led the way; and the four maidens (one of them had sea-green hair, another a bodice of oak-bark, a third sprinkled a shower of water-drops from her fingers' ends, and the fourth had some other oddity, which I have forgotten), all these followed behind, and hurried the guests along, until they entered a magnificent saloon. It was built in a perfect oval, and lighted from a crystal dome above. Around the walls were ranged two and twenty thrones, overhung by canopies of crimson and gold, and provided with the softest of cushions, which were tasseled and fringed with gold cord. Each of the strangers was invited to sit down; and there they were, two and twenty storm-beaten mariners, in worn and tattered garb, sitting on two and twenty cushioned and canopied thrones, so rich and gorgeous that the proudest monarch had nothing more splendid in his stateliest hall.

Then you might have seen the guests nodding, winking with one eye, and leaning from one throne to another, to communicate their satisfaction in hoarse whispers.

"Our good hostess has made kings of us all," said one. "Ha! do you smell the feast? I'll engage it will be fit to set before two-and-twenty kings."

"I hope," said another, "it will be, mainly, good substantial joints, sirloins, spareribs, and hinder quarters, without too many kickshaws. If I thought the good lady would not take it amiss, I should call for a fat slice of fried bacon to begin with."

Ah, the gluttons and gormandizers! You see how it was with them. In the loftiest seats of dignity, on royal thrones, they could think of nothing but their greedy appetite, which was the portion of their nature that they shared with wolves and swine; so that they resembled those vilest of animals far more than they

306

did kings, — if, indeed, kings were what they ought to be.

But the beautiful woman now clapped her hands; and immediately there entered a train of two and twenty serving-men, bringing dishes of the richest food, all hot from the kitchen fire, and sending up such a steam that it hung like a cloud below the crystal dome of the saloon. An equal number of attendants brought great flagons of wine, of various kinds, some of which sparkled as it was poured out, and went bubbling down the throat; while, of other sorts, the purple liquor was so clear that you could see the wrought figures at the bottom of the goblet. While the servants supplied the two and twenty guests with food and drink, the hostess and her four maidens went from one throne to another, exhorting them to eat their fill, and to quaff wine abundantly, and thus to recompense themselves, at this one banquet, for the many days when they had gone without a dinner. But, whenever the mariners were not looking at them (which was pretty often, as they looked chiefly into the basins and platters), the beautiful woman and her damsels turned aside and laughed. Even the servants, as they knelt down to present the dishes, might be seen to grin and sneer, while the guests were helping themselves to the offered dainties.

And once in a while the strangers seemed to taste something that they did not like.

"Here is an odd kind of a spice in this dish," said one. "I can't say it quite suits my palate. Down it goes, however."

307

"Send a good draught of wine down your throat," said his comrade on the next throne. "That is the stuff to make this sort of cookery relish well. Though I must needs say, the wine has a queer taste too. But the more I drink of it the better I like the flavor."

Whatever little fault they might find with the dishes, they sat at dinner a prodigiously long while; and it would really have made you ashamed to see how they swilled down the liquor and gobbled up the food. They sat on golden thrones, to be sure; but they behaved like pigs in a sty, and, if they had had their wits about them, they might have guessed that this was the opinion of their beautiful hostess and her maidens. It brings a blush into my face to reckon up, in my own mind, what mountains of meat and pudding, and what gallons of wine, these two and twenty guzzlers and gormandizers ate and drank. They forgot all about their homes, and their wives, and children, and all about Ulysses, and everything else, except this banquet, at which they wanted to keep feasting forever. But at length they began to give over, from mere incapacity to hold any more.

"That last bit of fat is too much for me," said one.

"And I have not room for another morsel," said his next neighbor, heaving a sigh. "What a pity! My appetite is as sharp as ever."

In short, they all left off eating, and leaned back on their thrones, with such a stupid and helpless aspect as made them ridiculous to behold. When their hostess saw this, she laughed aloud; so did her four damsels; so did the two-and-twenty serving men that bore the

dishes, and their two-and-twenty fellows that poured
out the wine. And the louder they all laughed, the
more stupid and helpless did the two-and-twenty gormandizers look. Then the beautiful woman took her
stand in the middle of the saloon, and stretching out
a slender rod (it had been all the while in her hand,
although they never noticed it till this moment), she
turned it from one guest to another, until each had felt
it pointed at himself. Beautiful as her face was, and
though there was a smile on it, it looked just as wicked
and mischievous as the ugliest serpent that ever was
seen; and fat-witted as the voyagers had made themselves, they began to suspect that they had fallen into
the power of an evil-minded enchantress.

"Wretches," cried she, "you have abused a lady's
hospitality; and in this princely saloon your behavior
has been suited to a hogpen. You are already swine
in everything but the human form, which you disgrace, and which I myself should be ashamed to keep
a moment longer, were you to share it with me. But
it will require only the slightest exercise of magic to
make the exterior conform to the hoggish disposition.
Assume your proper shapes, gormandizers, and begone
to the sty!"

Uttering these last words, she waved her wand; and
stamping her foot imperiously, each of the guests was
struck aghast at beholding, instead of his comrades in
human shape, one and twenty hogs sitting on the same
number of golden thrones. Each man (as he still supposed himself to be) essayed to give a cry of surprise,
but found that he could merely grunt, and that, in a

word, he was just such another beast as his companions. It looked so intolerably absurd to see hogs on cushioned thrones, that they made haste to wallow down upon all fours, like other swine. They tried to groan and beg for mercy, but forthwith emitted the most awful grunting and squealing that ever came out of swinish throats. They would have wrung their hands in despair, but, attemping to do so, grew all the more desperate for seeing themselves squatted on their hams, and pawing the air with their fore trotters. Dear me! what pendulous ears they had! what little red eyes, half buried in fat! and what long snouts, instead of Grecian noses!

But brutes as they certainly were, they yet had enough of human nature in them to be shocked at their own hideousness; and still intending to groan, they uttered a viler grunt and squeal than before. So harsh and ear-piercing it was, that you would have fancied a butcher was sticking his knife into each of their throats, or, at the very least, that somebody was pulling every hog by his funny little twist of a tail.

"Begone to your sty!" cried the enchantress, giving them some smart strokes with her wand; and then she turned to the serving-men. "Drive out these swine, and throw down some acorns for them to eat."

The door of the saloon being flung open, the drove of hogs ran in all directions save the right one, in accordance with their hoggish perversity, but were finally driven into the back yard of the palace. It was a sight to bring tears into one's eyes (and I hope none of you will be cruel enough to laugh at it) to see the poor creatures go snuffing along, picking up here a cabbage leaf and there a turnip-top, and rooting their noses in the earth for whatever they could find. In their sty, moreover, they behaved more piggishly than the pigs that had been born so; for they bit and snorted at one another, put their feet in the trough, and gobbled up their victuals in a ridiculous hurry; and, when there was nothing more to be had, they made a great pile of themselves among some unclean straw and fell fast asleep. If they had any human reason left, it was just enough to keep them wondering when they should be slaughtered, and what quality of bacon they should make.

Meantime, as I told you before, Eurylochus had waited, and waited, and waited, in the entrance-hall of the palace, without being able to comprehend what had befallen his friends. At last, when the swinish uproar resounded through the palace, and when he saw the image of a hog in the marble basin, he thought it best to hasten back to the vessel, and inform the wise Ulysses of these marvelous occurrences. So he ran as fast as he could down the steps, and never stopped to draw breath till he reached the shore.

"Why do you come alone?" asked King Ulysses, as soon as he saw him. "Where are your two and twenty comrades?"

At these questions Eurylochus burst into tears.

"Alas!" cried he, "I greatly fear that we shall never see one of their faces again."

Then he told Ulysses all that had happened, as far as he knew it, and added that he suspected the beautiful woman to be a vile enchantress, and the marble palace, magnificent as it looked, to be only a dismal cavern in reality. As for his companions, he could not imagine what had become of them, unless they had been given to the swine to be devoured alive. At this intelligence all the voyagers were greatly affrighted. But Ulysses lost no time in girding on his sword, and hanging his bow and quiver over his shoulders, and taking a spear in his right hand. When his followers saw their wise leader making these preparations, they inquired whither he was going, and earnestly besought him not to leave them.

"You are our king," cried they; "and what is more, you are the wisest man in the whole world, and nothing but your wisdom and courage can get us out of this danger. If you desert us, and go to the enchanted palace, you will suffer the same fate as our poor companions, and not a soul of us will ever see our dear Ithaca again."

"As I am your king," answered Ulysses, "and wiser than any of you, it is therefore the more my duty to see what has befallen our comrades, and whether anything can yet be done to rescue them. Wait for me here until to-morrow. If I do not then return, you must hoist sail, and endeavor to find your way to our native land. For my part, I am answerable for the fate of these poor mariners, who have stood by my side in battle, and been so often drenched to the skin, along with me, by the same tempestuous surges. I will either bring them back with me or perish."

Had his followers dared, they would have detained

him by force. But King Ulysses frowned sternly on them, and shook his spear, and bade them stop him at their peril. Seeing him so determined, they let him go, and sat down on the sand, as disconsolate a set of people as could be, waiting and praying for his return.

It happened to Ulysses, just as before, that, when he had gone a few steps from the edge of the cliff, the purple bird came fluttering towards him, crying, "Peep, peep, pe—weep!" and using all the art it could to persuade him to go no farther.

"What mean you, little bird?" cried Ulysses. "You are arrayed like a king in purple and gold, and wear a golden crown upon your head. Is it because I too am a king that you desire so earnestly to speak with me? If you can talk in human language, say what you would have me do."

"Peep!" answered the purple bird, very dolorously. "Peep, peep, pe—we—ep!"

Certainly there lay some heavy anguish at the little bird's heart; and it was a sorrowful predicament that he could not, at least, have the consolation of telling what it was. But Ulysses had no time to waste in trying to get at the mystery. He therefore quickened his pace, and had gone a good way along the pleasant wood-path, when there met him a young man of very brisk and intelligent aspect, and clad in a rather singular garb. He wore a short cloak, and a sort of cap that seemed to be furnished with a pair of wings; and from the lightness of his step, you would have supposed that there might likewise be wings on his feet. To enable him to walk still better (for he was always on one journey or another), he carried a winged staff, around which two serpents were wriggling and twisting. In short, I have said enough to make you guess that it was Quicksilver; and Ulysses (who knew him of old, and had learned a great deal of his wisdom from him) recognized him in a moment.

"Whither are you going in such a hurry, wise Ulysses?" asked Quicksilver. "Do you not know that this island is enchanted? The wicked enchantress (whose name is Circe, the sister of King Æetes) dwells in the marble palace which you see yonder among the trees. By her magic arts, she changes every human being into the brute, beast, or fowl whom he happens most to resemble."

"That little bird which met me at the edge of the cliff," exclaimed Ulysses; "was he a human being once?"

"Yes," answered Quicksilver. "He was once a king, named Picus, and a pretty good sort of a king too, only rather too proud of his purple robe, and his crown, and the golden chain about his neck; so he was forced to take the shape of a gaudy-feathered bird. The lions, and wolves, and tigers who will come running to meet you, in front of the palace, were formerly fierce and cruel men, resembling in their dispositions the wild beasts whose forms they now rightfully wear."

"And my poor companions," said Ulysses. "Have they undergone a similar change, through the arts of this wicked Circe?"

"You well know what gormandizers they were,"

replied Quicksilver; and, rogue that he was, he could not help laughing at the joke. "So you will not be surprised to hear that they have all taken the shapes of swine! If Circe had never done anything worse, I really should not think her so very much to blame."

"But can I do nothing to help them?" inquired Ulysses.

"It will require all your wisdom," said Quicksilver, "and a little of my own into the bargain, to keep your royal and sagacious self from being transformed into a fox. But do as I bid you, and the matter may end better than it has begun."

While he was speaking, Quicksilver seemed to be in search of something; he went stooping along the ground, and soon laid his hand on a little plant with a snow-white flower, which he plucked and smelt of. Ulysses had been looking at that very spot only just before; and it appeared to him that the plant had burst into full flower the instant when Quicksilver touched it with his fingers.

"Take this flower, King Ulysses," said he. "Guard it as you do your eyesight; for I can assure you it is exceedingly rare and precious, and you might seek the whole earth over without ever finding another like it. Keep it in your hand, and smell of it frequently after you enter the palace, and while you are talking with the enchantress. Especially when she offers you food, or a draught of wine out of her goblet, be careful to fill your nostrils with the flower's fragrance. Follow these directions, and you may defy her magic arts to change you into a fox."

Quicksilver then gave him some further advice how to behave, and, bidding him be bold and prudent, again assured him that, powerful as Circe was, he would have a fair prospect of coming safely out of her enchanted palace. After listening attentively, Ulysses thanked his good friend, and resumed his way. But he had taken only a few steps, when, recollecting some other questions which he wished to ask, he turned round again, and beheld nobody on the spot where Quicksilver had stood; for that winged cap of his, and those winged shoes with the help of the winged staff, had carried him quickly out of sight.

When Ulysses reached the lawn in front of the palace, the lions and other savage animals came bounding to meet him, and would have fawned upon him and licked his feet. But the wise king struck at them with his long spear, and sternly bade them begone out of his path; for he knew that they had once been bloodthirsty men, and would now tear him limb from limb, instead of fawning upon him, could they do the mischief that was in their hearts. The wild beasts yelped and glared at him, and stood at a distance while he ascended the palace steps.

On entering the hall, Ulysses saw the magic fountain in the centre of it. The up-gushing water had now again taken the shape of a man in a long, white, fleecy robe, who appeared to be making gestures of welcome. The king likewise heard the noise of the shuttle in the loom, and the sweet melody of the beautiful woman's song, and then the pleasant voices of herself and the four maidens talking together, with peals of merry laughter intermixed. But Ulysses did not waste much time in listening to the laughter or the song. He leaned his spear against one of the pillars of the hall, and then, after loosening his sword in the scabbard, stepped boldly forward, and threw the folding-doors wide open. The moment she beheld his stately figure standing in the doorway, the beautiful woman rose from the loom, and ran to meet him with a glad smile throwing its sunshine over her face, and both her hands extended.

"Welcome, brave stranger!" cried she. "We were expecting you."

And the nymph with the sea-green hair made a courtesy down to the ground, and likewise bade him welcome; so did her sister with the bodice of oaken bark, and she that sprinkled dew-drops from her fingers' ends, and the fourth one with some oddity which I cannot remember. And Circe, as the beautiful enchantress was called (who had deluded so many persons that she did not doubt of being able to delude Ulysses, not imagining how wise he was), again addressed him.

"Your companions," said she, "have already been received into my palace, and have enjoyed the hospitable treatment to which the propriety of their behavior so well entitles them. If such be your pleasure, you shall first take some refreshment, and then join them in the elegant apartments which they now occupy. See, I and my maidens have been weaving their figures into this piece of tapestry."

She pointed to the web of beautifully woven cloth

in the loom. Circe and the four nymphs must have
been very diligently at work since the arrival of the
mariners; for a great many yards of tapestry had now
been wrought, in addition to what I before described.
In this new part, Ulysses saw his two and twenty
friends represented as sitting on cushioned and canopied thrones, greedily devouring dainties and quaffing
deep draughts of wine. The work had not yet gone
any further. Oh, no, indeed! The enchantress was far
too cunning to let Ulysses see the mischief which her
magic arts had since brought upon the gormandizers.

"As for yourself, valiant sir," said Circe, "judging
by the dignity of your aspect, I take you to be nothing
less than a king. Deign to follow me, and you shall
be treated as befits your rank."

So Ulysses followed her into the oval saloon, where
his two and twenty comrades had devoured the banquet which ended so disastrously for themselves. But
all this while he had held the snow-white flower in
his hand, and had constantly smelt of it while Circe
was speaking; and as he crossed the threshold of the
saloon, he took good care to inhale several long and
deep snuffs of its fragrance. Instead of two and
twenty thrones, which had before been ranged around
the wall, there was now only a single throne, in the
centre of the apartment. But this was surely the most
magnificent seat that ever a king or an emperor re-
posed himself upon, all made of chased gold, studded
with precious stones, with a cushion that looked like
a soft heap of living roses, and overhung by a canopy of sunlight which Circe knew how to weave into

318

drapery. The enchantress took Ulysses by the hand, and made him sit down upon this dazzling throne. Then, clapping her hands, she summoned the chief butler.

"Bring hither," said she, "the goblet that is set apart for kings to drink out of. And fill it with the same delicious wine which my royal brother, King Æetes, praised so highly, when he visited me with my fair daughter Medea. That good and amiable child! Were she now here, it would delight her to see me offering this wine to my honored guest."

But Ulysses, while the butler was gone for the wine, held the snow-white flower to his nose.

"Is it a wholesome wine?" he asked.

At this the four maidens tittered; whereupon the enchantress looked round at them, with an aspect of severity.

"It is the wholesomest juice that ever was squeezed out of the grape," said she; "for, instead of disguising a man, as other liquor is apt to do, it brings him to his true self, and shows him as he ought to be."

The chief butler liked nothing better than to see people turned into swine, or making any kind of a beast of themselves; so he made haste to bring the royal goblet, filled with a liquid as bright as gold, and which kept sparkling upward, and throwing a sunny spray over the brim. But, delightfully as the wine looked, it was mingled with the most potent enchantments that Circe knew how to concoct. For every drop of the pure grape-juice there were two drops of the pure mischief; and the danger of the thing was, that the mischief made it taste all the better. The mere smell of the bubbles, which effervesced at the brim, was enough to turn a man's beard into pig's bristles, or make a lion's claws grow out of his fingers, or a fox's brush behind him.

"Drink, my noble guest," said Circe, smiling as she presented him with the goblet. "You will find in this draught a solace for all your troubles."

King Ulysses took the goblet with his right hand, while with his left he held the snow-white flower to his nostrils, and drew in so long a breath that his lungs were quite filled with its pure and simple fragrance. Then, drinking off all the wine, he looked the enchantress calmly in the face.

"Wretch," cried Circe, giving him a smart stroke with her wand, "how dare you keep your human shape a moment longer? Take the form of the brute whom you most resemble. If a hog, go join your fellow swine in the sty; if a lion, a wolf, a tiger, go howl with the wild beasts on the lawn; if a fox, go exercise your craft in stealing poultry. Thou hast quaffed off my wine, and canst be man no longer."

But, such was the virtue of the snow-white flower, instead of wallowing down from his throne in swinish shape or taking any other brutal form, Ulysses looked even more manly and kinglike than before. He gave the magic goblet a toss, and sent it clashing over the marble floor, to the farthest end of the saloon. Then, drawing his sword, he seized the enchantress by her beautiful ringlets, and made a gesture as if he meant to strike off her head at one blow.

"Wicked Circe," cried he, in a terrible voice, "this sword shall put an end to thy enchantments. Thou shalt die, vile wretch, and do no more mischief in the world, by tempting human beings into the vices which make beasts of them."

The tone and countenance of Ulysses were so awful, and his sword gleamed so brightly and seemed to have so intolerably keen an edge, that Circe was almost killed by the mere fright, without waiting for a blow. The chief butler scrambled out of the saloon, picking up the golden goblet as he went; and the enchantress and the four maidens fell on their knees, wringing their hands and screaming for mercy.

"Spare me!" cried Circe, — "spare me, royal and wise Ulysses. For now I know that thou art he of whom Quicksilver forewarned me, the most prudent of mortals, against whom no enchantments can prevail. Thou only couldst have conquered Circe. Spare me, wisest of men. I will show thee true hospitality, and even give myself to be thy slave, and this magnificent palace to be henceforth thy home."

The four nymphs, meanwhile, were making a most piteous ado; and especially the ocean nymph, with the sea-green hair, wept a great deal of salt water, and the fountain nymph, besides scattering dewdrops from her fingers' ends, nearly melted away into tears. But Ulysses would not be pacified until Circe had taken a solemn oath to change back his companions, and as many others as he should direct, from their present forms of beast or bird into their former shapes of men.

"On these conditions," said he, "I consent to spare your life. Otherwise you must die upon the spot."

With a drawn sword hanging over her, the enchantress would readily have consented to do as much good as she had hitherto done mischief, however little she might like such employment. She therefore led Ulysses out of the back entrance of the palace, and showed him the swine in their sty. There were about fifty of these unclean beasts in the whole herd; and though the greater part were hogs by birth and education, there was wonderfully little difference to be seen betwixt them and their new brethren who had so recently worn the human shape. To speak critically, indeed, the latter rather carried the thing to excess, and seemed to make it a point to wallow in the miriest part of the sty, and otherwise to outdo the original swine in their own natural vocation. When men once turn to brutes, the trifle of man's wit that remains in them adds tenfold to their brutality.

The comrades of Ulysses, however, had not quite lost the remembrance of having formerly stood erect. When he approached the sty, two and twenty enormous swine separated themselves from the herd, and scampered towards him, with such a chorus of horrible squealing as made him clap both hands to his ears. And yet they did not seem to know what they wanted, nor whether they were merely hungry or miserable from some other cause. It was curious, in the midst of their distress, to observe them thrusting their noses into the mire, in quest of something to eat. The nymph with the bodice of oaken bark (she was the hamadryad of an oak) threw a handful of acorns among them; and the two and twenty hogs scrambled and fought for the prize, as if they had tasted not so much as a noggin of sour milk for a twelvemonth.

"These must certainly be my comrades," said Ulysses. "I recognize their dispositions. They are hardly worth the trouble of changing them into the human form again. Nevertheless, we will have it done, lest their bad example should corrupt the other hogs. Let them take their original shapes, therefore, Dame Circe, if your skill is equal to the task. It will require greater magic, I trow, than it did to make swine of them."

So Circe waved her wand again, and repeated a few magic words, at the sound of which the two and twenty hogs pricked up their pendulous ears. It was a wonder to behold how their snouts grew shorter and shorter, and their mouths (which they seemed to be sorry for, because they could not gobble so expeditiously) smaller and smaller, and how one and another began to stand upon his hind legs, and scratch his nose with his fore trotters. At first the spectators hardly knew whether to call them hogs or men, but by and by came to the conclusion that they rather resembled the latter. Finally, there stood the twenty-two comrades of Ulysses, looking pretty much the same as when they left the vessel.

You must not imagine, however, that the swinish quality had entirely gone out of them. When once it fastens itself into a person's character, it is very difficult getting rid of it. This was proved by the hamadryad, who, being exceedingly fond of mischief, threw another handful of acorns before the twenty-two newly restored people; whereupon down they wallowed, in a moment, and gobbled them up in a very shameful way. Then, recollecting themselves, they scrambled to their feet, and looked more than commonly foolish.

"Thanks, noble Ulysses!" they cried. "From brute beasts you have restored us to the condition of men again."

"Do not put yourselves to the trouble of thanking me," said the wise king. "I fear I have done but little for you."

To say the truth, there was a suspicious kind of a grunt in their voices, and for a long time afterwards they spoke gruffly, and were apt to set up a squeal.

"It must depend on your own future behavior," added Ulysses, "whether you do not find your way back to the sty."

At this moment, the note of a bird sounded from the branch of a neighboring tree.

"Peep, peep, pe—wee—ep!"

It was the purple bird, who, all this while, had been sitting over their heads, watching what was going forward, and hoping that Ulysses would remember how he had done his utmost to keep him and his followers out of harm's way. Ulysses ordered Circe instantly to make a king of this good little fowl, and leave him exactly as she found him. Hardly were the words spoken, and before the bird had time to utter another "Pe—weep," King Picus leaped down from the bough of the tree, as majestic a sovereign as any in the world, dressed in a long purple robe and gorgeous yellow stockings, with a splendidly wrought collar about his neck, and a golden crown upon his head. He and King Ulysses exchanged with one another the courtesies which belonged to their elevated rank. But from that time forth, King Picus was no longer proud of his crown and his trappings of royalty, nor of the fact of his being a king; he felt himself merely the upper servant of his people, and that it must be his lifelong labor to make them better and happier.

As for the lions, tigers, and wolves (though Circe would have restored them to their former shapes at his slightest word), Ulysses thought it advisable that they should remain as they now were, and thus give warning of their cruel dispositions, instead of going about under the guise of men, and pretending to human sympathies, while their hearts had the blood-thirstiness of wild beasts. So he let them howl as much as they liked, but never troubled his head about them. And, when everything was settled according to his pleasure, he sent to summon the remainder of his comrades, whom he had left at the seashore. These being arrived, with the prudent Eurylochus at their head, they all made themselves comfortable in Circe's enchanted palace until quite rested and refreshed from the toils and hardships of their voyage.

THE SIRENS — SCYLLA AND CHARYBDIS

Translated by George Herbert Palmer

I TURNED me toward my ship, and called my crew to come on board and loose the cables. Quickly they came, took places at the pins, and sitting in order smote the foaming water with their oars. And for our aid behind our dark-bowed ship came a fair wind to fill our sail, a welcome comrade, sent us by fair-haired Circe, the mighty goddess, human of speech. When we had done our work at the several ropes about the ship, we sat us down, while wind and helmsman kept her steady.

Now to my men, with aching heart, I said, "My friends, it is not right for only one or two to know the oracles which Circe told, that heavenly goddess. Therefore I speak, that, knowing all, we so may die, or fleeing death and doom, we may escape. She warns us first against the marvelous Sirens, and bids us flee their voice and flowery meadow. Only myself she bade to hear their song; but bind me with galling cords, to hold me firm, upright upon the mast-block, — round it let the rope be wound. And if I should entreat you, and bid you set me free, thereat with still more fetters bind me fast."

Thus I, relating all my tale, talked with my comrades. Meanwhile our stanch ship swiftly neared the Sirens' island; a fair wind swept her on. On a sudden the wind ceased; there came a breathless calm; Heaven hushed the waves. My comrades, rising, furled the sail, stowed it on board the hollow ship, then sitting at their oars whitened the water with the polished blades. But I with my sharp sword cut a great cake of wax into small bits, which I then kneaded in my sturdy hands. Soon the wax warmed, forced by the powerful pressure and by the rays of the exalted sun, the lord of all. Then one by one I stopped the ears of all my crew; and on the deck they bound me hand and foot, upright upon the mast-block, round which they wound the rope; and sitting down they smote the foaming water with their oars. But when we were as far away as one can call, and driving swiftly onward, our speeding ship, as it drew near, did not escape the Sirens, and thus they lifted up their penetrating voice: —

"Come hither, come, Ulysses, whom all praise! great glory to the Achaians! Bring on your ship, and listen to our song. For none has ever passed us in a black-hulled ship till from our lips he heard ecstatic song, then went his way rejoicing and with larger knowledge. For we know all that on the plain of Troy Argives and Trojans suffered at the Gods' behest; we know whatever happens on the bounteous earth."

So spoke they, sending forth their glorious song, and my heart longed to listen. Knitting my brows, I signed my men to set me free; but bending forward, on they rowed. And straightway Perimedes and Eury-

lochus arose and laid upon me still more cords, and
drew them tighter. Then, after passing by, when we
could hear no more the Sirens' voice nor any singing,
quickly my trusty crew removed the wax with which
I stopped their ears, and set me free from bondage.

Soon after we left the island, I observed a smoke,
I saw high waves and heard a plunging sound. From
the hands of my frightened men down fell the oars,
and splashed against the current. There the ship
stayed, for they worked the tapering oars no more.
Along the ship I passed, inspiriting my men with cheer-
ing words, standing by each in turn: —

"Friends, hitherto we have not been untried in danger. Here is no greater danger than when the Cyclops
penned us with brutal might in the deep cave. Yet out
of that, through energy of mine, through will and wisdom, we escaped. These dangers, too, I think some day
we shall remember. Come then, and what I say let us
all follow. You with your oars strike the deep breakers
of the sea, while sitting at the pins, and see if Zeus will
set us free from present death and let us go in safety.
And, helmsman, these are my commands for you; lay
them to heart, for you control the rudders of our hollow
ship: keep the ship off that smoke and surf and hug
the crags, or else, before you know it, she may veer off
that way, and you will bring us into danger."

So I spoke, and my words they quickly heeded. But
Scylla I did not name, — that hopeless horror, — for
fear through fright my men might cease to row, and
huddle all together in the hold. I disregarded too the
hard behest of Circe, when she had said I must by

no means arm. Putting on my glittering armor and
taking in my hands my two long spears, I went upon
the ship's fore-deck, for thence I looked for the first
sight of Scylla of the rocks, who brought my men disaster. Nowhere could I descry her; I tried my eyes
with searching up and down the dusky cliff.

So up the strait we sailed in sadness; for here lay
Scylla, and there divine Charybdis fearfully sucked
the salt sea-water down. Whenever she belched it
forth, like a kettle in fierce flame all would foam swirl-
ing up, and overhead spray fell upon the tops of both
the crags. But when she gulped the salt sea-water
down, then all within seemed in a whirl; the rock
around roared fearfully, and down below the bottom
showed, dark with the sand. Pale terror seized my
men; on her we looked and feared to die.

And now it was that Scylla snatched from the hollow ship six of my comrades who were best in skill
and strength. Turning my eyes toward my swift ship
to seek my men, I saw their feet and hands already
in the air as they were carried up. They screamed
aloud and called my name for the last time, in agony
of heart. As when a fisher, on a jutting rock, with
long rod throws a bait to lure the little fishes, casting
into the deep the horn of stall-fed ox; then, catching
a fish, flings it ashore writhing, — even so were these
drawn writhing up the rocks. There at her door she
ate them, loudly shrieking and stretching forth their
hands in mortal pangs toward me. That was the sad-
dest sight my eyes have ever seen, in all my toils, searching the ocean pathways.

ULYSSES IN ITHACA

ULYSSES LANDS ON THE SHORE OF ITHACA

By F. S. Marvin, R. J. C. Mayor, and F. M.
Stowell

[For ten years Ulysses was driven hither and thither over the water, seeking for his homeland, Ithaca. At length he was shipwrecked on the shores of Phœacia. The king, Alcinous, entertained him most hospitably, and Ulysses related to him the story of his wanderings.]

WHEN Ulysses had finished his story, there was silence in the hall till Alcinous said, "Ulysses, now that you have come to my house after all these troubles, you shall return without more wandering to your home." And then he bade the princes go home for the night and meet again in the morning to bring their gifts.

So next day the Sea-kings went down to the ship and put their gifts on board and then returned to the palace and sacrificed an ox to Zeus. And then they feasted and drank their good wine and waited till the sun went down. And the minstrel sang to them, but Ulysses kept looking at the sun impatiently, like a hungry ploughman tired out at the close of day. At last the time arrived, and then Ulysses said, "Alcinous, let me go now, and fare you well. My escort and my

gifts are all prepared, and I could wish no more. May I but find my wife and my dear ones all safe and sound at home! And may Heaven grant you, too, happy home and every blessing and no distress among your people!'
And to Queen Arete he said, "Lady, may you live happily with your husband and children, and all this people, till old age comes to you and death, which must come to all!"

Then the herald led the way and Ulysses followed to the ship, and the queen sent her servants with him to carry warm clothing for the voyage and food and drink. And when they had stored the ship he lay down silently in the stern, and the rowers took their places in the benches and plied their oars, while a deep, sweet sleep fell upon him, like the sleep of death. Then the wonderful ship leapt forward on her way, like a team of chariot horses plunging beneath the whip, and the great dark wave roared round the stern. No hawk could fly so quickly as that ship flew through the waves, and the hawk is the swiftest of all birds. And as she sped, the man who had suffered so much and was as wise as the Gods lay peacefully asleep, and forgot his sufferings.

But when the bright star rose that tells of the approach of day, the ship drew near the island of Ithaca. There is a haven there between two steep headlands which break the waves, so that ships can ride in safety without a mooring rope, and at the head of it an olive-tree, and a shadowy cave where the water fairies come and tend their bees and weave their sea-blue garments on the hanging looms and mix their wine in bowls and jars of stone. There are springs of water in the cave, and two ways into it, one to the north for men to enter, and one to the south where none but the Gods may pass.

The Sea-kings knew this harbor and rowed straight into it and ran their ship half a keel's length ashore. Then they lifted Ulysses out of the stern, wrapt in the rugs and coverlet, and laid him still asleep upon the sand. And the gifts they placed in a heap by the trunk of the olive-tree, a little out of the road, so that no passer-by might rob him as he slept.

Then they sailed away; and after they were gone Ulysses awoke, but he could not recognize the land where he lay, for Athene had cast a mist about him so that everything looked strange, though he was the lord of it all. There were the mountain paths and the sheltering creeks, the high, steep rocks and the trees in bloom; but he could not see it aright, and started up and smote his hands upon his thighs and cried aloud, —

"What land have I come to now? And what can I do with all this treasure? If the Sea-kings did not really mean to send me back to Ithaca they should have conveyed me to some other people who would have sent me home." And then he counted the gifts over, the golden vessels, and the beautiful garments, and found nothing missing, but they gave him no pleasure; and he turned sadly to walk along the shore and dream of home, when a young herdsman met him, of noble figure, with a javelin in his hand and a fine mantle in double folds upon his shoulders. Ulysses was glad to greet him, and asked what country he had reached. It was Athene in disguise, and she answered, "Truly, stranger, you must have come from far indeed. For this is a famous island that all men know, whether they live in the east or in the west. It is a rugged land, and no place for horses and chariots, but though it is narrow, it is not so poor; for there are stores of corn and wine, plenty of water for the cattle and plenty of wood. Its name is Ithaca, and some men have heard of it even at Troy, which they say is a long way off."

Then brave Ulysses rejoiced in his heart to hear that it was his native land; but he would not tell the herdsman who he was, and made up a cunning story that he had escaped as an outlaw from Crete and had been left upon the island by a Phœnician crew. And the goddess smiled to hear him, and stood forth in her own true form, a wise and noble woman, tall and fair, and put her hand upon his shoulder, and said, —

"Come, let us practice no more craft on one another, Ulysses, for we are both famous for our wit and wiles, you among mortals and I among the Gods. I am Pallas Athene, daughter of Zeus, and I have stood beside you and protected you in all your wanderings and toil. And now I have come here to tell you of the troubles that await you in your house, and to help you with my counsel. But you must still endure in silence, and tell no one that Ulysses has returned."

And Ulysses made answer, "It is hard, goddess, for a mortal to know you, wise though he may be, for you come in many shapes. Truly I have known your kindness from of old in Troy, but when we went on board the ships, I never saw you at my side again.

Tell me, I pray you, if this is Ithaca indeed, my native land."

Then the goddess answered, "I see, Ulysses, that you keep your ready wit and steadfast mind. I could not show myself your friend before for fear of angering Neptune, my own father's brother. But come now, and I will show you Ithaca; there is the haven and the olive with its slender leaves, and the cave where you once made many an offering to the water nymphs."

And then she rolled away the mist, and the long-suffering hero rejoiced to see his native land again. He kissed the kindly earth, and vowed to the nymphs that he would bring them offerings as of old if he lived to see his dear son a man.

Then the goddess bade him be of good cheer, and showed him a hiding-place in the cavern for the gifts. And then they sat down by the trunk of the olive-tree, and Athene told him all the misdeeds of the suitors, and how his wife had beguiled them and kept them waiting till his return, and how he must avenge himself and her.

Then Ulysses said, "Truly, I should have perished in my own halls, like Agamemnon, if you had not warned me. Help me, therefore, with your wisdom, and stand beside me again and put strength and courage within me as in the days of Troy. For with you by my side I could fight against three hundred men."

And Pallas Athene made answer, "I will be with you, Ulysses, when the hour of the conflict is come, and the blood of the suitors who eat up your substance shall be shed at last. But now I will change you into a poor beggar, so old and so wretched that no one will know you, and in that guise you must go and stay with the herdsman Eumæus, who tends your swine, until I have brought your son Telemachus from Sparta, where he has gone to seek tidings of you."

Then she touched him with her magic wand, and the fair flesh withered on his limbs, and the golden locks fell from his head, and he was changed into an old man. His skin was shriveled and his bright eyes dimmed, and for his covering she gave him a tattered wrap, begrimed with smoke, and a worn deerskin on his shoulder, and a wallet and a staff in his hand.

Then she vanished, and left him to take his way alone across the hills.

ULYSSES AT THE HOUSE OF THE SWINEHERD

By F. S. Marvin, R. J. C. Mayor, and F. M. Stowell

ULYSSES went up along the rough mountain path, through the forest and over the hills, till he came to the house where his faithful steward lived. It stood in an open space, and there was a large courtyard in front with a wall of heavy stones and hawthorn boughs and a stout oak palisade. Inside the yard there were twelve sties for the pigs, and the swineherd kept four watch-dogs to guard the place, great beasts and fierce as wolves, that he had reared himself. Ulysses found him at home, sitting in the porch alone, and cutting himself a pair of sandals from a brown oxhide.

The dogs caught sight of the king as soon as he came up and flew at him, barking, but he had the wit to let go his staff and sit down at once on the ground. Still it might have gone hard with him there in front of his own servant's house had not Eumæus rushed out of the porch, dropping the leather in his haste, and scolded the dogs, driving them off with a volley of stones.

Then he said to Ulysses, "A little more, old man, and the dogs would have torn you in pieces, and disgraced me forever. And I have my full share of trouble as it is, for I have lost the best master in all the world and must sit here to mourn for him and fatten his swine for other men, while he is wandering somewhere in foreign lands, hungry and thirsty perhaps, if he is still alive at all. But now come in yourself, and let me give you food and drink and tell me your own tale."

So he took Ulysses into the house and made a seat for him with a pile of brushwood boughs and a great thick shaggy goat-skin which he used for his own bed, and all with so kind a welcome that it warmed the king's heart and made him pray the Gods to bless him for his goodness. But Eumæus only said, "How could I neglect a stranger, though he were a worse man than you? All strangers and beggars are sent to us by Zeus. Take my gift and welcome, though it is little enough I have to give, a servant such as I, with new masters to lord it over him. For we have lost the king who would have loved me and given me house and lands and all that a faithful servant ought to have, whose work is blest by the Gods and prospers, as mine does here. Alas! he is dead and gone! he went away with Agamemnon to fight at Troy and never came home again."

So saying, the good swineherd rose and fetched what meat and wine he had, and set it before Ulysses, grieving that he had nothing better for him because the shameless suitors plundered everything.

But Ulysses ate and drank eagerly, and when his strength had come again he asked Eumæus, "My friend, who is this master of yours you tell me of?

Did you not say he was lost for Agamemnon's sake? Perhaps I may have seen him, for I have traveled far."

But the swineherd answered, "Old man, his wife and son will believe no traveler's tale. They have heard too many such. Every wandering beggar who comes to Ithaca goes to my mistress with some empty story to get a meal for himself, and she welcomes him and treats him kindly and asks him about it all, with the tears running down her cheeks in a woman's way. Yes, even you, old man, might learn to weave such tales if you thought they would get you a cloak or a vest. No, he is dead, and dogs and birds have eaten him, or else he has fed the fishes and his bones lie somewhere on the seashore, buried in the sand. And he has left us all to grieve for him, but no one more than me, who can never have so kind a master again, not though I had my heart's desire and went back to my native land and saw my father and mother, and the dear home where I was born. It is Ulysses above all whom I long to see once more. There, stranger, I have called him by his name, and that I should not do; for he is still my dear master though he is far away."

Then Ulysses said, "My friend, your hope has gone and you will never believe me. But I tell you this and seal it with an oath: Ulysses will return! Poor as I am, I will take no reward for my news till he comes to his own again, but you shall give me a new vest and cloak that day, and I will wear them."

But the swineherd answered, "Ah, my friend, I shall never need to pay you that reward. He will never come back again. But now drink your wine in peace, and let us talk of something else, and do not call to mind the sorrow that almost breaks my heart. Tell me of yourself and your own troubles and who you are, and what ship brought you here, for you will not say you came afoot."

Then Ulysses pretended he was a Cretan and had fought at Troy, and told Eumæus a long tale of adventures and how he had been wrecked at last on the coast of Epirus. The king of the country, he said, had rescued him, and he had learned that Ulysses had been there a little while before, and was already on his way to Ithaca.

The swineherd listened eagerly to it all, but when Ulysses had finished he said, "Poor friend, my heart aches to hear of all your sufferings. But there is one thing you should not have said, one thing I can never believe, and that is that Ulysses will return. And why need you lie to please me? I can see for myself that you are old and unhappy, a wanderer whom the Gods have sent to me. It is not for such a tale I will show you the kindness that you need, but because I pity you myself and reverence the law of Zeus."

"If I lie," Ulysses answered, "you may have me thrown from the cliff as a warning to other cheats. I swear it, and call the Gods to witness."

But the true-hearted swineherd only said, "I should get a good name by that, my friend, if I took you into my house and had you for my guest, and then murdered you brutally! Do you think I could pray to Zeus after that without a fear? But now it is supper-time, and my men will be coming home."

While they spoke, the herdsmen came up with the swine, and the sows were driven into the pens, grunting and squealing noisily as they settled in for the night. Then Eumæus called out, "Bring in the fattest boar, and let us make a sacrifice in honor of our guest, and get some reward ourselves for all the trouble we have spent upon the drove, — trouble lost, since strangers take the fruit of it all."

So they brought in a big fat white-tusked boar, while Eumæus split the wood for the fire. And he did not forget the Immortals, for he had a pious heart: he made the due offerings first and prayed for his master's return, and then he stood up at the board to carve, and gave each man his share and a special slice for his guest from the whole length of the chine. Ulysses took it and thanked him with all his heart: —

"May Father Zeus be your friend, Eumæus, and give you what I would give you for your kindness to a poor old man like me."

But the swineherd said, "Take it, my good friend, take it and enjoy it. Zeus will give or withhold as it may please him, for he can do all things."

So they sat down to the feast, and after they had had their fill the swineherd's servant cleared everything away, and then they made ready for sleep. The evening closed in black and stormy, and a west wind sprang up bringing the rain with it, and blew hard all the night; so Eumæus made up a bed of fleeces for Ulysses by the fire and gave him a great thick cloak as well, that he kept for the roughest weather. But he could not bring himself to stay there too, away from his herd of pigs, and he wrapped himself up warmly and went out to sleep beside them in the open. Ulysses saw, and smiled to see, what care he took of everything, while he thought his master was far away.

[On the following morning] Ulysses and the swineherd were already preparing their breakfast when Telemachus came up. The dogs knew him and played round him lovingly. "Eumæus," said Ulysses, "some friend of yours is coming, for I hear footsteps, and the dogs are pleased and do not bark."

He had hardly finished speaking when his own dear son stood in the doorway. The swineherd started up and dropped the vessels in which he was mixing the wine. He went to meet his young master and fell on his neck and kissed him as a father would kiss an only son escaped from death. "Light of my eyes, dear son, have you come home at last? When you sailed away to Pylos, I never thought to see you again. But come in and let me feast my eyes upon you; for you do not often visit us, but are kept at home in the town, watching that crowd of ruinous suitors."

And Telemachus answered, "Gladly, good father; I have come to see you, and to hear tidings of my mother."

Then the swineherd told him that his mother still waited patiently at home, and spent her days and nights in weeping.

Then Telemachus went into the house, and as he came up Ulysses rose to give him his seat, but he would not take it, and said, "Keep your seat, stranger, this man shall make up another for me." So Ulysses sat

"DEAR SON, HAVE YOU COME HOME AT LAST? WHEN YOU SAILED
AWAY TO PYLOS, I NEVER THOUGHT TO SEE YOU AGAIN. BUT COME
IN AND LET ME FEAST MY EYES UPON YOU; FOR YOU DO NOT
OFTEN VISIT US, BUT ARE KEPT AT HOME IN THE TOWN, WATCH-
ING THAT CROWD OF RUINOUS SUITORS." AND TELEMACHUS AN-
SWERED, "GLADLY, GOOD FATHER; I HAVE COME TO SEE YOU,
AND TO HEAR TIDINGS OF MY MOTHER." THEN THE SWINEHERD
TOLD HIM THAT HIS MOTHER STILL WAITED PATIENTLY AT HOME

down again, and the swineherd made a seat for Telemachus of the green brushwood and put a fleece upon it. Then he set food before them, and when they had eaten, Telemachus asked who the stranger was, and how he had come to Ithaca. And Eumæus told him Ulysses's own story and begged him to protect the wanderer. But Telemachus thought of the suitors and did not wish to take him to the palace.

"I will give him a coat and a vest," he said, "and shoes for his feet, and a two-edged sword, and I will send him on his way. But I cannot take him into the house, where the suitors would mock at him and use him ill. One man cannot restrain them, and he so young as I."

Then Ulysses said, "Sir, if I may speak, I would say foul wrong is done you in your house, and my heart burns at the thought. Do your people hate you, or will your brothers give you no support? Would that I were as young as you are, and were Ulysses's son or Ulysses himself. I would go to the palace and fall upon all the throng, and die there, one man against a hundred, sooner than see the shameful deeds that are done in that glorious house."

And Telemachus answered, "Hear me, stranger, and I will tell you all. My people do not hate me, and I have no quarrel with them. But I have no brothers to stand by me, for Zeus has never given more than one son to each generation of our line. And there are many foemen in the house, all the princes of the islands, and they too woo my mother and threaten my life, and I cannot see how it will end."

Then he said to Eumæus, "Go up to the house, old father, as quickly as you can, and tell my mother that I am come back safe from Pylos, and I will wait for you here."

And Eumæus answered, "I hear, master, and understand. But shall I not go to Laertes on my way and tell him too? For since you set sail for Pylos, they say he has not eaten or drunk or gone about his work, but sits in his house sorrowing and wasting away with grief."

But Telemachus bade him go straight to the palace and return at once, and let the queen send word to Laertes by one of the maids. So Eumæus went forth, and when Athene saw him go, she drew near, and came and stood by the gateway and showed herself to Ulysses, a tall and beautiful woman, with wisdom in her look. The dogs saw her too and were afraid, and shrank away whining into the corner of the yard, but Telemachus could not see her. Then the goddess nodded to Ulysses, and he went out and stood before her, and she said, "Noble Ulysses, now is the time to reveal yourself to your son, and go forth with him to the town, with death and doom for the suitors. I shall be near you in the battle and eager to fight."

Then she touched him with her golden wand and gave him his beauty and stature once more, and his old bronzed color came back and his beard grew thick and his garments shone bright again: and so she sent him to the hut. And when Telemachus saw him, he marveled and turned away his eyes, for he thought it must be a god.

"Stranger," he said, "you are changed since a moment ago; your color is not the same, nor your garments. If you are one of the Immortals, be gracious to us, and let us offer you gifts and sacrifice."

Then Ulysses cried out, "I am no god, but your own dear father, for whose sake you are suffering cruel wrongs and the spite of men." And then he kissed his son and let his tears take their way at last.

But Telemachus could not believe it, and said, "You cannot be my father, but a god come down to deceive me and make me grieve still more. No mortal could do what you have done, for a moment since you were old and wretched, and poorly clad, and now you seem like one of the heavenly Gods."

Then his father answered, "My son, no other Ulysses will ever come back to you. Athene has done this wonder, for she is a goddess and can make men what she will, now poor, now rich, now old, now young; such power have the lords of heaven to exalt us or bring us low."

Then Telemachus fell on his neck, and they wept aloud together. And they would have wept out their hearts till evening, had not Telemachus asked his father how he had come to Ithaca at last; and Ulysses told him that the sea-kings had brought him and put him on shore asleep, and that Athene had sent him to the swineherd's hut. "But now tell me of the suitors. How many are they and what manner of men? Can the two of us make head against the throng?"

"Father," he answered, "I know well your fame, mighty and wise in war. But this we could never dare, two men against a host. They are a hundred and twenty in all, the best fighting men from Ithaca and the islands round. Think, if you can, of some champion who would befriend us and give us help."

And Ulysses made answer, "What think you, if Father Zeus and the goddess Athene stood by our side? Should we still need other help?"

"Truly they are the best of champions," said Telemachus, "though they sit on high among the clouds; and they rule both men and Gods." "And they will be with us," said his father, "when we come to the trial of war. Now at daybreak you must go home and mix with the suitors, and later on the swineherd will bring me to the town, disguised again as the old beggarman; and if they ill-treat me or even strike me or drag me out of the house, you must look on and bear it. You may check them by speaking, but they will not listen, for the day of their doom is at hand. And tell no one that Ulysses has come home, not even Laertes nor the swineherd nor Penelope herself; we must keep the secret until we are sure of our friends."

Then Telemachus said that his father might trust him, and so they talked on together. Meanwhile Eumæus had reached the palace with the tidings that Telemachus had returned; and the suitors who were in the hall heard it and were dismayed, for they saw that their plot had failed. They went out of the palace and sat down before the gates, and were talking of sending word to their ship that was lying in wait for Telemachus, when the ship itself came into the harbor, with the other princes on board. So they all went up together to the public square and debated what to do, and they resolved to murder Telemachus as soon as they found another chance. Then they went back and sat down again on the polished seats in the hall.

Now Medon the herald had heard them plotting together in the square, and went and told Penelope all they had said, and how they had purposed putting her son to death. She went down at once to the hall with her women, and stood in the doorway with her bright veil before her face and spoke to Antinous and said, "Wicked and insolent man, can it be that they call you in Ithaca one of their wisest men? No, it is a fool's work you are doing, plotting to kill my son. He is helpless before you now, but Zeus is the friend of the helpless and avenges their wrongs. Impious and ungrateful too! Did not Ulysses once shield your father from his enemies and save his life? Yet you waste his substance and would murder his son?"

Then Eurymachus spoke and tried to soothe her. No one, he said, should injure Telemachus while he was alive, for he loved him more than any man on earth. Eurymachus's words were fair, and Penelope could say no more; yet all the while he was planning the death of her son.

In the evening the swineherd reached his hut again, and found Ulysses changed to the old beggar-man once more, preparing supper with Telemachus.

"What news, good Eumæus?" said the young man. "Have the proud lords come home from their ambush, or are they still waiting out yonder to take me as I return?"

And Eumæus replied, "I did not stay, master, to go through the town and find out the news, for when I had given my message I wanted to be at home. But one thing I saw from the brow of the hill as I came along. A swift ship was entering the harbor, full of armor and armed men. They may have been the princes, but I cannot say."

As he heard this, Telemachus looked at his father and smiled, but he took good care that the swineherd should not see.

THE VENGEANCE OF ULYSSES

A. HIS RECEPTION AT THE PALACE

By F. S. Marvin, R. J. C. Mayor, and F. M. Stowell

EARLY next morning, when the rosy-fingered dawn was in the sky, Telemachus bound on his sandals and took his stout spear in his hand, and said to the swineherd, "Old friend, I must now be off to the city and let my mother see me, for I know she will weep and sigh until I am there myself. And as for this poor stranger, I would have you take him to the town and let him beg for bite and sup from door to door, and those who choose can give. For I cannot be host to every wanderer with all the trouble I have to bear. And if that makes him angry — well! it is only the worse for him; I am a man that speaks his mind."

Then Ulysses answered readily, "Sir, I do not ask to stay here myself; a beggar should not beg in the fields. Nor am I young enough to work on a farm at a master's beck and call. So go your ways, and your man shall take me with him to the town. But I will wait till the sun is high, for I am afraid of the morning frost with these threadbare rags of mine."

So Telemachus strode away until he reached the palace, and went into the hall. The old nurse Eurycleia was there with the maids, spreading fleeces on the inlaid stools and chairs; and she saw him at once and went up to him with tears in her eyes, and then all the women gathered round and kissed him and welcomed him home again. And Penelope came down from her chamber and flung her arms round her son, and kissed his head and both his eyes, and said to him tearfully, "You have come home, Telemachus, light of my eyes! I thought I should never see you again, when you sailed away to Pylos secretly, against my will, to get tidings of your father. And now tell me all you heard."

But Telemachus said to her, "Mother, why make me think of trouble now, when I have just escaped from death? Rather put on your fairest robes, and go and pray the Gods to grant us a day of vengeance. But I must be off to the public square to meet a guest of mine whom I brought here in my ship. I sent him on before me with the crew, and bade one of them take him to his house until I came myself."

So Penelope went away and prayed to the Gods, while the prince went down to the public square and found Theoclymenus and brought him back to the palace, and they sat down together in the hall. Then one of the old servants brought up a polished table and spread it for them with good things for their meal, and Penelope came and sat beside the door, spinning her fine soft yarn. She did not speak till they had finished, but then she said to her son, "Telemachus, I see I must go up to my room and lie down on my bed, the bed I have watered with my tears ever since Ulysses went away to Troy; for you are determined not to talk to me and tell me the news of your father before the suitors come into the hall!"

Then Telemachus said, "Mother, I will tell you all I know. We reached Pylos and found Nestor there, and he took me into his splendid house, and welcomed me as lovingly as though I had been a long-lost son of his own. But he could tell me nothing of my father, not even if he were alive or dead, and so he sent me on to Sparta, to the house of Menelaus. There I saw Helen, the fairest of women, for whom the Greeks and Trojans fought and suffered so long. Menelaus asked me why I came and I told him about the suitors and all the wrong they did. Then he cried, 'Curse on them! The dastards in the hero's place! Oh, that Ulysses would return! They would soon have cause enough to hate this suit of theirs!' And then he told me how he had heard tidings of my father from Proteus, the wizard of the sea. He was living still, so the wizard said, on an island far away, in the cave of a wood nymph called Calypso, who kept him there against his will, and he had no ship to carry him over the broad sea. That was all Menelaus could tell me; and when I had done my errand I came away, and the Gods have brought me home in safety."

And as Penelope listened her heart filled with sorrow; but Theoclymenus, the seer, said to her, "Listen to me, wife of Ulysses, and I will prophesy to you; for your son has heard nothing certain, but I have seen omens that are sure. I swear by Zeus, the ruler of the Gods, and by the board and the hearth of Ulysses himself where I am standing now, he is already here in Ithaca, he knows of all this wickedness, and is waiting to punish the suitors as they deserve."

At that moment the princes came in from their sport and flung their cloaks aside, and set about slaughtering the sheep and the fatted goats and the swine for their feast.

Meanwhile Ulysses was starting for the town, with the swineherd to show him the way. He had slung the tattered wallet across his shoulder, and Eumæus had given him a staff, and every one who met them would have taken the king for a poor old beggar-man, hobbling along with his crutch.

So they went down the rocky path till they reached a running spring by the wayside where the townsfolk got their water. There was a grove of tall poplars round it, and the cool stream bubbled down from the rock overhead, and above the fountain there was an altar to the nymphs where the passers-by laid their offerings.

There they chanced to meet Melanthius, the king's goatherd, driving his fattest goats to the town for the suitors' feast. He was a favorite of theirs, and did all he could to please them. Now as soon as he saw the two he broke out into scoffs and gibes, till the heart of Ulysses grew hot with anger.

"Look there!" he shouted, "one rascal leading another! Trust a man to find his mate! A plague on you, swineherd, where are you taking that pitiful wretch? Another beggar, I suppose, to hang about the doors and cringe for the scraps and spoil our feasts? Now

THE VENGEANCE OF ULYSSES

if you would only let me have him to watch my farm
and sweep out my stalls and fetch fodder for my kids,
he could drink as much whey as he liked and get some
flesh on his bones. But no! His tricks have spoilt him
for any honest work!"

So he jeered at them in his folly, and as he passed
he kicked Ulysses on the thigh, but the king stood
firm, and took the blow in silence, though he could have
found it in his heart to strike the man dead on the spot.
But Eumæus turned round fiercely, and cried to the
Gods for vengeance.

"Nymphs of the spring," he prayed, "if ever my
master honored you, hear my prayer, and send him
home again! He would make a sweep of all your
insolence, you good-for-nothing wretch, loitering here
in the city while your flocks are left to ruin!"

"Oho!" cried Melanthius. "Listen to the foul-
mouthed dog! I must put him on board a ship and
sell him in a foreign land, and make some use of him
that way! Why, Ulysses will never see the day of his
return! He is dead and gone; I wish his son would
follow him!"

With that he turned on his heel and hastened away
to the palace hall, where he sat down with the suitors
at their feast. And the other two followed slowly until
they reached the gate. There they paused, and Ulysses
caught the swineherd by the hand, and cried, —

"Eumæus, this must be the palace of the king!
No one could mistake it. See, there is room after room,
and a spacious courtyard with a wall and coping-
stones and solid double doors to make it safe. And I

am sure that a great company is seated there at the banquet, for I can smell the roasted meat and hear the sound of the lyre."

Then Eumæus said, "Your wits are quick enough; it is the very place. And now tell me: would you rather go in alone and face the princes while I wait here, or will you stay behind and let me go in first? But if you wait here, you must not wait too long, for some one might catch sight of you and strike you and drive you from the gate."

Then the hero said to him, "I understand; I knew what I had to meet. Do you go first and I will wait behind. For I have some knowledge of thrusts and blows, and my heart has learned to endure; for I have suffered much in storm and battle, and I can bear this like the rest."

But while they were talking, a dog who was lying there lifted his head and pricked his ears. It was the hound Argus, whom Ulysses had reared himself long ago before the war, but had to leave behind when he went away to Troy. Once he used to follow the hunters to the chase, but no one cared for him now when his master was away, and he lay there covered with vermin, on a dung-heap in front of the gates. Yet even so, when he felt that Ulysses was near him, he wagged his tail and dropped his ears; but he had not strength enough to drag himself up to his master. And when Ulysses saw it, he turned away his face so that Eumæus should not see the tears in his eyes, and said, "Eumæus, it is strange that they let that dog lie there in the dung. He looks a noble creature, but perhaps he has never been swift enough for the chase, and they have only kept him for his beauty."

"Ah, yes!" Eumæus answered, "it is easy to see that he has no master now. If you had been here when Ulysses went to Troy, you would have wondered at the creature's pace and strength. In the thickest depth of the forest no quarry could escape him, and no hound was ever keener-scented. But now he is old and wretched and his lord has perished far away, and the heedless women take no care of him. Slaves can do nothing as they ought when the master is not there, for a man loses half his manhood when he falls into slavery."

Then Eumæus went on into the palace and up to the hall where the suitors were. But Argus had seen his master again at last, and when he had seen him, he died.

As soon as the swineherd came in, Telemachus caught sight of him, and beckoned him to a stool at his side, and gave him his share of the feast. After a little while Ulysses came up too, and sat down on the threshold like a poor old beggar man. Then his son sent him meat and bread by the swineherd, and said that a beggar should be bold, and he ought to go among the princes and ask each man for a dole. So he went round from one to the other, stretching out his hand for a morsel in the true beggar's way. And every one else felt some pity and gave him an alms, but Antinous mocked at them all and told them they were ready enough to be generous with another's wealth. And at last he grew angry and cursed Ulysses for a whining rascal, and hurled a footstool at his head, bidding him begone and trouble them no more. The stool struck Ulysses on the shoulder, but he stood like a rock, motionless and silent, with black thoughts in his heart. Then he went back straight to the threshold and sat down and spoke to all the company:—

"Listen to me, my lords! No man bears any rancor for a blow in open war, but Antinous has struck me because I am a beggar and know the curse of hunger. If there be any gods who avenge the poor man's cause, I pray that he may die before his marriage day!"

At that the others felt shame, and told Antinous he did wrong to strike the homeless wanderer.

"Who knows?" they said. "He might be one of the heavenly Gods, and woe to you if he were! For sometimes the Immortals take upon themselves the likeness of strangers, and enter our cities, and go about among men, watching the good and evil that they do."

Thus they warned him, but he cared little for all they said. And Telemachus sat there full of rage and grief to see his father struck, but he kept back the tears and held his peace.

Now Penelope was sitting in her room behind the hall, and she saw what had happened, and was angry with Antinous, and called the swineherd to her side.

"Go, good Eumæus, and tell the stranger to come here. And I will ask him if he has ever heard of Ulysses, for he looks like a man who has wandered far."

And the swineherd said, "Yes, he is a Cretan, and has had all kinds of adventures before he was driven here, and he could tell you stories that would charm you like a minstrel's sweetest song, and you would

never tire of listening. And he says that he has heard
of Ulysses, near home, in the rich land of Epirus, and
that he is already on his way to us, bringing a store of
treasures with him."

Then Penelope said, "Quick, bring the stranger
here at once, and let him speak with me face to face.
And if I see that he tells the truth I will give him a vest
and a cloak for himself."

So the swineherd hurried back with the message;
but Ulysses said he dared not face the princes a second
time and it would be better to speak with Penelope
later in the evening, alone by the fireside; and when
the queen heard this, she said that the stranger was
right. By this time it was afternoon, and Eumæus
went up to Telemachus and whispered that he must
be off to his work again. Telemachus said he might
go, but bade him have supper first and told him to
come back next morning without fail. So the swineherd took his food in the hall, and then started home
for his farm, to look after his pigs and everything that
he had charge of there.

B. THE TRIAL OF THE BOW

Translated by George Herbert Palmer

AND now the goddess, clear-eyed Athene, put in
the mind of Icarius's daughter, heedful Penelope,
to offer to the suitors in the hall the bow and the
gray steel, as means of sport and harbingers of death.
She mounted the long stairway of her house, holding

a crooked key in her firm hand, — a goodly key of bronze, having an ivory handle, — and hastened with her damsels to a far-off room where her lord's treasure lay, bronze, gold, and well-wrought steel. Here also lay his curved bow and the quiver for his arrows, — and many grievous shafts were in it still, — gifts which a friend had given Ulysses when he met him once in Lacedæmon, — Iphitus, son of Eurytus, a man like the Immortals. At Messene the two met, in the house of wise Orsilochus. Ulysses had come hither to claim a debt, which the whole district owed him; for upon ships of many oars Messenians carried off from Ithaca three hundred sheep together with their herdsmen. In the long quest for these, Ulysses took the journey when he was but a youth; for his father and the other elders sent him forth. Iphitus, on the other hand, was seeking horses; for twelve mares had been lost, which had as foals twelve hardy mules. These afterwards became the death and doom of Iphitus when he met the stalwart son of Zeus, the hero Hercules, who well knew deeds of daring; for Hercules slew Iphitus in his own house, although his guest, and recklessly did not regard the anger of the Gods nor yet the proffered table, but slew the man and kept at his own hall the strong-hoofed mares. It was when seeking these that Iphitus had met Ulysses and given the bow which in old days great Eurytus was wont to bear, and which on dying in his lofty hall he left his son. To Iphitus Ulysses gave a sharp-edged sword and a stout spear, as the beginning of a loving friendship. They never sat, however, at one another's table; ere

that could be, the son of Zeus slew godlike Iphitus,
the son of Eurytus, who gave the bow. Royal Ulysses, when going off to war in the black ships, would
never take this bow. It always stood in its own place
at home, as a memorial of his honored friend. In his
own land he bore it.

Now when the royal lady reached this room and
stood on the oaken threshold, — which long ago the car-
penter had smoothed with skill and leveled to the line,
fitting the posts thereto and setting the shining doors,
— then quickly from its ring she loosed the strap,
thrust in the key, and with a careful aim shot back
the door-bolts. As a bull roars when feeding in the
field, so roared the goodly door touched by the key,
and open flew before her. She stepped to a raised
dais where stood some chests in which lay fragrant
garments. Thence reaching up, she took from its peg
the bow in the glittering case which held it. And now
she sat her down and laid the case upon her lap, and
loudly weeping drew her lord's bow forth. But when
she had had her fill of tears and sighs, she hastened
to the hall to meet the lordly suitors, bearing in hand
the curved bow and the quiver for the arrows, and
many grievous shafts were in it still. Beside her, damsels bore a box in which lay many a piece of steel
and bronze, implements of her lord's for games like
these. And when the royal lady reached the suitors,
she stood beside a column of the strong-built roof,
holding before her face her delicate wimple, the while
a faithful damsel stood on either hand. And straightway she addressed the suitors, speaking thus: —

"Hearken, you haughty suitors who beset this house, eating and drinking ever, now my husband is long gone; no word of excuse can you suggest except your wish to marry me and win me for your wife. Well then, my suitors, — since before you stands your prize, — I offer you the mighty bow of prince Ulysses; and whoever with his hands shall lightliest bend the bow and shoot through all twelve axes, him will I follow and forsake this home, this bridal home, so very beautiful and full of wealth, a place I think I ever shall remember, even in my dreams."

So saying, she bade Eumæus, the noble swineherd, deliver to the suitors the bow and the gray steel. With tears Eumæus took the arms and laid them down before them. Near by, the neatherd also wept to see his master's bow. But Antinous rebuked them, and spoke to them and said, —

"You stupid boors, who only mind the passing minute, wretched pair, what do you mean by shedding tears, troubling this lady's heart, when already her heart is prostrated with grief at losing her dear husband? Sit down and eat in silence, or else go forth and weep, but leave the bow behind, a dread ordeal for the suitors; for I am sure this polished bow will not be bent with ease. There is not a man of all now here so powerful as Ulysses. I saw him once myself, and well recall him, though I was then a child."

He spoke, but in his breast his heart was hoping to draw the string and send an arrow through the steel; yet he was to be the first to taste the shaft of good Ulysses, whom he now wronged though seated in his hall, while to like outrage he encouraged all his comrades. To these now spoke revered Telemachus: —

"Ha! Zeus the son of Cronos has made me play the fool! My mother — and wise she is — says she will follow some strange man and quit this house; and I but laugh and in my silly soul am glad. Come then, you suitors, since before you stands your prize, a lady whose like cannot be found throughout Achaian land, in sacred Pÿlos, Argos, or Mycenæ, in Ithaca itself, or the dark mainland, as you yourselves well know, — what needs my mother praise? — come then, delay not with excuse nor longer hesitate to bend the bow, but let us learn what is to be. I too might try the bow. And if I stretch it and send an arrow through the steel, then with no shame to me my honored mother may forsake this house and follow some one else, leaving me here behind; for I shall then be able to wield my father's arms."

He spoke, and flung his red cloak from his shoulders, rising full height, and put away the sharp sword also from his shoulder. First then he set the axes, marking one long furrow for them all, aligned by cord. The earth on the two sides he stamped down flat. Surprise filled all beholders to see how properly he set them, though he had never seen the game before. Then he went and stood upon the threshold and began to try the bow. Three times he made it tremble as he sought to make it bend. Three times he slacked his strain, still hoping in his heart to draw the string and send an arrow through the steel. And now he might have drawn it by force of a fourth tug, had not Ulysses shaken his head and stayed the eager boy. So to the suitors once more spoke revered Telemachus: —

"Fie! Shall I ever be a coward and a weakling, or am I still but young and cannot trust my arm to right me with the man who wrongs me first? But come, you who are stronger men than I, come try the bow and end the contest."

So saying, he laid by the bow and stood it on the ground, leaning it on the firm-set polished door. The swift shaft, too, he likewise leaned against the bow's fair knob, and once more took the seat from which he first arose. Then said to them Antinous, Eupeithes' son, —

"Rise up in order all, from left to right, beginning where the cupbearer begins to pour the wine."

So said Antinous, and his saying pleased them. Then first arose Leiodes, son of Œnops, who was their soothsayer and had his place beside the goodly mixer, farthest along the hall. To him alone their lawlessness was hateful; he abhorred the suitor crowd. He it was now who first took up the bow and the swift shaft; and going to the threshold, he stood and tried the bow. He could not bend it. Tugging the string wearied his hands, — his soft, unhorny hands, — and to the suitors thus he spoke: —

"No, friends, I cannot bend it. Let some other take the bow. Ah, many chiefs this bow shall rob of life and breath! Yet better far to die than live and still to fail in that for which we constantly are gathered, waiting expectantly from day to day! Now each man hopes and purposes at heart to win Penelope, Ulysses' wife. But when he shall have tried the bow and seen his failure, then to some other fair-robed woman of Achaia let each go, and offer her his suit and woo her with his gifts. So may Penelope marry the man who gives her most and comes with fate to favor!"

When he had spoken, he laid by the bow, leaning it on the firm-set polished door. The swift shaft, too, he likewise leaned against the bow's fair knob, and once more took the seat from which he first arose. But Antinous rebuked him, and spoke to him, and said, —

"Leiodes, what words have passed the barrier of your teeth? Strange words and harsh! Vexatious words to hear! As if this bow must rob our chiefs of life and breath because you cannot bend it! Why, your good mother did not bear you for a brandisher of bows and arrows. But others among the lordly suitors will bend it by and by."

So saying, he gave an order to Melanthius, the goatherd: "Hasten, Melanthius, and light a fire in the hall and set a long bench near, with fleeces on it; then bring me the large cake of fat which lies inside the door, that after we have warmed the bow and greased it well, we young men may try the bow and end the contest."

He spoke, and straightway Melanthius kindled a steady fire, and set a bench beside it with a fleece thereon, and brought out the large cake of fat which lay inside the door, and so the young men warmed the bow and made their trial. But yet they could not bend it; they fell far short of power. Antinous, however, still held back, and prince Eurymachus, who were the suitors' leaders; for they in manly excellence were quite the best of all.

Meanwhile out of the house at the same moment came two men, princely Ulysses' herdsmen of the oxen and the swine; and after them came royal Ulysses also from the house. And when they were outside the gate, beyond the yard, speaking in gentle words Ulysses said, —

"Neatherd, and you too, swincherd, may I tell a certain tale, or shall I hide it still? My heart bids me speak. How ready would you be to aid Ulysses if he should come from somewhere, thus, on a sudden, and a god should bring him home? Would you support the suitors or Ulysses? Speak freely, as your heart and spirit bid you speak."

Then said to him the herdsman of the cattle, "O father Zeus, grant this my prayer! May he return and Heaven be his guide! Then shall you know what might is mine and how my hands obey."

So prayed Eumæus too to all the Gods, that wise Ulysses might return to his own home. So when he knew with certainty the heart of each, finding his words once more Ulysses said, —

"Lo, it is I, through many grievous toils now in the twentieth year come to my native land! And yet I know that of my servants none but you desire my coming. From all the rest I have not heard one prayer that I return. To you then I will truly tell what shall hereafter be. If God by me subdues the lordly suitors, I will obtain you wives and give you wealth and homes established near my own; and henceforth in my eyes you shall be friends and brethren of Telemachus. Come, then, and I will show you too a very trusty sign, — that you may know me certainly and be assured in heart, — the scar the boar dealt long ago with his white tusk, when I once journeyed to Parnassus with Autolycus's sons."

So saying, he drew aside his rags from the great scar. And when the two beheld and understood it all, their tears burst forth; they threw their arms round wise Ulysses, and passionately kissed his face and neck. So likewise did Ulysses kiss their heads and hands. And daylight had gone down upon their weeping had not Ulysses stayed their tears and said, —

"Have done with grief and wailing, or somebody in coming from the hall may see, and tell the tale indoors. Nay, go in one by one, not all together. I will go first, you after. And let this be agreed: the rest within, the lordly suitors, will not allow me to receive the bow and quiver. But, noble Eumæus, bring the bow along the room and lay it in my hands. Then tell the women to lock the hall's close-fitting doors; and if from their inner room they hear a moaning or a strife within our walls, let no one venture forth, but stay in silence at her work. And noble Philœtius, in your care I put the courtyard gates. Bolt with the bar and quickly lash the fastening."

So saying, Ulysses made his way into the stately house, and went and took the seat from which he first arose. And soon the serving-men of princely Ulysses entered too.

Now Eurymachus held the bow and turned it up and down, trying to heat it at the glowing fire. But still, with all his pains, he could not bend it; his proud soul groaned aloud. Then bitterly he spoke; these were the words he said, —

"Ah! here is woe for me and woe for all! Not that I so much mourn missing the marriage, though vexed I am at that. Still, there are enough more women of Achaia, both here in sea-girt Ithaca and in the other cities. But if in strength we fall so short of princely Ulysses that we cannot bend his bow — oh, the disgrace for future times to know!"

Then said Antinous, Eupeithes' son, "Not so, Eurymachus, and you yourself know better. To-day throughout the land is the archer-god's high feast. Who then could bend a bow? Nay, quietly lay it by; and for the axes, what if we leave them standing? Nobody, I am sure, will carry one away and trespass on the house of Laertes' son, Ulysses. Come then, and let the wine-pourer give pious portions to our cups, that after a libation we may lay aside curved bows. To-morrow morning tell Melanthius, the goatherd, to drive us here the choicest goats of all his flock; and we will set the thighs before the archer-god, Apollo, then try the bow and end the contest."

So said Antinous, and his saying pleased them. Pages poured water on their hands; young men brimmed bowls with drink and served to all, with a first pious portion for the cups. And after they had poured and drunk as their hearts would, then in his subtlety said wise Ulysses, —

THE VENGEANCE OF ULYSSES

"Hearken, you suitors of the illustrious queen, and let me tell you what the heart within me bids. I beg a special favor of Eurymachus, and great Antinous too; for his advice was wise, that you now drop the bow and leave the matter with the Gods, and in the morning God shall grant the power to whom he may. But give me now the polished bow, and let me in your presence prove my skill and power and see if I have yet such vigor left as once there was within my supple limbs, or whether wanderings and neglect have ruined all."

At these his words all were exceeding wroth, fearing that he might bend the polished bow. But Antinous rebuked him, and spoke to him and said, "You scurvy stranger, with not a whit of sense, are you not satisfied to eat in peace with us, your betters, unstinted in your food and hearing all we say? Nobody else, stranger or beggar, hears our talk. 'T is wine that goads you, honeyed wine, a thing that has brought others trouble, when taken greedily and drunk without due measure. Wine crazed the Centaur, famed Eurytion, at the house of bold Peirithous, on his visit to the Lapithæ. And when his wits were crazed with wine, he madly wrought foul outrage on the household of Peirithous. So indignation seized the heroes. Through the porch and out of doors they rushed, dragging Eurytion forth, shorn by the pitiless sword of ears and nose. Crazed in his wits, he went his way, bearing in his bewildered heart the burden of his guilt. And hence arose a feud between the Centaurs and mankind; but the beginning of the woe he himself caused by wine. Even so I prophesy great harm to you, if you shall bend the bow. No kindness will you meet from any in our land, but we will send you by black ship straight to King Echetus, the bane of all mankind, out of whose hands you never shall come clear. Be quiet, then, and take your drink! Do not presume to vie with younger men!"

Then said to him heedful Penelope, "Antinous, it is neither honorable nor fitting to worry strangers who may reach this palace of Telemachus. Do you suppose the stranger, if he bends the great bow of Ulysses, confident in his skill and strength of arm, will lead me home and take me for his wife? He in his inmost soul imagines no such thing. Let none of you sit at the table disturbed by such a thought; for that could never, never, be!"

Then answered her Eurymachus, the son of Polybus, "Daughter of Icarius, heedful Penelope, we do not think the man will marry you. Of course that could not be. And yet we dread the talk of men and women, and fear that one of the baser sort of the Achaians say, 'Men far inferior sue for a good man's wife, and cannot bend his polished bow. But somebody else — a wandering beggar — came, and easily bent the bow and sent an arrow through the steel.' This they will say, to us a shame indeed."

Then said to him heedful Penelope, "Eurymachus, men cannot be in honor in the land and rudely rob the household of their prince. Why, then, count this a shame? The stranger is right tall, and well-knit too, and calls himself the son of a good father. Give him the polished bow, and let us see. For this I tell you, and it shall be done: if he shall bend it and Apollo grants his prayer, I will clothe him in a coat and tunic, goodly garments, give him a pointed spear to keep off dogs and men, a two-edged sword, and sandals for his feet, and I will send him where his heart and soul may bid him go."

Then answered her discreet Telemachus, "My mother, no Achaian has better right than I to give or to refuse the bow to any as I will. And out of all who rule in rocky Ithaca, or in the islands off toward grazing Elis, none may oppose my will, even if I wished to put the bows into the stranger's hands and let him take them once for all away. Then seek your chamber and attend to matters of your own, — the loom, the distaff, — and bid the women ply their tasks. Bows are for men, for all, especially for me; for power within this house rests here."

Amazed, she turned to her own room again, for the wise saying of her son she laid to heart. And coming to the upper chamber with her maids, she there bewailed Ulysses, her dear husband, till on her lids clear-eyed Athene caused a sweet sleep to fall.

Meanwhile the noble swineherd, taking the curved bow, was bearing it away. But the suitors all broke into uproar in the hall, and a rude youth would say, "Where are you carrying the curved bow, you miserable swineherd? Crazy fool! Soon out among the swine, away from men, swift dogs shall eat you, — dogs you yourself have bred, — will but Apollo and the other deathless Gods be gracious!"

At these their words the bearer of the bow laid it down where he stood, frightened because the crowd within the hall cried out upon him. But from the other side Telemachus called threatening aloud, "Nay, father! Carry on the bow! You cannot well heed all. Take care, or I, a nimbler man than you, will drive you to the fields with pelting stones. Superior in strength I am to you. Ah, would I were as much beyond the others in the house, beyond these suitors, in my skill and strength of arm! Then would I soon send somebody away in sorrow from my house; for men work evil here."

He spoke, and all burst into merry laughter and laid aside their bitter anger with Telemachus. And so the swineherd, bearing the bow along the hall, drew near to wise Ulysses and put it in his hands; then calling aside nurse Eurycleia, thus he said, —

"Telemachus bids you, heedful Eurycleia, to lock the hall's close-fitting doors; and if a woman from the inner room hears moaning or a strife within our walls, let her not venture forth, but stay in silence at her work."

Such were his words; unwinged, they rested with her. She locked the doors of the stately hall. Then silently from the house Philœtius stole forth and straightway barred the gates of the fenced court. Beneath the portico there lay a curved ship's cable, made of biblus plant. With this he lashed the gates, then passed indoors himself, and went and took the seat from which he first arose, eyeing Ulysses. Now Ulysses already held the bow and turned it round and round, trying it here and there to see if worms had gnawed the horn while its lord was far away. And glancing at his neighbor one would say, —

"A sort of fancier and a trickster with the bow this fellow is. No doubt at home he has himself a bow like that, or means to make one like it. See how he turns it in his hands this way and that, ready for mischief, — rascal!"

Then would another rude youth answer thus: "Oh, may he always meet with luck as good as when he is unable now to bend the bow!"

So talked the suitors. Meantime wise Ulysses, when he had handled the great bow and scanned it closely, — even as one well skilled to play the lyre and sing stretches with ease round its new peg a string, securing at each end the twisted sheep-gut, so without effort did Ulysses string the mighty bow. Holding it now with his right hand, he tried its cord; and clear to the touch it sang, voiced like the swallow. Great consternation came upon the suitors. All faces then changed color. Zeus thundered loud for signal. And glad was long-tried royal Ulysses to think the son of crafty Cronos had sent an omen. He picked up a swift shaft which lay beside him on the table, drawn. Within the hollow quiver still remained the rest, which the Achaians soon should prove. Then laying the arrow on the arch, he drew the string and arrow notches, and forth from the bench on which he sat let fly the shaft, with careful aim, and did not miss an axe's ring from first to last, but clean through all sped on the bronze-tipped arrow; and to Telemachus he said, —

"Telemachus, the guest now sitting in your hall brings you no shame. I did not miss my mark, nor in the bending of the bow make a long labor. My strength is sound as ever, not what the mocking suitors here despised. But it is time for the Achaians to make supper ready, while it is daylight still; and then for us in other ways to make them sport, — with dance and lyre; for these attend a feast."

He spoke and frowned the sign. His sharp sword then Telemachus girt on, the son of princely Ulysses clasped his right hand around his spear, and close beside his father's seat he took his stand, armed with the gleaming bronze.

C. THE SLAYING OF THE SUITORS

By F. S. Marvin, R. J. C. Mayor, and F. M. Stowell

ULYSSES sprang to the great threshold with the bow and quiver in his hand. He poured out the arrows at his feet, and shouted to the princes, "So ends the game you could not play! Now for another mark which no man has ever hit before!"

With that he shot at Antinous. He, as it chanced, was just lifting a golden cup from the board, never dreaming that death would meet him there with all his comrades round him at the feast. But before the wine touched his lips the arrow struck him in the throat, and the cup dropped from his hand, and he fell dying to the floor. The princes sprang to their feet when they saw their comrade fallen, and looked round the walls for armor, but there was not a spear or shield to be found. Then they turned in fury on Ulysses: "Madman, are you shooting at men? You have slain the noblest youth in Ithaca, and you shall not live to draw bow again."

But Ulysses faced them sternly and said, "Dogs, you thought that I should never return. You have rioted in my home, and outraged the women of my household, and you have wooed my own wife while I was yet a living man. You took no thought for the Gods who rule in heaven, nor for the indignation of men in days hereafter. Now your time is come."

All grew pale as he spoke, and Eurymachus alone found words: "If you are in truth King Ulysses, your words are just; there have been many shameful deeds done upon your lands and in your house. But Antinous, who was the cause of all, lies dead; it was he who lead us on, hoping that he might take your kingdom for himself. Spare us now that he has met his doom, for we are your own people; and we will make you full atonement for all that has been eaten and drunk in your halls."

"Eurymachus, you might give me all you have, but even then I would not hold my hands until I had taken vengeance for every wrong. You have your choice. Fight, or fly, if you think that flight can save you."

At that their knees shook beneath them, but Eurymachus cried, "Comrades, this man will have no mercy. He has got the bow in his hands, and he will shoot us down from the threshold, so long as there is one of us left alive. Draw your swords, and guard yourselves with the tables; and let us all set upon him at once and drive him from the doorway. If we can reach the city, we are safe."

As he spoke he drew his sword and sprang forward with a cry; and at the same moment Ulysses shot. The arrow struck him in the breast, and he dropped forward over the table, while the mist of death sank upon his eyes. Then Amphinomus made a rush on the doorway. But Telemachus was too quick for him; he hurled his spear and struck him from behind between the shoulders, and he fell crashing on the floor. Telemachus sprang back, leaving the spear, for he dared not wait to draw it out. He darted to his father's side. "Father, we ought to have armor; I will go and get weapons for us."

"Run and bring them," said Ulysses, "while I have arrows left; when these are gone I cannot hold the doorway against them all."

So Telemachus ran to the armory and hurried back with helmets and shields and spears; and he armed himself and made the two servants do the same, and they took their stand beside the king. While the arrows lasted, Ulysses shot, and struck down the wooers man by man. And then he leant the bow against the doorpost, and slung the shield about him and put on the helmet and took two spears in his hand.

Now there was a postern in the hall, close beside the great doorway and opening on the corridor. Ulysses had put the swineherd to guard it, and now the boldest of the suitors said to the rest, "Could not some of us force a passage there and raise the cry for rescue ?"

"Little use in that," said Melanthius, "the great doorway is too close, and one brave man might stop us all before we reached the court. I have a better plan. Ulysses and his son have stowed away the weapons, and I think I know where they are. I will go and fetch you what you need."

With these words he clambered up through the lights of the hall and got into the armory, and fetched out twelve shields and as many spears and helmets, and brought them to the princes. The heart of Ulysses misgave him when he saw the armor and the long spears in their hands; and he felt that the fight would go hard, and said to Telemachus, "Melanthius or one of the women has betrayed us."

"Father, it was my fault," said Telemachus; "I left the door of the armory open, and one of them must have kept sharper watch than I did. Go, Eumæus, make fast the door, and see whether this is the doing of Melanthius, as I guess."

While they spoke, Melanthius went again to fetch more armor, and the swineherd spied him and said, "There is the villain going to the armory, as we thought; tell me, shall I kill him, if I can master him, or shall I bring him here to suffer for his sins ?" "Telemachus and I will guard the doorway here," said Ulysses, "and you and the shepherd shall bind him hand and foot and leave him in the chamber to wait his doom."

So the two went up to the armory, and stood in wait on either side of the door; and as Melanthius came out, they leapt upon him and dragged him back by the hair and flung him on the ground and bound him tightly to a pillar hand and foot. "Lie there," said Eumæus, "and take your ease: the dawn will not find you sleeping, when it is time for you to rise and drive out your goats." With that they went back to join Ulysses, and the four stood together at the threshold, — four men against a host.

Then Athene came among them in the likeness of Mentor, and Ulysses knew her and rejoiced. "Mentor," he shouted, "help me in my need, for we are comrades from of old." And the wooers sent up another shout, "Do not listen to him, Mentor; or your turn will come when he is slain." But Athene taunted Ulysses and spurred him to the fight: "Have you lost your strength and courage, Ulysses? It was not thus you did battle for Helen in the ten years' war at Troy. Is it so hard to face the suitors in your own house and home? Come, stand by me, and see if Mentor forgets old friendship." Yet she left the victory still uncertain, that she might prove his courage to the full. She turned herself into a swallow and flew up into the roof and perched on a blackened rafter overhead.

Then the wooers took courage, when they saw that Mentor was gone, and that the four stood alone in the doorway. And one of them said to the rest, "Let six of us hurl our spears together at Ulysses. If once he falls, there will be little trouble with the rest." So they flung their spears as he bade them; but all of them missed the mark. Then Ulysses gave the word to his men, and they all took steady aim and threw, and each one killed his man; and the wooers fell back into the farther end of the hall, while the four dashed on together and drew out their spears from the bodies of the slain. Once more the suitors hurled, and Telemachus and the swineherd were wounded; but the other spears fell wide. Then at last Athene lifted her shield of war high overhead, — the shield that brings death to men, — and panic seized the wooers, and they fled through the hall like a drove of cattle when the gadfly stings them. But the four leapt on them like vultures swooping from the clouds; and they fled left and right through the hall, but there was no escape.

Only Phemius, the minstrel, whom the wooers had forced to sing before them, sprang forward and clasped the knees of Ulysses and said, "Have mercy on me, Ulysses: you would not slay a minstrel, who gladdens the hearts of Gods and men? The princes forced me here against my will."

And Telemachus heard and said to his father, "Do not hurt him, for he is not to blame; and let us save the herald too, if he is yet alive, for he took care of me when I was a child."

Now the herald had hidden himself under a stool and pulled an ox-hide over him, and when he heard this he crept out and clasped the knees of Telemachus and begged that he would plead for him. "Have no fear," said Ulysses; "my son has saved your life. Go out, you and the minstrel, and wait in the courtyard, for I have other work to do within." So the two went out into the courtyard, and sat down beside the altar, looking for their death each moment.

Then Ulysses searched through the hall, to see if any one was yet lurking alive. But they all lay round him fallen in the dust and blood, heaped upon each other like fishes on a sunny beach when the fisherman has drawn his net to land. Then he told Telemachus to call out the old nurse Eurycleia. She came and found Ulysses standing among the bodies of the slain, with his hands and feet all stained with blood, and she was ready to shout aloud for triumph when she saw the great work accomplished. But Ulysses checked her cry and said, "Keep your joy unspoken, old nurse; there should be no shout of triumph over the slain. It is the judgment of Heaven that has repaid them for the evil deeds they did."

Then he gave orders that the bodies of the dead should be carried out and that the blood should be washed away. And when this was done he turned to Eurycleia and said, "Bring fire and sulphur now and I will purify the hall. Then bid Penelope meet me here."

"Yes, my child," said the old nurse, "I will obey you. But let me bring you a mantle first: it is not fitting that you should stand here with only your rags to cover you." But Ulysses said that she must do his bidding at once. So she brought sulphur and lit a fire, and Ulysses purified the hall.

D. PENELOPE RECOGNIZES ULYSSES

Translated by George Herbert Palmer

THE old woman, full of glee, went to the upper chamber to tell her mistress her dear lord was in the house. Her knees grew strong; her feet outran themselves. By Penelope's head she paused, and thus she spoke: —

"Awake, Penelope, dear child, to see with your own eyes what you have hoped to see this many a day! Ulysses is here! He has come home at last, and slain the haughty suitors, the men who vexed his house, devoured his substance, and oppressed his son."

Then heedful Penelope said to her, "Dear nurse, the Gods have crazed you. They can befool one who is very wise, and often they have set the simple in the paths of prudence. They have confused you; you were sober-minded heretofore. Why mock me when my heart is full of sorrow, telling wild tales like these? And why arouse me from the sleep that sweetly bound me and kept my eyelids closed? I have not slept so soundly since Ulysses went away to see accursed Ilium, — name never to be named. Nay then, go down, back to the hall. If any other of my maids had come and told me this and waked me out of sleep, I would soon have sent her off in sorry wise into the hall once more. This time age serves you well."

Then said to her the good nurse Eurycleia, "Dear child, I do not mock you. In very truth it is Ulysses;

he is come, as I have said. He is the stranger whom everybody in the hall has set at naught. Telemachus knew long ago that he was here, but out of prudence hid his knowledge of his father till he should have revenge from those bold men for wicked deeds."

So spoke she; and Penelope was glad, and, springing from her bed, fell on the woman's neck, and let the tears burst from her eyes; and, speaking in winged words, she said, —

"Nay, tell me, then, dear nurse, and tell me truly; if he is really come as you declare, how was it he laid hands upon the shameless suitors, being alone, while they were always here together?"

Then answered her the good nurse Eurycleia, "I did not see; I did not ask; I only heard the groans of dying men. In a corner of our protected chamber we sat and trembled, — the doors were tightly closed, — until your son Telemachus called to me from the hall; for his father bade him call. And there among the bodies of the slain I found Ulysses standing. All around, covering the trodden floor, they lay, one on another. It would have warmed your heart to see him, like a lion, dabbled with blood and gore. Now all the bodies are collected at the courtyard gate, while he is fumigating the fair house by lighting a great fire. He sent me here to call you. Follow me, then, that you may come to gladness in your true hearts together, for sorely have you suffered. Now the long hope has been at last fulfilled. He has come back alive to his own hearth, and found you still, you and his son, within his hall; and upon those who did him wrong, the suitors, on all of them here in his home he has obtained revenge."

Then heedful Penelope said to her, "Dear nurse, be not too boastful yet, nor filled with glee. You know how welcome here the sight of him would be to all, and most to me and to the son we had. But this is no true tale you tell. Nay, rather some immortal slew the lordly suitors, in anger at their galling insolence and wicked deeds; for they respected nobody on earth, bad man or good, who came among them. So for their sins they suffered. But Ulysses, far from Achaia, lost the hope of coming home; nay, he himself was lost."

Then answered her the good nurse Eurycleia, "My child, what word has passed the barrier of your teeth, to say your husband, who is now beside your hearth, will never come! Your heart is always doubting. Come, then, and let me name another sign most sure, — the scar the boar dealt long ago with his white tusk. I found it as I washed him, and I would have told you then; but he laid his hand upon my mouth, and in his watchful wisdom would not let me speak. But follow me. I stake my very life; if I deceive you, slay me by the vilest death."

Then heedful Penelope answered her, "Dear nurse, 't is hard for you to trace the counsels of the everlasting Gods, however wise you are. Nevertheless, let us go down to meet my son, and see the suitors who are dead, and him who slew them."

So saying, she went from her chamber to the hall, and much her heart debated whether aloof to question her dear husband, or to draw near and kiss his face and take his hand. But when she entered, crossing the stone threshold, she sat down opposite Ulysses, in the firelight, beside the farther wall. He sat by a tall pillar, looking down, waiting to hear if his stately wife would speak when she should look his way. But she sat silent long; amazement filled her heart. Now she would gaze with a long look upon his face, and now she would not know him for the mean clothes that he wore. But Telemachus rebuked her, and spoke to her and said, —

"Mother, hard mother, of ungentle heart, why do you hold aloof so from my father, and do not sit beside him, plying him with words and questions? There is no other woman of such stubborn spirit to stand off from the husband who, after many grievous toils, comes in the twentieth year home to his native land. Your heart is always harder than a stone!"

Then said to him heedful Penelope, "My child, my soul within is dazed with wonder. I cannot speak to him, nor ask a question, nor look him in the face. But if this indeed is Ulysses, come at last, we certainly shall know each other better than others know; for we have signs which we two understand, — signs hidden from the rest."

As she, long tried, spoke thus, royal Ulysses smiled, and said to Telemachus forthwith in winged words, "Telemachus, leave your mother in the hall to try my truth. She soon will know me better. Now, because I am foul and dressed in sorry clothes, she holds me in dishonor, and says I am not he. But you and

I have yet to plan how all may turn out well. For whoso kills one man among a tribe, though the man leaves few champions behind, becomes an exile, quitting kin and country. We have destroyed the pillars of the state, the very noblest youths of Ithaca. Form, then, a plan, I pray."

Then answered him discreet Telemachus, "Look you to that, dear father. Your wisdom is, they say, the best among mankind. No mortal man can rival you. Zealously will we follow, and not fail, I think, in daring, so far as power is ours."

Then wise Ulysses answered him and said, "Then I will tell you what seems best to me. First wash and put on tunics, and bid the maids about the house array themselves. Then let the sacred bard with tuneful lyre lead us in sportive dancing, that men may say, hearing us from without, 'It is a wedding,' whether such men be passers-by or neighboring folk; and so broad rumor may not reach the town about the suitors' murder till we are gone to our well-wooded farm. There will we plan as the Olympian shall grant us wisdom."

So he spoke, and willingly they heeded and obeyed. For first they washed themselves and put on tunics, and the women also put on their attire. And then the noble bard took up his hollow lyre, and in them stirred desire for merry music and the gallant dance; and the great house resounded to the tread of lusty men and gay-girt women. And one who heard the dancing from without would say, "Well, well! some man has married the long-courted queen. Hard-hearted! For the husband of her youth she would not guard her great house to the end, till he should come." So they would say, but knew not how things were.

Meanwhile within the house Eurynome, the housekeeper, bathed resolute Ulysses and anointed him with oil, and on him put a goodly robe and tunic. Upon his face Athene cast great beauty; she made him taller than before, and stouter to behold, and made the curling locks to fall round his head as on the hyacinth flower. As when a man lays gold on silver, — some skillful man whom Vulcan and Pallas Athene have trained in every art, and he fashions graceful work, so did she cast a grace upon his head and shoulders. Forth from the bath he came, in bearing like the Immortals, and once more took the seat from which he first arose, facing his wife, and spoke to her these words: —

"Lady, a heart impenetrable beyond the sex of women the dwellers on Olýmpus gave to you. There is no other woman of such stubborn spirit to stand off from the husband who, after many grievous toils, comes in the twentieth year home to his native land. Come, then, good nurse, and make my bed, that I may lie alone. For certainly of iron is the heart within her breast."

Then said to him heedful Penelope, "Nay, sir, I am not proud, nor contemptuous of you, nor too much dazed with wonder. I very well remember what you were when you went upon your long-oared ship away from Ithaca. However, Eurycleia, make up his massive bed outside that stately chamber which he himself once built. Move the massive frame out there, and throw the bedding on, — the fleeces, robes, and bright-hued rugs."

She said this in the hope to prove her husband, but Ulysses spoke in anger to his faithful wife: "Woman, these are bitter words which you have said! Who set my bed elsewhere? A hard task that would be for one, however skilled, — unless a god should come and by his will set it with ease upon some other spot; but among men no living being, even in his prime, could lightly shift it; for a great token is inwrought into its curious frame. I built it; no one else. There grew a thick-leaved olive shrub inside the yard, full-grown and vigorous, in girth much like a pillar. Round this I formed my chamber, and I worked till it was done, building it out of close-set stones, and roofing it over well. Framed and tight-fitting doors I added to it. Then I lopped the thick-leaved olive's crest, cutting the stem high up above the roots, neatly and skillfully smoothed with my axe the sides, and to the line I kept all true to shape my post, and with an auger I bored it all along. Starting with this, I fashioned me the bed till it was finished, and I inlaid it well with gold, with silver, and with ivory. On it I stretched a thong of ox-hide, gay with purple. This is the token I now tell. I do not know whether the bed still stands there, wife, or whether somebody has set it elsewhere, cutting the olive trunk."

As he spoke thus, her knees grew feeble and her very soul, when she recognized the tokens which Ulysses exactly told. Then bursting into tears, she ran straight toward him, threw her arms round Ulysses' neck and kissed his face, and said, —

"Ulysses, do not scorn me! Ever before, you were the wisest of mankind. The Gods have sent us sorrow, and grudged our staying side by side to share the joys of youth and reach the threshold of old age. But do not be angry with me now, nor take it ill that then when I first saw you I did not greet you thus; for the heart within my breast was always trembling. I feared some man might come and cheat me with his tale. Many a man makes wicked schemes for gain. Nay, Argive Helen, the daughter of Zeus, would not have given herself to love a stranger if she had known how warrior sons of the Achaians would bring her home again, back to her native land. And yet it was a god prompted her deed of shame. Before, she did not cherish in her heart such sin, such grievous sin, from which began the woe which stretched to us. But now, when you have clearly told the tokens of our bed, which no one else has seen, but only you and I and the single servant, Actoris, whom my father gave me on my coming here to keep the door of our closed chamber, — you make even my ungentle heart believe."

So she spoke, and stirred still more his yearning after tears; and he began to weep, holding his loved and faithful wife. As when the welcome land appears to swimmers, whose sturdy ship Neptune wrecked at sea, confounded by the winds and solid waters; a few escape the foaming sea and swim ashore; thick salt foam crusts their flesh; they climb the welcome land, and are escaped from danger; so welcome to her gazing eyes appeared her husband. From round his neck she never let her white arms go. And rosy-fingered dawn had found them weeping, but a different plan the goddess formed, clear-eyed Athene. She checked the long night in its passage, and at the ocean-stream she stayed the gold-throned dawn, and did not suffer it to yoke the swift-paced horses which carry light to men, Lampus and Phaethon, which bear the dawn. And now to his wife said wise Ulysses, —

"O wife, we have not reached the end of all our trials yet. Hereafter comes a task immeasurable, long and severe, which I must needs fulfill; for so the spirit of Tiresias told me, that day when I descended to the house of Hades to learn about the journey of my comrades and myself. But come, my wife, let us to bed, that there at last we may refresh ourselves with pleasant sleep."

Then said to him heedful Penelope, "The bed shall be prepared whenever your heart wills, now that the Gods have let you reach your stately house and native land. But since you speak of this, and God inspires your heart, come, tell that trial. In time to come, I know, I shall experience it. To learn about it now, makes it no worse."

Then wise Ulysses answered her and said, "Lady, why urge me so insistently to tell? Well, I will speak it out; I will not hide it. Yet your heart will feel no joy; I have no joy myself; for Tiresias bade me go to many a peopled town, bearing in hand a shapely oar, till I should reach the men that know no sea and do not eat food mixed with salt. These, therefore, have no knowledge of the red-cheeked ships, nor of the shapely oars which are the wings of ships. And this was the sign, he said, easy to be observed. I will not hide it from you. When another traveler, meeting me, should say I had a winnowing-fan on my white shoulder, there in the ground he bade me fix my oar and make fit offerings to lord Neptune, — a ram, a bull, and the sow's mate, a boar, — and, turning homeward, to offer sacred hecatombs to the immortal gods who hold the open sky, all in the order due. And on myself death from the sea shall very gently come and cut me off, bowed down with hale old age. Round me shall be a prosperous people. All this, he said, should be fulfilled."

Then said to him heedful Penelope, "If gods can make old age the better time, then there is hope there will be rest from trouble."

So they conversed together. Meanwhile, Eurynome and the nurse prepared their bed with clothing soft, under the light of blazing torches. And after they had spread the comfortable bed, with busy speed, the old woman departed to her room to rest; while the chamber-servant, Eurynome, with torch in hand, walked on before, as they two came to bed. She brought them to their chamber, and then she went her way. So they came gladly to their old bed's rites. And now Telemachus, the neatherd, and the swineherd stayed their feet from dancing, and bade the women stay, and all betook themselves to rest throughout the dusky halls.

So when the pair had joyed in happy love, they

joyed in talking too, each one relating; she, the royal lady, what she endured at home, watching the wasteful throng of suitors, who, making excuse of her, slew many cattle, beeves, and sturdy sheep, and stores of wine were drained from out the casks; he, high-born Ulysses, what miseries he brought on other men and what he bore himself in anguish, — all he told, and she was glad to listen. No sleep fell on her eyelids till he had told her all.

He began with how at first he conquered the Ciconians, and came thereafter to the fruitful land of Lotus-Eaters; then what the Cyclops did, and how he took revenge for the brave comrades whom the Cyclops ate, and never pitied; then how he came to Æolus, who gave him hearty welcome and sent him on his way; but it was fated that he should not reach his dear land yet, for a sweeping storm bore him once more along the swarming sea, loudly lamenting; how he came to Telepylus in Læstrygonia, where the men destroyed his ships and his mailed comrades, all of them; Ulysses fled in his black ship alone. He told of Circe, too, and all her crafty guile; and how on a ship of many oars he came to the mouldering house of Hades, there to consult the spirit of Teiresias of Thebes, and looked on all his comrades, and on the mother who had borne him and cared for him when little; how he had heard the full-voiced Sirens' song; how he came to the Wandering Rocks, to dire Charybdis and to Scylla, past whom none goes unharmed; how then his crew slew the Sun's kine; how Zeus with a blazing bolt smote his swift ship, — Zeus, thundering from on high, — and his good comrades perished, utterly, all, while he escaped their evil doom; how he came to the island of Ogygia and to the nymph Calypso, who held him in her hollow grotto, wishing him to be her husband, cherishing him, and saying she would make him an immortal, young forever, but she never beguiled the heart within his breast; then how he came through many toils to the Phæacians, who honored him exceedingly, as if he were a god, and brought him on his way to his native land, giving him stores of bronze and gold and clothing. This was the latest tale he told, when pleasant sleep fell on him, easing his limbs and from his heart removing care.

THE WANDERINGS OF THE TROJAN ÆNEAS

THE FLIGHT OF ÆNEAS FROM THE RUINS OF TROY

By Alfred J. Church

ÆNEAS, a famous Trojan warrior, fought bravely as long as the city stood; but when it had fallen, he bethought himself of his father Anchises, and his wife Creusa, and of his little son Ascanius, and how he had left them without defense at home. But as he turned to seek them, the night being now, by reason of many fires, as clear as the day, he espied Helen sitting in the temple of Vesta, where she had sought sanctuary; for she feared the men of Troy, to whom she had brought ruin and destruction, and not less her own husband, whom she had deceived. Then was his wrath kindled, and he spake to himself, "Shall this evil woman return safe to Sparta? Shall she see again her home and her children, with Trojan women forsooth to be her handmaidens? Shall Troy be burnt and King Priam be slain, and she take no harm? Not so; for though there be no glory to be won from such a deed, yet shall I satisfy myself, taking vengeance upon her for my kinsmen and my countrymen." But while he thought these things in his heart, lo! there appeared unto him Venus, his mother, made manifest as he had never seen her before, as fair and as tall as the dwellers in heaven behold her. Then Venus spake thus: "What meaneth all this rage, my son? Hast thou no care for me? Hast thou forgotten thy father Anchises, and thy wife, and thy little son? Of a surety the fire and the sword had consumed them long since but that I cared for them and saved them. It is not Helen, no, nor Paris, that hath laid low this great city of Troy, but the wrath of the Gods. See now, for I will take away the mist that covers thine eyes; see how Neptune with his trident is overthrowing the walls and rooting up the city from its foundations; and how Juno stands with spear and shield in the Scæan Gate and calls fresh hosts from the ships; and how Pallas sits on the height with the storm-cloud about her and her Gorgon shield; and how Father Jupiter himself stirs up the enemy against Troy. Fly, therefore, my son. I will not leave thee till thou shalt reach thy father's house." And as she spake she vanished in the darkness.

Then did Æneas see dreadful forms and gods who were enemies of Troy, and before his eyes the whole city seemed to sink down into the fire. Even as a mountain oak upon the hills on which the woodmen ply their axes bows its head while all its boughs shake about it, till at last, as blow comes after blow, with a mighty groan it falls crashing down from the height, even so the city seemed to fall. Then did Æneas pass on his way, the goddess leading him, and the flames gave place to him, and the javelins harmed him not.

But when he was come to his house he bethought him first of the old man his father; but when he would have carried him to the hills, Anchises would not, being loath to live in some strange country when Troy had perished. "Nay," said he, "fly ye who are strong and in the flower of your days. But as for me, if the Gods had willed that I should live, they had saved this dwelling for me. Enough it is, yea, and more than enough, that once I have seen this city taken, and lived. Bid me, then, farewell as though I were dead. Death will I find for myself. And truly I have long lingered here a useless stock and hated of the Gods, since Jupiter smote me with the blast of his thunder."

Nor could the old man be moved from his purpose, though his son and his son's wife, and even the child Ascanius, besought him with many tears that he should not make yet heavier the doom that was upon them. Then was Æneas minded to go back to the battle and die. For what hope was left? "Thoughtest thou, my father," he cried, "that I should flee and leave thee behind? What evil word is this that has fallen from thy lips? If the Gods will have it that nought of Troy should be left, and thou be minded that thou and thine should perish with the city, be it so. The way is easy; soon will Pyrrhus be here: Pyrrhus, red with Priam's blood; Pyrrhus, who slays the son before the face of the father, and the father at the altar. Was it for this, kind Mother Venus, that thou broughtest me safe through fire and sword, to see the enemy in my home, and my father and my wife and my son lying slaughtered together? Comrades, give me my arms, and take me back to the battle. At the least I will die avenged."

But as he girded on his arms and would have departed from the house, his wife Creusa caught his feet upon the threshold, staying him, and held out the little Ascanius, saying, "If thou goest to thy death, take wife and child with thee; but if thou hopest aught from arms, guard first the house where thou hast father and wife and child."

And lo! as she spake there befell a mighty marvel, for before the face of father and mother there was seen to shine a light on the head of the boy Ascanius, and to play upon his waving hair and glitter on his temples. And when they feared to see this thing, and would have stifled the flame or quenched it with water, the old man Anchises in great joy raised his eyes to heaven, and cried aloud, "O Father Jupiter, if prayer move thee at all, give thine aid and make this omen sure." And even as he spake the thunder rolled on his left hand, and a star shot through the skies, leaving a long trail of light behind, and passed over the house-tops till it was hidden in the woods of Ida. Then the old man lifted himself up and did obeisance to the star, and said, "I delay no more: whithersoever ye lead I will follow. Gods of my country, save my house and my grandson. This omen is of you. And now, my son, I refuse not to go."

Then said Æneas, and as he spake the fire came nearer, and the light was clearer to see, and the heat more fierce, "Climb, dear father, on my shoulders; I will bear thee, nor grow weary with the weight. We will be saved or perish together. The little Ascanius shall go with me, and my wife follow behind, not over near. And ye, servants of my house, hearken to me; ye mind how that to one who passes out of the city there is a tomb and a temple of Ceres in a lonely place, and an ancient cypress-tree hard by. There will we gather by divers ways. And do thou, my father, take the holy images in thy hands, for as for me, who have but newly come from battle, I may not touch them till I have washed me in the running stream."

And as he spake he put a cloak of lion's skin upon his shoulders, and the old man sat thereon. Ascanius also laid hold of his hand, and Creusa followed behind. So he went in much dread and trembling. For indeed before sword and spear of the enemy he had not feared, but now he feared for them that were with him. But when he was come nigh unto the gates, and the journey was well-nigh finished, there befell a grievous mischance, for there was heard a sound as of many feet through the darkness; and the old man cried to him, "Fly, my son, fly; they are coming. I see the flashing of shields and swords." But as Æneas hasted to go, Creusa his wife was severed from him. But whether she wandered from the way or sat down in weariness, no man may say. Only he saw her no more, nor knew her to be lost, till all his company being met at the temple of Ceres, she only was found wanting. Very grievous did the thing seem to him, nor did he cease to cry out in his wrath against Gods and men. Also he bade his comrades have a care of his father and his son, and of the household gods, and girded him again with arms, and so passed into the city. And first he went to the wall and to the gate by which he had come forth, and then to his house, if haply she had returned thither. But there indeed the men of Greece were come, and the fire had well-nigh mastered it. And after that he went to the citadel and to the palace of King Priam. And lo! in the porch of Juno's temple, Phœnix and Ulysses were keeping guard over the spoil, even the treasure of the temples, tables of the Gods, and solid cups of gold, and raiment, and a long array of them that had been taken captive, children and women. But not the less did he seek his wife through all the streets of the city, yea, and called her aloud by name. But lo! as he called, the image of her whom he sought seemed to stand before him, only greater than she had been while she was yet alive. And the spirit spake, saying, "Why art thou vainly troubled? These things have not befallen us against the pleasure of the Gods. The ruler of Olympus willeth not that Creusa should bear thee company in thy journey. For thou hast a long journey to take, and many seas to cross, till thou come to the Hesperian shore, where Lydian Tiber flows softly through a good land and a fertile. There shalt thou have great prosperity, and take to thyself a wife of royal race. Weep not, then, for Creusa, whom thou lovest, nor think that I shall be carried away to be a bond-slave to some Grecian woman. Such fate befits not a daughter of Dardanus and daughter-in-law of Venus. The mighty mother of the Gods keepeth me in this land to serve her. And now, farewell, and love the young Ascanius, even thy son and mine."

So spake the spirit, and when Æneas wept and would have spoken, vanished out of his sight. Thrice he would have cast his arms about her neck, and thrice the image mocked him, being thin as air and fleeting

AND AS HE SPAKE HE PUT A CLOAK OF LION'S SKIN UPON HIS
SHOULDERS, AND THE OLD MAN SAT THEREON. ASCANIUS ALSO
LAID HOLD OF HIS HAND, AND CREUSA FOLLOWED BEHIND. SO
HE WENT IN MUCH DREAD AND TREMBLING, FOR INDEED BE-
FORE SWORD AND SPEAR OF THE ENEMY HE HAD NOT FEARED,
BUT NOW HE FEARED MUCH FOR THEM THAT WERE WITH HIM

FLIGHT OF ÆNEAS FROM TROY

as a dream. Then, the night being now spent, he sought
his comrades, and found with much joy and wonder
that a great company of men and women were gathered together, and were willing, all of them, to follow
him whithersoever he went. And now the morning
star rose over Mount Ida, and Æneas, seeing that the
Greeks held the city, and that there was no longer
any hope of succor, went his way to the mountains,
taking with him his father.

ÆNEAS'S ADVENTURE WITH THE HARPIES

By Charles Henry Hanson

[For three days the vessels of Æneas were tossed about by terrible storm winds.]

AT last, on the fourth day, the fury of the storm abated, and they came in sight of land, — at first lofty mountains, and afterwards, as they drew nearer, rich grassy plains, on which the wanderers saw herds of cattle and flocks of goats grazing without a keeper. As soon as the storm-beaten vessels could be brought to the shore, the Trojans hastened to land, and slaughtered some of the cattle, preparing a luxurious banquet. But this they were not destined to enjoy in peace; for scarcely had they stretched themselves on the couches they had hurriedly prepared beside the food when there was a sudden rushing of wings, and three ghastly creatures swooped down upon the feast, devoured a large part of it, and so defiled the rest with their loathsome touch that very little was eatable. These were the Harpies, and by their appearance Æneas knew that he and his companions had arrived at the Strophades, two islands in the Ionian Sea which for many years had been given up to the monsters. They were fearful of aspect: down to the

402

breast they resembled women, with scanty black hair and glaring red-rimmed eyes, and on their faces ever a famine-stricken look; but they had wings instead of arms, and their bodies and lower limbs were those of huge birds, foul and uncleanly. These hateful creatures had long before been sent by the Gods to plague Pheneus the Blind, king of Thrace, who had cruelly treated his sons. Whenever a meal was spread for the king, the Harpies used to descend and devour it. At last some brave warriors, who were passing through Thrace, were persuaded by the promise of rewards from Pheneus to rid him of the monsters, and drove them to the far Strophades, where they had ever since dwelt.

Irritated at the loss of their feast, Æneas and his companions prepared more food, and determined, if necessary, to defend it with their swords. They accordingly concealed their weapons in the grass, and stationed one of their number on the watch, to give notice with the sound of a trumpet when the Harpies were approaching. This was done accordingly, and the obscene creatures, when they again swooped down to seize on the cooked meats, which they relished more than any other food, were driven off, though not without difficulty. But one of them, perching on a high rock, croaked forth to the astonished mariners this dismal prophecy:—

"Woe to you, Trojans! Do you dare to make war upon us after having slain our oxen, and to banish the innocent Harpies from the kingdom which is theirs by right? Fix, then, in your minds these words, which

403

the father of Gods and men revealed to Phœbus Apollo, and Apollo to me. Italy is the land you seek, and Italy you shall reach at last, after many perils; but you shall not build up the walls of your new-founded city until dire famine and suffering, visiting you because you have injured us, shall compel you to devour your tables as well as the food that is upon them."

The gloomy prediction terrified most of the wanderers, and they urged Æneas to endeavor to propitiate the unclean monsters with invocations and sacrifices. But Anchises, after imploring Jupiter to ward off the threatened calamities, commanded that the expedition should at once quit that melancholy shore. After passing the rugged cliffs of Ithaca, and uttering maledictions on the land that bred Ulysses, the most cunning enemy of Troy, the exiles arrived in safety at the harbor of Leucadia, where the ships were anchored, and the travelers landed to rest awhile after the fatigues of the voyage. Here they celebrated the games of their country; and Æneas hung on the door-posts of an ancient and famous temple of Apollo a suit of armor, which he had taken from a Greek warrior slain before Troy, placing above it an inscription, "These arms Æneas won from the victorious Greeks."

ÆNEAS IN THE LAND OF THE CYCLOPS

By Charles Henry Hanson

A DAY'S sail over the blue Mediterranean brought Æneas and his followers in sight of the southeastern shores of Italy; and as they saw the swelling hills and grassy plains of the promised land, they broke into cries of joy. The ships were run into a secure harbor, and sacrifices offered up for the propitiation of Minerva and of Juno; after which, mindful of the injunctions of Helenus to avoid those parts of Italy which lay nearest to Greece, the adventurers resumed their voyage. Keeping near the coast, they passed the Bay of Tarentum and the lofty promontories of Calabria. Now came in sight the immense bulk of Etna, lifting its fire-crowned head into the clouds; and the roaring of the terrible Charybdis could be distinctly heard. Remembering the warnings of Helenus, they hastily turned to the left, and avoided the perilous strait, but sought refuge in a place scarcely less dangerous; for they landed in the country of the Cyclops, where, only a little while before, Ulysses had been with his comrades, and had endured great sufferings at the hands of the giant Polyphemus. The Cyclops, it will be remembered, were a race of savage shepherds, of immense stature, having each but one eye in the middle

405

of his forehead. They dwelt in caves, and kept great flocks and herds. Polyphemus was the largest and fiercest of them all; and when Ulysses and his companions entered his cave he kept them prisoners, and devoured several of them. The hero himself and the rest of his followers had escaped him by making him drunk with wine they had brought on shore from their ships, and then putting out his eye with a sharpened stake, the point of which they had hardened in the fire. The knowledge of this adventure came to Æneas and his Trojans in a strange fashion. On the morning after their arrival in the country of the Cyclops, they were on the shore, when they were surprised to see a man emerge from the woods, and approach them with suppliant gestures. His appearance was wild and emaciated, his beard overgrown, his garments ragged; but nevertheless it was easy to perceive that he was a Greek. When he saw that the voyagers wore Trojan dress and arms, he paused in fear, but the next moment he hurried toward them with tears and entreaties.

"I conjure you," he cried, "by the stars, by the powers above, by the light of heaven, ye Trojans, take me hence. Carry me where you will, do with me what you will, I shall be content. I confess that I was one who bore arms against Troy; if you deem that a crime, put me to death for it. At least I shall have the satisfaction of dying by the hands of men."

Æneas and Anchises received the stranger kindly, assured him of his safety, and asked him who he was, and how he came to be in that desolate country. He answered that he was an Ithacan, his name Achæmenides, and that he had been one of the companions of Ulysses in his wanderings. He related the adventures of the Ithacan hero in the cave of Polyphemus, and told how he himself, having been by accident left behind when his comrades escaped, had since led a wretched existence in the woods, living on wild berries and roots, and continually in dread lest he should be seen by the Cyclops. He advised Æneas to lose no time in quitting the country, lest the ferocious shepherds should discover and destroy them. Even as Achæmenides spoke, Polyphemus was seen accompanying his flock to their pasture. So tall was he of stature that he carried the trunk of a pine-tree as a staff to guide his footsteps. Reaching the sea he stepped into it, and bent down to bathe the wound inflicted by Ulysses. The Trojans hastened to cut their cables, and rowed out to sea. The giant heard the sound of their oars, and turned to follow them; but in his blindness he dared not follow far, and therefore he called on his brethren with a cry so loud that the very sea was shaken in its depths. Forthwith the huge Cyclops came trooping to the shore, like a wood of lofty trees endued with life and motion; but by this time the Trojan vessels had got beyond their reach.

ÆNEAS AND QUEEN DIDO

By Alfred J. Church

[Æneas was driven by a storm upon the shores of Carthage.]

NOW it came to pass on the next day that Æneas, having first hidden his ships in a bay that was well covered with trees, went forth to spy out the new land whither he was come, and Achates only went with him. And Æneas had in each hand a broad-pointed spear. And as he went there met him in the middle of the wood his mother, but habited as a Spartan virgin, for she had hung a bow from her shoulders after the fashion of a huntress, and her hair was loose, and her tunic short to the knees, and her garments gathered in a knot upon her breast. Then first the false huntress spake: "If perchance ye have seen one of my sisters wandering hereabouts, make known to me the place. She is girded with a quiver, and is clothed with the skin of a spotted lynx, or, maybe, she hunts a wild boar with horn and hound."

To whom Æneas, "I have not seen nor heard sister of thine, O virgin — for what shall I call thee? for, of a surety, neither is thy look as of a mortal woman, nor yet thy voice. A goddess certainly thou art, sister of Phœbus, or, haply, one of the nymphs. But whosoever thou art, look favorably upon us and help us.

Tell us in what land we be, for the winds have driven us hither, and we know not aught of place or people."

And Venus said, "Nay, stranger, I am not such as ye think. We virgins of Tyre are wont to carry a quiver and to wear a buskin of purple. For indeed it is a Tyrian city that is hard by, though the land be Libya. And of this city Dido is queen, having come hither from Tyre, flying from the wrong-doing of her brother. And indeed the story of the thing is long, but I will recount the chief matter thereof to thee. The husband of this Dido was one Sichæus, richest among all the men of Phœnicia, and greatly beloved of his wife, whom he married from a virgin. Now the brother of this Sichæus was Pygmalion, the king of the country, and he exceeded all men in wickedness. And when there arose a quarrel between them, the king, being exceedingly mad after gold, took him unaware, even as he did sacrifice at the altar, and slew him. And the king hid the matter many days from Dido, and cheated her with false hopes. But at the last there came to her in her dreams the likeness of the dead man, baring his wounds and showing the wickedness which had been done. Also he bade her make haste and fly from that land, and, that she might do this the more easily, told her of great treasure, gold and silver, that was hidden in the earth. And Dido, being much moved by these things, made ready for flight; also she sought for companions, and there came together to her as many as hated the king or feared him. Then did they seize ships that chanced to be ready and laded them with gold, even the treasure of King Pygmalion, and so fled across the sea. And in all this was a woman the leader. Then came they to this place, where thou seest the walls and citadel of Carthage, and bought so much land as they could cover with a bull's hide. And now do ye answer me this, Whence come ye, and whither do ye go?"

Then answered Æneas, "Should I tell the whole story of our wanderings, and thou have leisure to hear, evening would come ere I could make an end. We are men of Troy, who, having journeyed over many seas, have now been driven by storms to this shore of Libya. And as for me, men call me Prince Æneas. The land I seek is Italy, and my race is from Jupiter himself. With twenty ships did I set sail, going in the way whereon the Gods sent me. And of these scarce seven are left. And now, seeing that Europe and Asia endure me not, I wander over the desert places of Africa."

But Venus suffered him not to speak more, but said, "Whoever thou art, stranger, that art come to this Tyrian city, thou art surely beloved by the Gods. And now go, show thyself to the queen. And as for thy ships and thy companions, I tell thee that they are safe in the haven, if I have not learnt augury in vain. See those twenty swans, how joyously they fly! And now there cometh an eagle swooping down from the sky, putting them to confusion, but now again they move in due order, and some are settling on the earth and some are preparing to settle. Even so doth it fare with thy ships, for either are they already in the haven or enter thereinto with sails full set."

And as she spoke she turned away, and there shone

a rosy light from her neck, also there came from her hair a sweet savor as of ambrosia, and her garments grew under her feet; and Aneas perceived that she was his mother, and cried aloud, —

"O my mother, why dost thou mock me so often with false shows, nor sufferest me to join my hand unto thy hand, and to speak with thee face to face?"

And he went towards the walls of the city. But Venus covered him and his companions with a mist, that no man might see them, or hinder them, or inquire of their business, and then departed to Paphos, where was her temple and also many altars of incense. Then the men hastened on their way, and mounting a hill which hung over the city, marveled to behold it, for indeed it was very great and noble, with mighty gates and streets, and a multitude that walked therein. For some built the walls and the citadel, rolling great stones with their hands, and others marked out places for houses. Also they chose those that should give judgment and bear rule in the city. Some, too, digged out harbors, and others laid the foundations of a theatre, and cut out great pillars of stone. Like to bees they were, when, the summer being newly come, the young swarms go forth, or when they labor filling the cells with honey, and some receive the burdens of those that return from the fields, and others keep off the drones from the hive. Even so labored the men of Tyre. And when Æneas beheld them he cried, "Happy ye, who even now have a city to dwell in!" And being yet hidden by the mist, he went in at the gate and mingled with the men, being seen of none.

411

Now in the midst of the city was a wood, very thick with trees, and here the men of Carthage, first come to the land from their voyage, had digged out of the ground that which Juno had said should be a sign to them, even a horse's head; for that, finding this, their city would be mighty in war, and full of riches. Here, then, Dido was building a temple to Juno, very splendid, with threshold of bronze, and many steps thereunto; of bronze also were the door-posts and the gates. And here befell a thing which gave much comfort and courage to Æneas; for as he stood and regarded the place, waiting also for the queen, he saw set forth in order upon the walls the battles that had been fought at Troy, the sons of Atreus also, and King Priam, and fierce Achilles. Then said he, not without tears, "Is there any land, O Achates, that is not filled with our sorrows? Seest thou Priam? Yet withal there is a reward for virtue here also, and tears and pity for the troubles of men. Fear not, therefore. Surely the fame of these things shall profit us."

Then he looked, satisfying his soul with the paintings on the walls. For there was the city of Troy. In this part of the field the Greeks fled and the youth of Troy pursued them, and in that the men of Troy fled, and Achilles followed hard upon them in his chariot. Also he saw the white tents of Rhesus, king of Thrace, whom the fierce Diomed slew in his sleep, when he was newly come to Troy, and drave his horses to the camp before they ate of the grass of the fields of Troy or drank the waters of Xanthus. There also Troilus was pictured, ill matched in battle with Achilles. His horses bare him along; but he lay on his back in the chariot, yet holding the reins, and his neck and head were dragged upon the earth, and the spear-point made a trail in the dust. And in another place the women of Troy went suppliant-wise to the temple of Minerva, bearing a great and beautiful robe, sad and beating their breasts, and with hair unbound; but the goddess regarded them not. Also Achilles dragged the body of Hector three times round the walls of Troy, and was selling it for gold. And Æneas groaned when he saw the man whom he loved, and the old man Priam reaching out helpless hands. Also he knew himself, fighting in the midst of the Grecian chiefs; black Memnon also he knew, and the hosts of the East; and Penthesilea leading the army of the Amazons with shields shaped as the moon. Fierce she was to see, with one breast bared for battle, and a golden girdle beneath it, a damsel daring to fight with men.

But while Æneas marveled to see these things, lo! there came, with a great throng of youths behind her, Dido, most beautiful of women, fair as Diana, when, on the banks of Eurotas or on the hills of Cynthus, she leads the dance with a thousand nymphs of the mountains about her. On her shoulder she bears a quiver, and overtops them all, and her mother, even Latona, silently rejoices to behold her. So fair and seemly to see was Dido as she bare herself right nobly in the midst, being busy in the work of her kingdom. Then she sat herself down on a lofty throne in the gate of the temple, with many armed men about her. And she did justice between man and man; also she divided

413

the work of the city, sharing it equally or parting it by lot.

Then of a sudden Æneas heard a great clamor, and saw a company of men come quickly to the place, among whom were Antheus and Sergestus and Cloanthus, and others of the men of Troy that had been parted from him in the storm. Right glad was he to behold them, yet was not without fear; and though he would fain have come forth and caught them by the hand, yet did he tarry, waiting to hear how the men had fared, where they had left their ships, and wherefore they were come.

Then Ilioneus, leave being now given that he should speak, thus began: "O Queen, whom Jupiter permits to build a new city in these lands, we men of Troy, whom the winds have carried over many seas, pray thee that thou save our ships from fire, and spare a people that serveth the Gods. For, indeed, we are not come to waste the dwellings of this land, or to carry off spoils to our ships. For, of a truth, they who have suffered so much think not of such deeds. There is a land which the Greeks call Hesperia, but the people themselves Italy, after the name of their chief; an ancient land, mighty in arms and fertile of corn. Hither were we journeying, when a storm arising scattered our ships, and only these few that thou seest escaped to the land. And can there be nation so savage that it receiveth not shipwrecked men on its shore, but beareth arms against them, and forbiddeth them to land? Nay, but if ye care not for men, yet regard the Gods, who forget neither them that do righteously nor them that transgress. We had a king, Æneas, than whom there lived not a man more dutiful to Gods and men, and greater in war. If indeed he be yet alive, then we fear not at all. For of a truth it will not repent thee to have helped us. And if not, other friends have we, as Acestes of Sicily. Grant us, therefore, to shelter our ships from the wind; also to fit them with fresh timber from the woods, and to make ready oars for rowing, so that, finding again our king and our companions, we may gain the land of Italy. But if he be dead, and Ascanius his son lost also, then there is a dwelling ready for us in the land of Sicily, with Acestes, who is our friend."

Then Dido, her eyes bent on the ground, thus spake: "Fear not, men of Troy. If we have seemed to deal harshly with you, pardon us, seeing that, being newly settled in this land, we must keep watch and ward over our coasts. But as for the men of Troy, and their deeds in arms, who knows them not? Think not that we in Carthage are so dull of heart, or dwell so remote from man, that we are ignorant of these things. Whether, therefore, ye will journey to Italy or rather return to Sicily and King Acestes, know that I will give you all help, and protect you; or, if ye will, settle in this land of ours. Yours is this city which I am building. I will make no difference between man of Troy and man of Tyre. Would that your king also were here! Surely I will send those that shall seek him in all parts of Libya, lest haply he should be gone astray in any forest or strange city of the land."

And when Æneas and Achates heard these things

they were glad, and would have come forth from the cloud, and Achates said, "What thinkest thou? Lo, thy comrades are safe, saving him whom we saw with our own eyes drowned in the waves; and all other things are according as thy mother said."

And even as he spake the cloud parted from about them, and Æneas stood forth, very bright to behold, with face and breast as of a god, for his mother had given to him hair beautiful to see, and cast about him the purple light of youth, even as a workman sets ivory in some fair ornament, or compasseth about silver or marble of Paros with gold. Then spake he to the queen: "Lo! I am he whom ye seek, even Æneas of Troy, scarcely saved from the waters of the sea. And as for thee, O Queen, seeing that thou only hast been found to pity the unspeakable sorrows of Troy, and biddest us, though we be but poor exiles and lacking all things, to share thy city and thy home, may the Gods do so to thee as thou deservest. And, of a truth, so long as the rivers run to the seas, and the shadows fall on the hollows of the hills, so long will thy name and thy glory survive, whatever be the land to which the Gods shall bring me." Then gave he his right hand to Ilioneus, and his left hand to Sergestus, and greeted them with great joy.

And Dido, hearing these things, was silent for a while, but at the last she spake. "What ill fortune brings thee into perils so great? what power drave thee to these savage shores? Well do I mind me how in days gone by there came to Sidon one Teucer, who, having been banished from his country, sought help from

Belus that he might find a kingdom for himself. And it chanced that in those days Belus, my father, had newly conquered the land of Cyprus. From that day did I know the tale of Troy, and thy name also, and the chiefs of Greece. Also I remember that Teucer spake honorably of the men of Troy, saying that he was himself sprung of the old Teucrian stock. Come ye, therefore to my palace. I too have wandered far, even as you, and so have come to this land, and having suffered much, have learnt to succor them that suffer."

So saying she led Æneas into her palace; also she sent to his companions in the ships great store of provisions, even twenty oxen and a hundred bristly swine and a hundred ewe sheep with their lambs. But in the palace a great feast was set forth, couches covered with broidered purple and silver vessels without end, and cups of gold, whereon were embossed the mighty deeds of the men of old time.

And in the mean time Æneas sent Achates in haste to the ships, that he might fetch Ascanius to the feast. Also he bade that the boy should bring with him gifts of such things as they had saved from the ruins of Troy, — a mantle stiff with broidery of gold and a veil bordered with yellow acanthus, which the fair Helen had taken with her, flying from her home; but Leda, her mother, had given them to Helen; a sceptre likewise which Ilione, first-born of the daughters of Priam, had carried, and a necklace of pearls and a double crown of jewels and gold.

But Venus was troubled in heart, fearing evil to her

son should the men of Tyre be treacherous, after their wont, and Juno remember her wrath. Wherefore, taking counsel with herself, she called to the winged boy, even Love, that was her son, and spake: "My son, who art all my power and strength, who laughest at the thunders of Jupiter, thou knowest how Juno, being exceedingly wroth against thy brother Æneas, causeth him to wander out of the way over all lands. This day Dido hath him in her palace, and speaketh him fair; but I fear me much how these things may end. Wherefore hear thou that which I purpose. Thy brother hath even now sent for the boy Ascanius, that he may come to the palace, bringing with him gifts of such things as they saved from the ruins of Troy. Him will I cause to fall into a deep sleep and hide in Cythera or Idalium, and do thou for one night take upon thee his likeness. And when Queen Dido at the feast shall hold thee in her lap, and kiss and embrace thee, do thou breathe by stealth thy fire into her heart."

Then did Love as his mother bade him, and put off his wings, and took upon him the shape of Ascanius, but on the boy Venus caused there to fall a deep sleep, and carried him to the woods of Idalium, and lapped him in sweet-smelling flowers. And in his stead Love carried the gifts to the queen. And when he was come they sat down to the feast, the queen being in the midst under a canopy. Æneas also and the men of Troy lay on coverlets of purple, to whom serving-men brought water and bread in baskets and napkins; and within fifty handmaids were ready to replenish the store of victual and to fan the fire; and a hundred others, with pages as many, loaded the tables with dishes and drinking-cups. Many men of Tyre also were bidden to the feast. Much they marveled at the gifts of Æneas, and much at the false Ascanius. Dido also could not satisfy herself with looking on him, nor knew what trouble he was preparing for her in the time to come. And he, having first embraced the father who was not his father, and clung about his neck, addressed himself to Queen Dido, and she ever followed him with her eyes, and sometimes would hold him on her lap. And still he worked upon her that she should forget the dead Sichæus and conceive a new love in her heart.

But when they first paused from the feast, lo! men set great bowls upon the table and filled them to the brim with wine. Then did the queen call for a great vessel of gold, with many jewels upon it, from which Belus, and all the kings from Belus, had drunk, and called for wine, and having filled it she cried, "O Jupiter, whom they call the god of hosts and guests, cause that this be a day of joy for the men of Troy and for them of Tyre, and that our children remember it forever. Also Bacchus, giver of joy, be present, and kindly Juno." And when she had touched the wine with her lips, she handed the great cup to Prince Bitias, who drank thereout a mighty draught, and the other princes after him. Then the minstrel Iopas, whom Altas himself had taught, sang to the harp, of the moon, how she goes on her way, and of the sun, how his light is darkened. He sang also of men, and of the beasts of the field, whence they come; and of the stars, Arcturus, and the Greater Bear and the Less, and the Hyades; and of the winter sun, why he hastens to dip himself in the ocean; and of the winter nights, why they tarry so long. The queen also talked much of the story of Troy, of Priam, and of Hector, asking many things, as of the arms of Memnon, and of the horses of Diomed, and of Achilles, how great he was. And at last she said to Æneas, "Tell us now thy story, how Troy was taken, and thy wanderings over land and sea." And Æneas made answer, "Nay, O Queen, but thou biddest me renew a sorrow unspeakable. Yet, if thou art minded to hear these things, hearken." And he told her all that had befallen him, even to the day when his father Anchises died.

Much was Queen Dido moved by the story, and much did she marvel at him that told it, and scarce could sleep for thinking of him. And the next day she spake to Anna, her sister, "O my sister, I have been troubled this night with ill dreams, and my heart is disquieted within me. What a man is this stranger that hath come to our shores! How noble of mien! How bold in war! Sure I am that he is of the sons of the Gods. What fortunes have been his! Of what wars he told us! Surely were I not steadfastly purposed that I would not yoke me again in marriage, this were the man to whom I might yield. Only he — for I will tell thee the truth, my sister — only he, since the day when Sichæus died by our brother's hand, hath moved my heart. But may the earth swallow me up, or the almighty Father strike me with lightning, ere I stoop to such baseness. The husband of my youth hath carried with him my love, and he shall keep it in his grave."

So she spake, with many tears. And her sister made answer, "Why wilt thou waste thy youth in sorrow, without child or husband? Thinkest thou that there is care or remembrance of such things in the grave? No suitors indeed have pleased thee here or in Tyre, but wilt thou also contend with a love that is after thine own heart? Think too of the nations among whom thou dwellest, how fierce they are, and of thy brother at Tyre, what he threatens against thee. Surely it was by the will of the Gods, and of Juno chiefly, that the ships of Troy came hither. And this city, which thou buildest, to what greatness will it grow if only thou wilt make for thyself such alliance! How great will be the glory of Carthage if the strength of Troy be joined unto her! Only do thou pray to the Gods and offer sacrifices; and, for the present, seeing that the time of sailing is now past, make excuse that these strangers tarry with thee awhile."

Thus did Anna comfort her sister and encourage her. And first the two offered sacrifice to the Gods, chiefly to Juno, who careth for the bond of marriage. Also, examining the entrails of slain beasts, they sought to learn the things that should happen thereafter. And ever Dido would company with Æneas, leading him about the walls of the city which she builded. And often she would begin to speak and stay in the midst of her words. And when even was come, she would hear again and again at the banquet the tale of Troy, and while others slept would watch, and while he was far away would seem to see him and to hear him. Ascanius, too, she would embrace for love of his father, if so she might cheat her own heart. But the work of the city was stayed meanwhile; nor did the towers rise in their places, nor the youth practice themselves in arms.

Then Juno, seeing how it fared with the queen, spake to Venus: "Are ye satisfied with your victory, thou and thy son, that ye have vanquished, the two of you, one woman? Well I knew that thou fearedst lest this Carthage should harm thy favorite. But why should there be war between us? Thou hast what thou seekest. Let us make alliance. Let Dido obey a Phrygian husband, and bring the men of Tyre as her dowry."

But Venus knew that she spake with ill intent, to the end that the men of Troy should not reign in the land of Italy. Nevertheless she dissembled with her tongue, and spake: "Who would not rather have peace with thee than war? Only I doubt whether this thing shall be to the pleasure of Jupiter. This thou must learn, seeing that thou art his wife, and where thou leadest I will follow."

So the two, taking counsel together, ordered things in this wise. The next day a great hunting was prepared. For as soon as ever the sun was risen upon the earth, the youth of the city assembled, with nets and hunting spears and dogs that ran by scent. And the princes of Carthage waited for the queen at the palace door, where her horse stood champing the bit, with trappings of purple and gold. And after a while she came forth, with many following her. And she had upon her a Sidonian mantle, with a border wrought with divers colors; of gold was her quiver, and of gold the knot of her hair, and of gold the clasp to her mantle. Æneas likewise came forth, beautiful as is Apollo when he leaveth Lydia and the stream of Xanthus, coming to Delos, and hath about his hair a wreath of bay-leaves and a circlet of gold. So fair was Æneas to see. And when the hunters came to the hills they found great store of goats and stags, which they chased. And of all the company Ascanius was the foremost, thinking scorn of such hunting, and wishing that a wild boar or a lion out of the hills would come forth to be his prey.

And now befell a great storm, with much thunder and hail, from which the hunters sought shelter. But Æneas and the queen, being left of all their company, came together to the same cave. And there they plighted their troth one to the other. Nor did the queen after that make secret of her love, but called Æneas her husband.

Straightway went Rumor and told these things through the cities of Libya. Now Rumor, men say, is the youngest daughter of Earth, a marvelous creature, moving very swiftly with feet and wings, and having many feathers upon her, and under every feather an eye and a tongue and a mouth and an ear. In the night she flieth between heaven and earth, and sleepeth not; and in the day she sitteth on some housetop or lofty tower, or spreadeth fear over mighty cities; and she loveth that which is false even as she loveth that which is true. So now she went telling through Libya how Æneas of Troy was come, and Dido was wedded to him, and how they lived careless and at ease, and thinking not of the work to which they were called.

And first of all she went to Prince Iarbas, who himself had sought Dido in marriage. And Iarbas was very wroth when he heard it, and, coming to the temple of Jupiter, spread his grief before the Gods, how that he had given a place on his coasts to this Dido, and would have taken her to wife, but that she had married a stranger from Phrygia, another Paris, whose dress and adornments were of a woman rather than of a man.

And Jupiter saw that this was so, and he said to Mercury, who was his messenger, " Go speak to Æneas these words: ' Thus saith the king of Gods and men. Is this what thy mother promised of thee, twice saving thee from the spear of the Greeks? Art thou he that shall rule Italy and its mighty men of war, and spread thy dominion to the ends of the world ? If thou thyself forgettest these things, dost thou grudge to thy son the citadels of Rome? What doest thou here? Why lookest thou not to Italy? Depart and tarry not.'"

Then Mercury fitted the winged sandals to his feet, and took the wand with which he driveth the spirits of the dead, and came right soon to Mount Atlas, which standeth bearing the heaven on his head, and having always clouds about his top, and snow upon his shoulders, and a beard that is stiff with ice. There Mercury stood awhile; then, as a bird which seeks its prey in the sea, shot headlong down, and came to

Æneas where he stood, with a yellow jasper in his sword-hilt, and a cloak of purple shot with gold about his shoulders, and spake: "Buildest thou Carthage, for-getting thine own work? The Almighty Father saith to thee, 'What meanest thou? Why tarriest thou here? If thou carest not for thyself, yet think of thy son, and that the Fates have given to him Italy and Rome.'"

And Æneas saw him no more. And he stood stricken with fear and doubt. Fain would he obey the voice, and go as the Gods commanded. But how should he tell this purpose to the queen? But at the last it seemed good to him to call certain of the chiefs, as Mnestheus, and Sergestus, and Antheus, and bid them make ready the ships in silence, and gather together the people, but dissemble the cause, and he himself would watch a fitting time to speak and unfold the matter to the queen.

Yet was not Dido deceived, for love is keen of sight. Rumor also told her that they made ready the ships for sailing. Then, flying through the city, even as one on whom has come the frenzy of Bacchus flies by night over Mount Cithæron, she came upon Æneas, and spake: "Thoughtest thou to hide thy crime, and to depart in silence from this land? Carest thou not for her whom thou leavest to die? And hast thou no fear of winter storms that vex the sea? By all that I have done for thee and given thee, if there be yet any place for repentance, repent thee of this purpose. For thy sake I suffer the wrath of the princes of Libya and of my own people; and if thou leavest me, for what should I live? — till my brother overthrow my city,

or Iarbas carry me away captive? If but I had a little
Æneas to play in my halls I should not seem so altogether desolate."

But Æneas, fearing the words of Jupiter, stood with
eyes that relented not. At the last he spake: "I deny
not, O Queen, the benefits that thou hast done unto
me, nor ever, while I live, shall I forget Dido. I sought
not to fly by stealth; yet did I never promise that I
would abide in this place. Could I have chosen according to my will I had built again the city of Troy where
it stood; but the Gods command that I should seek
Italy. Thou hast thy Carthage; why dost thou grudge
Italy to us? Nor may I tarry. Night after night have
I seen my father Anchises warning me in dreams.
Also even now the messenger of Jupiter came to me —
with these ears I heard him — and bade me depart."

Then, in great wrath, with eyes askance, did Dido
break forth upon him: "Surely no goddess was thy
mother, nor art thou come of the race of Dardanus.
The rocks of Caucasus brought thee forth, and an
Hyrcanian tigress gave thee suck. For why should
I dissemble? Was he moved at all my tears? Did he
pity my love? Nay, the very Gods are against me.
This man I took to myself when he was shipwrecked
and ready to perish. I brought back his ships, his companions from destruction. And now forsooth comes
the messenger of Jupiter with dreadful commands
from the Gods. As for thee, I keep thee not. Go,
seek thy Italy across the seas: only, if there is any
vengeance in heaven, thou wilt pay the penalty for
this wrong, being wrecked on some rock in their midst.

Then wilt thou call on Dido in vain. Aye, and where-ever thou shalt go I will haunt thee, and rejoice in the dwellings below to hear thy doom."

Then she turned, and hasted to go into the house. But her spirit left her, so that her maidens bare her to her chamber and laid her on her bed.

Then Æneas, though indeed he was much troubled in heart, and would fain have comforted the queen, was obedient to the heavenly word, and departed to his ships. And the men of Troy busied themselves in making them ready for the voyage. Even as the ants spoil a great heap of corn and store it in their dwellings against winter, moving in a black line across the field, and some carry the great grains, and some chide those that linger, even so did the Trojans swarm along the ways and labor at the work.

But when Dido saw it she called to Anna her sister and said, "Seest thou how they hasten the work along the shore? Even now the sails are ready for the winds, and the sailors have wreathed the ships with garlands, as if for departure. Go thou — the deceiver always trusted thee, and thou knowest how best to move him — go and entreat him. I harmed not him nor his people; let him then grant me this only. Let him wait for a fairer time for his journey. I ask not that he give up his purpose; only that he grant me a short breathing space, till I may learn how to bear this sorrow."

And Anna hearkened to her sister, and took the message to Æneas, yet profited nothing, for the Gods shut his ears that he should not hear. Even as the oak stands firm when the north wind would root it up from

the earth, — its leaves are scattered all around, yet
doth it remain firm, for its roots go down to the regions
below, even as far as its branches reach to heaven, —
so stood Æneas firm, and, though he wept many tears,
changed not his purpose.

Then did Dido grow weary of her life. For when
she did sacrifice, the pure water would grow black and
the wine be changed to blood. Also from the shrine of
her husband, which was in the midst of her palace,
was heard a voice calling her, and the owl cried aloud
from the house-top. And in her dreams the cruel
Æneas seemed to drive her before him; or she seemed
to be going a long way with none to bear her company,
and be seeking her own people in a land that was
desert. Therefore, hiding the thing that was in her
heart, she spake to her sister, saying, "I have found a
way, my sister, that shall bring him back to me or set
me free from him. Near the shore of the Great Sea,
where the Æthiopians dwell, is a priestess, who guards
the temple of the daughters of Hesperus, being wont
to feed the dragons that kept the apples of gold. She
is able by her charms to loose the heart from care or
to bind it, and to stay rivers also, and to turn the courses
of the stars, and to call up the spirits of the dead. Do
thou, therefore — for this is what the priestess commands — build a pile in the open court, and put thereon
the sword which he left hanging in our chamber, and
the garments he wore, and the couch on which he lay,
even all that was his, so that they may perish together."

And when these things were done — for Anna knew
not of her purpose — and also an image of Æneas was

428

laid upon the pile, the priestess, with her hair unbound, called upon all the gods that dwell below, sprinkling thereon water that was drawn, she said, from the lake of Avernus, and scattering evil herbs that had been cut at the full moon with a sickle of bronze. Dido also, with one foot bare and her garments loosened, threw meal upon the fire and called upon the gods, if haply there be any, that look upon those that love and suffer wrong.

In the mean time Æneas lay asleep in the hind part of his ship, when there appeared to him in a dream the god Mercury, even as he had seen him when he brought the commandment of Jupiter. And Mercury spake, saying, "Son of Venus, canst thou sleep? seest thou not what perils surround thee, nor hearest how the favorable west wind calls? The queen purposes evil against thee. If thou lingerest till the morning come thou wilt see the shore covered with them that wish thee harm. Fly, then, and tarry not; for a woman is ever of many minds."

Then did Æneas in great fear start from his sleep, and call his companions, saying, "Wake, and sit on the benches, and loose the sails. 'T is a god thus bids us fly." And even as he spake he cut the cable with his sword. And all hasted to follow him, and sped over the sea.

And now it was morning, and Queen Dido, from her watch-tower, saw the ships upon the sea. Then she smote upon her breast and tore her hair, and cried, "Shall this stranger mock us thus? Hasten to follow him. Bring down the ships from the docks, make ready sword and fire. And this was the man who bare upon his shoulders his aged father. Why did I not tear him to pieces, and slay his companions with the sword, and serve up the young Ascanius at his meal? And if I had perished, what then? for I die to-day. O Sun, that regardest all the earth, and Juno, that carest for marriage bonds, and Hecate, Queen of the dead, and ye Furies that take vengeance on evil-doers, hear me. If it be ordered that he reach that land, yet grant that he suffer many things from his enemies, and be driven from his city, and beg for help from strangers, and see his people cruelly slain with the sword; and, when he shall have made peace on ill conditions, that he enjoy not long his kingdoms, but die before his day, and lie unburied on the plain. And ye, men of Tyre, hate his children and his people forever. Let there be no love or peace between you. And may some avenger arise from my grave who shall persecute the race of Dardanus with fire and sword. So shall there be war forever between him and me."

Then she spake to old Barce, who had been nurse to her husband Sichæus, "Bid my sister bathe herself in water, and bring with her beasts for sacrifice. And do thou also put a garland about thy head, for I am minded to finish this sacrifice which I have begun, and to burn the image of the man of Troy."

And when the old woman made haste to do her bidding, Queen Dido ran to the court where the pile was made for the burning, and mounted on the pile, and drew the sword of Æneas from the scabbard. Then did she throw herself upon the bed, and cry,

"Now do I yield up my life. I have finished my course. I have built a mighty city. I have avenged my husband on him that slew him. Happy had I been, yea, too happy! had the ships of Troy never come to this land." Then she kissed the bed and cried, "Shall I die unavenged? Nevertheless let me die. The man of Troy shall see this fire from the sea whereon he journeys, and carry with him an augury of death."

And when her maidens looked, lo! she had fallen upon the sword, and the blood was upon her hands. And a great cry went up through the palace, exceeding loud and bitter, even as if the enemy had taken Carthage or ancient Tyre, and the fire were mounting over the dwellings of men and of Gods. And Anna her sister heard it, and rushing through the midst called her by name: "O my sister, was this thy purpose? Were the pile and the sword and the fire for this? Why wouldst thou not suffer that I should die with thee? For surely, my sister, thou hast slain thyself, and me, and thy people, and thy city. But give me water, ye maidens, that I may wash her wounds, and if there be any breath left in her, we may yet stay it."

Then she climbed on to the pile, and caught her sister in her arms, and sought to staunch the blood with her garments. Three times did Dido strive to raise her eyes; three times did her spirit leave her. Three times she would have raised herself upon her elbow; three times she fell back upon the bed, looking with wandering eyes for the light, and groaning that she yet beheld it.

Then Juno, looking down from heaven, saw that

her pain was long, and pitied her, and sent down Iris, her messenger, that she might loose the soul that struggled to be free. For, seeing that she died not by nature, nor yet by the hand of man, but before her time and of her own madness, Queen Proserpine had not shred the ringlet from her head which she shreds from them that die. Wherefore Iris, flying down with dewy wings from heaven, with a thousand colors about her from the light of the sun, stood about her head and said, "I give thee to death, even as I am bidden, and loose thee from thy body." Then she shred the lock, and Queen Dido gave up the ghost.

THE FUNERAL GAMES OF
ANCHISES

By Charles Henry Hanson

ÆNEAS called together all his followers, and reminded them that a year had now passed since the death of his father. Not of their own purpose, but doubtless by the will of the Gods, they had now returned to the friendly land where his bones had been laid. It was therefore his intention to celebrate funeral games. For eight days there should be feasting, for which Acestes had generously provided two oxen for each ship; and on the ninth day he would give prizes to be contested in the foot-race, in shooting with the bow, and in boxing with the cestus.

Having thus spoken, the hero, according to the custom of that time, placed a wreath of myrtle upon his head and proceeded to the tomb of his father, where he poured out, as a libation to the Gods, two bowls of wine, two of new milk, and two of sacred blood. Then he scattered flowers over the tomb, and offered up a prayer to his father's shade. Immediately there came forth from the tomb a huge snake with glittering scales of blue and gold, which, after tasting of what had been poured out, retired again to the recesses of the vault. Believing this creature to be an attendant on his father's spirit, Æneas offered rich sacrifices — ewes, sows, and bullocks — and his companions followed his example. The eight days of feasting passed pleasantly enough, and the morning appointed for the funeral games dawned bright and serene. A joyous crowd assembled on the shore, some to take part in the contests, and others to watch them. The first of the games was a race between galleys, and four ships had been entered to take part in it. The first was the Pristis, or Shark, of which Mnestheus was the captain. The Chimera, a vessel of immense size, was commanded by Gyas. The other vessels were the Centaur and the Scylla, — the first commanded by Sergestus, and the second by Cloanthus. Some way out in the sea, opposite to the starting-point, a rock rose amid the restless waters. The galleys were to round this rock, on which Æneas had planted an oak-tree as a mark, and then return to the shore. The vessels were assigned their places by lot, and the captain of each took his place on the poop; while the rowers, stripped to the waist, their shoulders glistening with oil, sat with their arms stretched to the oars, eager for the signal. At the blast of a trumpet all the oars struck the sea at once, and beat it into foam, and the vessels shot forward amid the loud shouts of the multitude. The Chimera, under Gyas's skillful guidance, took the lead; next followed the Scylla, whose rowers were more efficient, but were unable to make such progress, because the vessel was naturally slower. Behind the Shark and the Centaur followed close together, and first the one and then the other gained a slight advantage. The two leading vessels were rapidly nearing the rock when Gyas perceived that

his helmsman, Menœtes, was keeping a course too far
to the right, in fear of some hidden crags, and was
thus losing the advantage that had been gained. He
urged him to steer more to the left, nor to care even if
the oars grazed the rock; but Menœtes was afraid to
obey the command. And now Cloanthus in the Scylla,
taking the very course Gyas had wished to follow, ran
boldly between the Chimera and the rock, and so got
round the goal in front of his antagonist. When Gyas
beheld this he was full of wrath. Rushing to the helm,
he seized the over-cautious Menœtes and hurled him
into the sea; then he himself took the helm, and at once
guided his ship and issued commands and cries of encouragement to his oarsmen. The luckless Menœtes
with difficulty contrived to scramble out of the sea
onto the rock, and sat there in his dripping garments,
while the spectators roared with laughter at his misadventure. But now Mnestheus in the Shark and Sergestus in the Centaur pushed forward with redoubled
zeal in the hope of obtaining the lead. Sergestus got
a little in front of his competitor, but Mnestheus, walking among his rowers, urged them to put forth their
utmost strength, and at least not to suffer the disgrace of
being last. In response to his appeal they bent to the oar
with new vigor; the ship trembled under their strokes
and the water seemed to fly from beneath her keel.
Suddenly, while the Centaur, in full career, was pressing close to the rock to prevent the Shark from passing
on the inner side, she ran upon a jutting point where
she remained fast, while the oars were shattered against
the hard rocks. In a moment the Shark shot past,

and having rounded the goal, dashed on the homeward
way. Ere long Mnestheus had overtaken the Chimera,
which had lost ground because she was deprived of
her steersman. Cloanthus in the Scylla was now alone
in front of the Shark; and though the race was nearly
over, the frantic efforts of Mnestheus' crew might have
gained him the victory, but that Cloanthus poured forth
passionate prayers to the marine deities, and promised
them ample offerings if the first prize became his.
They heard his vows, and gathering underneath his
vessel, pushed it forward, so that it entered the harbor
just in front of the Shark. Then Æneas proclaimed
Cloanthus the victor, and gave him a mantle embroidered
with gold and ornamented with a thick fringe of the
costly Melibœan purple. On Mnestheus, who had so
gallantly gained the second place, he bestowed a ponderous coat of mail worked in gold and brass, which
he had himself taken from a famous Greek warrior,
Demoleus, whom he had slain before Troy. Gyas
received two caldrons of brass, and some silver bowls
ornamented with rich carvings. Lastly, when Sergestus had slowly brought back to port his crippled
galley, his chief bestowed on him, in reward for having
rescued the vessel from her perilous position, a Cretan
female slave with her two children.

Thus ended the galley race; and the assembled
multitude now proceeded to a grassy plain a little way
inland, where thrones were placed for Acestes, Æneas,
and the other leaders. Here the remaining games
were to be celebrated, and first of all a foot race. Among
the competitors in this were Euryalus, a Trojan youth

distinguished for his personal beauty; Nisus, a brave warrior, who was his constant friend and companion; Diores, Salius, and Patron, three other Trojans; and two Sicilian youths famous for their speed, named Elymus and Panopes. Æneas announced that he would give two Cretan javelins of bright steel and a carved battle-axe of silver to each who took part in the race, and to the three who came in first other rich prizes: to the first a war-horse with costly trappings; to the second a quiver full of Thracian arrows, with a gold belt and jeweled buckle; and to the third a Grecian helmet. The runners having been placed in proper order, the signal was given, and they darted forward like a tempest. Nisus led the way, Salius coming second, and Euryalus third, with the rest following close behind. Already Nisus was near the goal, when unluckily his foot slipped at a spot where some victims had been sacrificed for the altar, and the blood soaking into the grass had made it slippery. Down he fell into the puddle, and in a moment his chance of victory had disappeared. But even then, in spite of his disappointment, he was mindful of his affection for Euryalus, and resolved that since he could not win the race, his friend should do so. He rose to his feet just as Salius was coming up, and contrived to stand in his way so as to overturn him. Euryalus, who had still kept the third place, now sprang forward, and was easily victorious amid the applause of the crowd. Elymus came in next, and close behind him Diores. But Salius loudly demanded that the first prize of right belonged to him, because he had been deprived of the victory by unfair means. The spectators, however, favored the claim of Euryalus because of his youth and beauty; and Diores vehemently took the same side, since, if Salius were adjudged the victory, he would not receive a prize at all. Æneas speedily silenced all contention by declaring that the promised rewards should go to the three who had arrived first at the winning-post; but he added that he would show his sympathy for the disaster which had befallen Salius, and therefore bestowed on him the shaggy hide of a Getulian lion, still retaining the claws, which had been gilt. Upon this, Nisus also merrily asked for some consolation, since but for an accident the first prize would have been his, and he showed his face and limbs all besmeared with mud. His chief entered into the jest, and gave him a buckler, finely carved, which had once hung on the walls of Neptune's temple at Troy.

The next contest was that with the cestus, the boxing-glove of the ancients, a formidable implement, intended not to soften the blows dealt by the boxers, but to make them more painful, for it was composed of strips of hardened oxhide. To the competitors in this sport — if such it could be called — Æneas offered two prizes, — the first a bullock, decked with gold and fillets, and the second a sword and a shining helmet. A noted Trojan warrior named Dares, a man of immense strength and bulk, who was also celebrated for his skill with the cestus, presented himself to contest this prize. He brandished his huge fists in the air, and paced vaingloriously backward and forward in the arena, challenging any one in the assembly to meet

HE ROSE TO HIS FEET JUST AT THE MOMENT THAT SALIUS WAS
COMING UP, AND CONTRIVED TO STAND IN HIS WAY SO AS TO
OVERTURN HIM. EURYALUS, WHO HAD STILL KEPT THE THIRD
PLACE, NOW SPRANG FORWARD, AND WAS EASILY VICTORIOUS
AMID THE APPLAUSE OF THE CROWD. ELYMUS CAME IN NEXT,
AND CLOSE BEHIND HIM DIORES. BUT SALIUS LOUDLY DE-
MANDED THAT THE FIRST PRIZE OF RIGHT BELONGED TO HIM.

him. But there was no response; his friends were too well acquainted with his skill, and the Sicilians were awed by his formidable appearance. At last, therefore, imagining that nobody would venture to encounter him, he advanced to Æneas and asked that the prize might be given up to him. It seemed, indeed, that this would have to be done, when King Acestes turned to one of his elders, a venerable Sicilian chief named Entellus, and asked how it was that he thus allowed such splendid prizes to be taken before his eyes without striking a blow for them. Entellus had, in his younger days, been a great champion with the cestus, having been taught the use of the weapon by none other than Eryx, at that time king of Sicily, and one of the most expert boxers in the world. So confident had Eryx been in his powers, that when the mighty Hercules passed through Sicily on his way from Spain, where he had slain King Geryon and carried off his splendid cattle, the Sicilian monarch ventured to challenge the hero to a combat with the cestus, staking his kingdom against the cattle which Hercules was bearing away to Greece. Hercules had accepted the challenge, and had slain Eryx in the encounter; but the tradition of his skill had been preserved by his pupil Entellus. The chief was now old, and disinclined for exertion; but when thus urged by King Acestes, he slowly rose and threw into the arena the gauntlets which King Eryx had been accustomed to use. Terrible weapons indeed they were, with heavy pieces of iron and lead sewn into them underneath the oxhide. At the mere sight of them Dares shrank back appalled, and refused to fight with such implements. "These," said Entellus, "were the gauntlets with which my master Eryx encountered Hercules; and these, after his death, I myself was accustomed to use. But if Dares likes not such gloves, let Æneas provide others for both of us." With these words he threw off his upper garments and bared his massive shoulders and sinewy arms. The Trojan chief brought out two pairs of gauntlets of less formidable make, with which the two champions armed themselves; and then they stood face to face, and both raised their arms for the encounter. For some time they stood parrying each other's blows and watching for an opportunity. Presently, as they grew warmer, many heavy strokes were given on each side, now on the head, now on the breast. Entellus stood stiff and unmoved in the same firm posture, only bending to evade Dares's blows, and always closely watching his antagonist, who, more active, wheeled round him, trying first one method of attack, then another. At last Entellus uplifted his right arm, thinking he saw an opportunity for delivering a decisive stroke; but Dares with great agility slipped out of the way, and as the arm of Entellus encountered no resistance save from the empty air, he fell forward on the ground through the violence of his own effort. Acclamations burst from all the onlookers, and Acestes himself stepped forward to assist his old companion to his feet. But the mishap had only aroused Entellus's anger; he no longer acted on the defensive, but rushed upon his opponent with irresistible ardor, and smote blow after blow, driving Dares headlong over the field, pouring down strokes as incessantly as a shower of hail rattles upon the house-tops. Æneas now deemed it high time to put a stop to the combat, and called upon Dares, who indeed was quite overpowered, to yield. His comrades led the beaten champion to the ships, with the blood flowing from his battered head and face, and on his behalf they took away the helmet and sword, leaving the bull to the conqueror. Entellus, proud of his victory, laid hold of the animal, and exclaimed, "Behold, O chief, and you Trojans, from this what my strength once was, and also from what death you have saved Dares." With these words he smote the bull on the forehead with the cestus so mightily that the skull was battered in and the brute sank dead at his feet.

After this exciting competition came a more peaceful sport, — a trial of skill with the bow. A mast was planted on a sward, and to the top of it a living dove was secured by a cord. This was the mark, and four archers came forward to contend for the prizes, — Hippocoön, the brother of Nisus and one of Æneas's dearest friends; Mnestheus, the winner of the second prize in the galley race; Eurytion, a brother of that Pandarus who was one of the most skillful archers that fought in the Trojan war, and who, after wounding Menelaus, was slain by Diomedes; and lastly, King Acestes himself. Hippocoön shot first, and his arrow, whizzing past the fluttering dove, pierced the pole to which she was fastened. This, though it did not hit the mark, was an excellent shot, and it won loud applause from the spectators. Mnestheus next discharged his dart, taking a long and steady aim ; but his arrow, instead of striking the bird, cut in two the cord by which she was fastened, and, spreading her wings, the dove at once flew away. Instantly, however, Eurytion raised his bow, and shot with so true an aim that he struck the bird even in mid-flight, and brought her lifeless to the earth. There was thus no longer a mark at which Acestes could aim; but notwithstanding he drew his bow and discharged a shaft high into the air. And now a strange prodigy happened; for the arrow, soaring upward, took fire as it flew, and marked out a path of flame, till, being quite consumed, it vanished into the air. This spectacle naturally excited the wonder and reverence of the assembled multitude; and Æneas, embracing Acestes, declared that the incident was an omen from the Gods awarding to him the first prize. He therefore bestowed on him a splendid bowl, embossed with figures, which had once belonged to Anchises, nor did the other competitors dispute the justice of the decision.

But the games were not yet ended. The Trojan chief had prepared a closing spectacle as a surprise for the spectators. He sent a messenger to summon Ascanius, and in the mean time ordered a large space of ground to be cleared. Then suddenly his son entered on horseback at the head of a numerous company, — all the youths of the expedition. They were attired alike, with garlands on their heads and circles of gold about their necks; and each carried two spears of cornel-wood, tipped with steel. The young equestrians were divided into three companies; one was commanded by Ascanius himself, mounted on a beautiful Sidonian steed which had been given him by Queen Dido; a second by the youthful Priam, a son of that Polites whom Pyrrhus slew at the fall of Troy; and the third by Atys, a boy who was Ascanius' especial friend and companion. They went through a series of evolutions, now advancing in line, again forming in different bands and pretending to charge one another, and afterwards going through many other intricate manœuvres. The scene was a most picturesque one, and gave great pleasure to those who witnessed it.

ÆNEAS'S VISIT TO THE LOWER WORLD

By Charles Henry Hanson

CONTINUING his voyage, Æneas reached the shore of the country afterwards named Campania, the modern province of Naples. Here the ships were carefully moored, and the crews disembarked. Some busied themselves in kindling fires and preparing a meal; others explored the country in search of game. Æneas, however, hastened at once to seek the temple of Apollo and the adjoining cave of the Cumæan Sibyl, — the most famous of all the oracles of antiquity. The temple and cave were situated in a thick wood, closely adjoining the gloomy lake of Avernus, a black pool of unknown depth, hedged in by precipitous cliffs, and emitting gases so poisonous that no bird was able to fly over it in safety. In the rocks at one side of the lake there yawned a sombre cavern, which was believed in those days to be the entrance to the kingdom of Pluto — the abode of the dead.

Æneas was surveying the temple, — an edifice of great splendor, adorned with pictures wrought in metal by the cunning hand of Dædalus, — when Achates, whom he had sent before him to the Sibyl's cave, approached, conducting the priestess. "O prince," she

said, "this is not the time for admiring the works of
men. It will be more fitting for you to propitiate the
god with sacrifices, so that he may inspire me." With
this mandate the hero at once complied, and then
the Sibyl summoned him and his followers to the
entrance of her cave, — a vast apartment carved out
of the living rock, whence issued a hundred corridors.
Scarcely had the Trojans approached the threshold
when the virgin exclaimed, "Now is the time to consult your fate! The god! lo, the god!" As she cried
out thus her looks suddenly changed, her color came
and went, her hair fell in disorder over her shoulders,
her bosom heaved, and she was shaken by an uncon-
trollable passion. Her very form seemed to dilate,
and the tone of her voice was no longer that of a mere
mortal, since she was inspired by the influence of the
god. "Trojan Æneas!" she exclaimed, "delay no
longer to offer thy prayers for the knowledge which
thou seekest; for not till then can I reveal to thee the
secrets of the future."

Earnestly did Æneas implore pity and aid from
Apollo; and of the Sibyl he entreated that she should
proclaim her revelations by word of mouth, and not,
as was her custom, write them on leaves of trees, lest
they should become the sport of the winds. At first
the prophetess did not answer; she was not yet fully
possessed by the spirit of the god, and raved in wild
ecstasy in the cave, struggling, as it were, to resist
the will of Phœbus, who, on his part, wearied her
foaming lips, subdued her fierce heart, and moulded
her to his will. Then all at once the hundred doors

THE WANDERINGS OF ÆNEAS

of the cavern flew open of their own accord, and the
Sibyl proclaimed the divine response, —

"O thou who hast at length overpassed the perils
of the ocean, yet more terrible trials await thee on
shore. Thou and thy Trojans shall indeed reach the
promised land — that is assured; but ye shall wish
that ye had never come thither. Wars, horrid wars,
I foresee, and Tiber foaming with a deluge of blood.
Another Achilles awaits thee in Latium — he also
the son of a goddess. Nor shall the persecutions of
Juno cease to follow the Trojans wherever they may
be; and in your distress you will humbly supplicate
all the surrounding Italian states for aid. Once more
shall a marriage with a foreign wife be a source of
affliction to you. But yield not under your sufferings;
encounter them resolutely in the teeth of adverse
fortune, and when you least expect it, the means of
deliverance shall come to you from a Greek city."

So, under the inspiration of Apollo, spoke the Sibyl.
When she had ceased, Æneas answered that no prospect of further trials could appall him, for he was prepared to endure the worst that could befall. But he now
entreated, since it was said that the entrance to the
shades was near, that the Sibyl should conduct him
into those dark regions, in order that he might obtain
an interview with the spectre of his father. It was
Anchises' self, he added, who had bidden him make
this request; and filial devotion would enable him to
perform a task which Orpheus had achieved out of
love for his wife Eurydice, and Pollux through his attachment to his brother Castor.

446

"Æneas," replied the priestess, "easy is the descent into Hades: grim Pluto's gate stands open night and day, but to retrace your steps and escape to the upper regions will be a difficult task indeed, and one which few have hitherto been able to accomplish. If, however, you are fixed in the resolve to pursue so desperate an enterprise, learn what first is to be done. There is in the dark woods which surround the Lake of Avernus a certain tree, dense of foliage, on which grows a single bough of gold, with leaves and twigs of the same precious metal, and no living mortal can enter Hades unless he has first found and plucked this bough, which is demanded by Proserpine, the consort of Pluto and queen of the infernal realms, as her peculiar tribute. When the bough is torn off, another always grows in its place. Therefore search for it diligently, and when you have discovered it grasp it with your hand. If the Fates are propitious to your enterprise, you will be able to pluck it easily; if otherwise, your whole strength could not tear it from the tree, nor could you ever sever it with your sword. In the mean time the body of one of your friends lies lifeless, and demands the funeral rites. First bury him with proper ceremonies, and then return to me with black cattle for the sacrifices; and then you shall be able to visit the realms of Hades, to which most living men are denied an entrance."

With sorrowful thoughts Æneas, closely followed by Achates, now withdrew from the shrine, and took the way to the shore. Both were greatly perplexed to know what was the corpse needing burial of which the Sibyl had spoken. But while they were wondering they came to the beach, and there, before them, they saw lying the body of Misenus, who had come to a lamentable end. Misenus was the most skilled among all the Trojans in the art of blowing the trumpet. He had been, besides, a famous warrior, and during the siege of Troy was accustomed to be the companion of Hector in the field, and to fight by his side. When Hector fell, he attached himself to Æneas, scorning to follow any less illustrious chief, and so had formed one of the band which the hero was conducting to Latium. But he was inordinately vain of his skill with the trumpet, and believed himself superior even to the Tritons, the sea-deities whose especial province it was to lull the seas at the command of Neptune by blowing upon instruments made of shells. These Tritons Misenus had challenged to a trial of skill, and by way of defiance had blown so loud a note that the deities were afraid to respond to his challenge; but being full of jealousy, they had now contrived to lure him into the sea and drown him. The discovery of his lifeless body filled all his comrades with sadness. They gathered about him with loud lamentations, and then prepared to erect his funeral pyre, hastening with axes into the thick surrounding woods, and cutting down huge oaks and pines and ash-trees.

Æneas himself led the way in the performance of this task, and while he was engaged in it he could not help exclaiming, as his glance surveyed the wide forest, "Would that I could now perceive the golden bough which I must find before entering Hades; for in this

ample forest, how can I begin to search for it ? " Scarcely
had he spoken when two pigeons suddenly swooped
down from the upper air and alighted at his feet. He
guessed at once that these doves, his mother's favorite birds, had been sent for his guidance, and he entreated them to conduct him to the place where the
precious bough was growing. The doves, feeding and
flying by turns, advanced through the wood at such
a speed that Æneas could easily keep them in sight,
and presently, having reached the very edge of Lake
Avernus, both rose at once into the air, and settled on
a great tree of very dense foliage. The hero hastened
to the spot, and there indeed, on one of the lower
limbs of the tree, gleamed the bough, the rich yellow
lustre of its leaves and twigs contrasting vividly with
the deep green of the surrounding foliage. Æneas
with delight grasped it, and plucked it from its place,
and, bearing it carefully in his hand, hastened to rejoin his companions.

They, in the mean time, had reared on the shore a
vast pile of logs of pine and oak, the sides of which
they had interlaced with smaller boughs. After having
carefully washed and purified the body of Misenus,
they first made a couch upon the pyre, with the apparel of the dead man, and then, with renewed cries of
grief, placed the body upon it. His arms, too, they
laid beside him, and having poured incense and oil
abundantly upon the pile, they set it on fire. When only
smouldering embers were left, these were quenched
with wine, and the ashes of the dead were carefully
collected and placed in a brazen urn. This urn was

afterwards deposited in a lofty tomb which Æneas erected on a promontory that henceforth bore the name of Misenus.

The funeral ceremonies having thus duly been performed, the hero proceeded to the cave of the Sibyl, and called upon her to fulfill her promise, and accompany him to the kingdom of the dead. She led him to the mouth of the black cavern at the side of Lake Avernus, and there offered up sacrifices of black cattle and sheep, uttering various invocations. Presently the ground began to rumble beneath their feet; upon which the Sibyl ordered those of Æneas's followers who had attended him to withdraw from the spot, and exhorted the chief himself, drawing his sword from its sheath, to march firmly forward. So saying she plunged into the cave, nor did he hesitate to follow.

At first they moved along through a region that was utterly waste, void, and covered with an intense gloom, deep as that of a winter's night when the moon is obscured by clouds. But this desolate tract was not wholly untenanted, for Æneas saw flitting about certain hideous shadowy forms. The spirits of Grief and Revenge and pale Disease, Fear and Famine and deformed Indigence, had their abode in this vestibule of Hades; and so, too, Death and Toil, and murderous War, and frantic Discord, her head crowned with curling vipers and bound by a blood-dyed fillet. Here, also, were the iron chambers in which dwelt the terrible Furies. In the midst rose a gloomy elm, which was the haunt of vain Dreams, who dwelt under every leaf. Beyond this tree were many huge and misshapen monsters, —

Centaurs, and double-formed Scyllas, and the great dragon of the Lernæan lake, which, when it plagued the upper earth, was slain by Hercules. Here, also, was the huge Chimæra, with its three heads vomiting flames; Gorgons, Harpies, and other ghastly forms flitted about. At so fearful a sight Æneas was seized with sudden fear; he drew his sword, and would have struck at the monsters, if the Sibyl had not restrained his hand and reminded him that they were but disembodied shadows.

The path now led them to a place where the three infernal rivers, Acheron, Cocytus, and Styx, met in one deep, black, and boiling flood. Here there kept guard the grim ferryman Charon, an infernal deity of fearful aspect. A long gray beard fell all tangled and neglected from his chin; his filthy and ragged garments were knotted over his shoulders; his eyes glittered with baleful light. He sat on a great black barge, which he pushed to and fro across the river with a pole. An immense crowd of shades was incessantly pouring to the banks, — young and old, matrons and virgins, warriors who had endured the toils of a long life and tender boys who had died while yet under the care of their parents. All were eager to cross the stream, and stretched their hands in earnest entreaty to Charon to admit them into his boat. But the sullen ferryman only consented to receive some; others he drove back with his pole, and would on no account permit them to cross.

Æneas was amazed at this scene, and asked the Sibyl to explain to him its meaning. "You see before you," she replied, "the deep pools of Cocytus, and the Stygian lake, by which the Gods are accustomed to swear when they take an oath which they dare not violate. All that crowd which Charon will not ferry across is composed of persons who after death received not the rites of burial; those only are permitted to enter the boat who have been interred with proper ceremonies. As for the others, they wander unquiet about these shores for a hundred years before they are allowed to cross to the regions beyond."

When Æneas heard this he was filled with sadness, for among the spectres of the unburied who crowded on the bank he saw many of his own comrades who had perished during the storms he had had to encounter during his long voyages. As he looked, there advanced, slow and mournful, the pilot Palinurus, who had been thrown overboard by Somnus during the recent voyage from Sicily. The hero accosted him, and asked him what god had torn him from his post and overwhelmed him in the midst of the ocean. The oracle of Apollo, he said, had assured him that Palinurus would be safe on the sea, and would arrive on the Italian coast; and yet it would seem that the oracle had been falsified. The shade of Palinurus, knowing nothing of the enchantment which had been wrought on him by Somnus, replied that no god had destroyed him, and that the oracle had spoken truly. He had fallen into the sea through being overcome by slumber, and having kept afloat for three days and nights, had on the fourth day reached the Italian shore alive, but had been cruelly murdered by the savage people while clambering up the cliffs. Now his body was tossing on the waves, sometimes thrown on the shore and then washed off again. But he passionately entreated Æneas either to find his corpse and inter it with proper solemnities, or else to contrive some means of taking him as his companion across the black waters of Styx, unburied as he was, that at last his soul might find rest. The Sibyl, however, rebuked him for expressing so impious a desire, and for hoping that the fixed decrees of the Gods could be violated for the benefit of one insignificant mortal. But by way of consolation she informed him that the people of the country where he had met with his death, compelled by terrible plagues sent by Jupiter, would offer solemn atonement to his remains, erect a tomb to his memory, and give his name to the place where it stood.

Æneas and the Sibyl now advanced toward the river; but when Charon saw them approaching, he called out, "Whoever thou mayest be that art now coming armed and in life to our rivers, say quickly on what errand thou art coming. This is the region of ghosts and death; to waft over the bodies of the living in my boat is not permitted. Nor was it joyful to me to receive Hercules when he came, nor Theseus and Pirithous, though they were descendants of the Gods and unconquerable in war. Hercules dared to bind in chains Cerberus himself, the keeper of the gate of Tartarus, and dragged him trembling from the very throne of Pluto. The others attempted a feat scarcely less perilous, for they sought to carry off our queen Proserpine."

"Be not disturbed," answered the Sibyl; "we at least meditate no such plots, nor does this mortal bring with him his arms for any purpose of violence. He is Æneas of Troy, illustrious for piety and skill in arms, and he penetrates these gloomy abodes to have converse with his father Anchises. If your compassion is not moved by his filial devotion, at least pay regard to this branch." And so saying, she produced the golden bough. The surly ferryman, though filled with rage at being forced to obey, was at once silenced. He brought his boat to the bank, and silently received into it Æneas and his companion, driving back the ghosts that at the same time eagerly strove to enter the vessel. It was old and leaky, and sank deep in the black flood under the unaccustomed weight of living mortals; but Charon ferried them safely across, and landed them on the farther side, where, in a huge den at the gate of the infernal regions, lay Cerberus, the terrible three-headed dog which was the guardian of the place — a ferocious brute which only Hercules among living men had been able to subdue. When Æneas approached he opened his huge jaws and made all Hades resound with his barking; but the Sibyl threw to him a medicated cake, which he at once devoured, and was thereby lulled into profound sleep. The way was now safe; the Trojan chief and his companion passed quickly through the open gate, and entered the dread region where Minos and his fellow judges pronounced on the fate of each ghost that came before them.

The first place within the gate was assigned to the

shades of infants, cut off in the very beginning of life, who filled their allotted region with loud wailings and weeping. Beyond these were placed persons who had been put to death in consequence of false accusations. Not even the unjust suffering which such persons had endured on earth could at once procure for them a place among those happy spirits declared free of guilt. Here they were doomed to wait till the inexorable Minos examined each case and gave his award. Immediately adjoining was the place allotted to those who, though unstained by crime, had become weary of life and had committed self-destruction. Gladly, indeed, would they have now returned to the upper world they had despised, but no such return was possible to them.

Æneas and his companion next viewed a region named the Fields of Mourning, — a wide tract, with shady paths and thick myrtle groves, dedicated to those who had died through unrequited love, and were held to have been emancipated by the miseries they had endured on earth from suffering any punishment below. Here were to be seen, wandering disconsolately, many women of whom Æneas had heard in old legends of Greece and Troy. Among them he beheld, with sorrow and pity, the ill-starred Queen of Carthage, the wound she had herself inflicted yet gaping in her fair bosom. "Dido!" he exclaimed with tears, "was it then a true rumor that reached me of your having died after my departure, and by your own hand? If I have been the cause of your death, I am indeed unhappy. By all I hold sacred, fair queen, I swear to you that it was against my own will I quitted Carthage. The will of the Gods, which now has brought me, while yet living, into these melancholy realms, drove me from you; but I dreamt not that our separation would bring upon you such extreme suffering. Why will you not speak to me? Why do you fly from me? Never again will the Fates permit us to meet together."

But all his entreaties and his tears were vain. The spectre gazed upon him awhile with eyes of inexorable hate, and then turned away, with a gesture of unrelenting aversion, to a shady recess near by, where she was joined by the ghost of her first lord, Sichæus, who by the compassion of Pluto had been permitted to bear her company. Æneas resumed his journey, pondering sadly over the fate of the woman who but a little since had loved him so ardently and to whom he had unwillingly brought such misfortunes. He and his guide now came to a place dedicated to the shades of renowned warriors. Here he saw numbers of those brave Trojans, once his companions in arms, who had fallen before Troy. They eagerly crowded around him, pressed his hands, and questioned him as to the circumstances which had brought him, while yet alive, amongst them. There, too, were many Greeks who had perished during the Trojan war; but when they beheld the hero in the flesh, and wearing his gleaming armor, they fled from him in dismay. As he passed on, after exchanging affectionate words with many of his old comrades, he met Deiphobus, that son of Priam who, after the death of Paris, became the husband of Helen. The spectre of the prince was cruelly mutilated, — so that Æneas scarcely knew him. "Who, O Deiphobus," he exclaimed, "could have inflicted such shameful wounds upon you? After I had escaped from Troy a story was brought to me that you had indeed perished, but honorably and in fair fight, having slain many of the enemy. Then I erected in your honor an empty tomb on the shore under Mount Ida, and offered proper funeral rites, for your body I was unable to find."

"You, my friend," answered Deiphobus, "omitted no duty towards my corpse that you could perform. But I owe my death and these infamous wounds to the wickedness of Helen; they are the marks of her love. On the night after the fatal horse was brought into Troy, I was lying asleep in my chamber, enjoying needful repose. Then my faithless wife removed all the arms from my palace, and even took away my sword from the side of my couch. That done, she threw open the gates, and herself summoned her former husband, Menelaus, and he and Ulysses burst into my apartment and inflicted on me these wounds, for which I pray the Gods that they may be requited."

Æneas would have spent yet more time in conversing with the shades of his former comrades; but the Sibyl reminded him that the hour was approaching when he must return to the upper world. "Here," she said, "the path is divided. To the right, past the palace of Pluto, lies our way to the Elysian Fields; on the left is the way to Tartarus, the place of punishment for the wicked."

As they proceeded toward Elysium, Æneas looked around him, and beheld to the left a vast prison, en-

closed by mighty walls, at the foot of which ran Phlege-
thon, the river of fire, whirling along great rocks in its
furious current. Across the stream, just opposite to
where he was standing, was a lofty gate, with columns
of solid adamant. In an iron tower adjoining sat Tisi-
phone, the eldest of the Furies, watching the gate.
From within sounds were heard — groans of pain,
the sound of cruel lashes, and the clanking of chains.
Æneas asked his companion what punishments were
being inflicted within, and who were the sufferers.
"This," replied the Sibyl, "is Tartarus, whereinto no
righteous person can enter. Here Rhadamanthus pre-
sides: he searches into the deeds of all who are sent
hither, obliges them to confess all the crimes they have
committed in the upper world, and awards the punishment. As soon as the sentence is pronounced, Tisi-
phone scourges the doomed one with a whip of scor-
pions, and then consigns him to the fierce attendants
of her sister Furies. Immediately the gates, creaking
on their hinges, fly open. Within, the entrance is
guarded by a hideous Hydra, with fifty black and gaping
mouths. In the pit of Tartarus beyond, the giants who
waged war against the ruler of the Gods lie prostrated
by his thunderbolts. Beside them, enduring terrible
tortures, is Salmoneus. He was a king of Elis in Greece,
and was so puffed up by pride that he rode through his
city on a high chariot drawn by four prancing horses,
waving in his hand a torch, and pretending to be Jupiter himself, wielding his thunderbolts. The Almighty
Sire punished his impiety by hurling from Olympus
a real thunderbolt, which deprived him of life; and

now he pays the penalty of his mad pride by eternal
sufferings in Tartarus. There also lies Tityus, the huge
giant who, having insulted the goddess Latona, was
slain by the darts of her children, Apollo and Diana,
and whose writhing body now lies extended over
nine acres of ground, while insatiable vultures per-
petually prey on his vitals, that are renewed as fast
as they are devoured. Beyond him is Ixion, bound
to a wheel that never ceases to revolve, while he is
scourged by attendant Furies. He it was who, being
admitted to Olympus by the generosity of Jupiter himself, dared to seek the love of the queen of the Gods.
Not less dreadful is the punishment allotted to Pirithous, who, along with Theseus, endeavored to carry
off the Queen of Hades, Proserpine, from the side of
Pluto. Over his head hangs a huge rock, which every
moment seems about to fall and crush him, but yet
never actually descends; moreover, he is plagued with
a gnawing hunger, and a rich banquet is always before
him, which yet he is never able to reach. Myriads of
other unhappy shades, whose course on earth has
been stained by detestable crime, here expiate the evil
they have done; but had I a hundred mouths and a
hundred tongues, I could not recount all their offenses
and the varieties of their punishment. It is necessary
that we should go forward, since yonder stands the
palace of Pluto, where thou, O Æneas, must deposit
the bough which has gained thee admission here."

Obedient to his guide, Æneas advanced to the vast
portals of the palace where Pluto, the brother of Jupiter
and monarch of the infernal kingdom, had his abode

with his lovely queen Proserpine, the daughter of Ceres, whom ages before he had carried off from the upper world. There he made due reverence before the goddess, and deposited the golden bough at her feet. Advancing beyond, Æneas and the Sibyl came at last to the Elysian Fields, — the abode of joy assigned to those who during life had been distinguished for piety, virtue, and heroic actions. Here were lovely green fields and pleasant groves; the air was pure and balmy, the sky was blue, and all was glowing in the light of the blessed sun. Some of the happy spirits who dwelt in this region were amusing themselves by wrestling on the greensward, and other sports in which they had delighted on earth, such as chariot-racing, exercises with the spear and the bow. Others were dancing and singing to the delicious notes which Orpheus, the most skillful of musicians, produced from his lyre. On the bank of the river Eridanus, which pours its clear waters through Elysium over sands of gold, were gathered a band whose heads were adorned with snow-white fillets. These were priests who had kept unstained the purity and sanctity of their office; poets who had sung the praises of the Gods in immortal verse; and those who had made human life more happy by the invention of useful arts. Among them the Sibyl sought out Musæus, the father of the poets, and besought him to reveal in what retreat they should find Anchises, on whose account she and her companion had traversed all the regions of the shades.

"None of us," answered the venerable shade, "have here any fixed abode. We wander at our will among

the shady groves and by the pleasant banks of the
river. But if you mount with me this little eminence,
I will show you him whom you seek."

As he spoke, he led them to a spot where they could
survey all the shining plains around, and pointed to
where Anchises, reclined in a secluded vale, was surveying the souls of his descendants who were destined
in future times to visit the earth, and were enacting
beforehand the achievements they were fated to accomplish during life. As soon as he saw Æneas advancing
toward him, he rose with hands stretched out and
joyful tears pouring down his face.

"Are you indeed," he exclaimed, "come to me at
last, my son? Am I permitted once more to see your
face, and to listen to the tones of your dear voice?
Now indeed the hopes which I cherished are fulfilled.
By how many dangers have you been threatened since
we parted! I was filled with dread lest you should be
prevented from accomplishing your task by the temp-
tations which beset you at Carthage."

"Thy apparition, beloved father," answered Æneas,
"continually appearing to me in dreams, urged me
forward even to these regions. Permit me now to clasp
thee in my arms, and do not withdraw from my embrace." Thrice did he attempt to throw his arms about
the shade, which being only composed of thin air, was
not perceptible to his touch. While the two conversed
together, Æneas observed at no great distance from
them a stream, at which prodigious numbers of ghosts
were incessantly crowding to drink, swarming like bees
round their hive. Astonished at this spectacle, the hero

inquired of his father what that stream was, and why those spectres were so eager to drink of it. "These," answered Anchises, "are souls destined by fate to occupy other bodies in the upper world; and the stream is Lethe, one draught of which is sufficient to destroy all recollection of their former condition."

"But surely," said Æneas, "it is not to be believed that any souls which have tasted the delights of this abode will be desirous to return again to the life of earth, with its uncertainties and its miseries. How comes it that this impulse possesses them?"

In reply to this question, Anchises entered into a long explanation, the substance of which was that all the spirits of the departed had to endure in the regions below a process of expiation for their earthly sins, longer or shorter according to the nature of their transgressions. Those that were not consigned to the pains of Tartarus entered the Elysian Fields, where, after they had remained a thousand years, they were summoned to drink of the waters of Lethe, and thus lose all recollection of their former lives; after which, being purified from all stain, they were fitted to return to the upper world and inhabit new bodies. Anchises added that he would show to his son the forms of his own descendants in the Italian kingdom he was destined to establish, and would trace for him their achievements. Leading Æneas and the Sibyl onto a rising ground, in the midst of the souls which were crowding about the magic stream of Lethe, he pointed out to him a long array of future kings of Latium, — Silvius, who was to be the son of Æneas's old age by his consort

Lavinia; Procas, Capys, and Numitor, destined to be
monarchs of Alba Longa; and Romulus, the future
founder of the great city of Rome, which would extend
over seven hills, and would spread her dominion over
the whole earth. Not far from these were the souls
of Romulus's successors in the early days of Rome,
— Numa Pompilius, who first would give his country
laws, and encourage the arts of peace; Tullus Hostilius, who would wage victorious wars, and extend the
territories of Rome; Ancus Martius, not less success-
ful in the field; and Tarquin, destined to lose the throne
through his oppressive reign. Anchises proceeded to
indicate to his wondering son many of the patriots
and generals who in future years were to contribute
to the glory and power of the Roman State, — more
especially the great Julius Cæsar, the lineal descendant
of Æneas himself; and Augustus, who would once more
establish the golden age in Latium, and whose empire
would extend to countries as yet unknown. The venerable shade concluded his forecast of the future with a
splendid description of the part which Rome was destined to play in the world's history: —

> "Let others better mould the running mass
> Of metals, and inform the breathing brass,
> And soften into flesh a marble face;
> Plead better at the bar; describes the skies,
> And when the stars descend, and when they rise:
> But Rome! 't is thine alone, with awful sway
> To rule mankind, and make the world obey,
> Disposing peace and war thy own majestic way;
> To tame the proud, the fettered slave to free, —
> These are imperial arts, and worthy thee."

Having thus inspired Æneas with renewed determination by showing him the brilliant future that was awaiting his descendants, Anchises conducted him over those parts of the Elysian Fields which he had not yet visited, and showed him everything that was of peculiar interest. As they went, he discoursed to him respecting the wars which he would have to wage in Latium, and gave him counsel as to the means by which he should overcome every difficulty. Then at last, having brought him to the ivory gate whence the gods were accustomed to send false dreams to the upper world, he bade him farewell. By that gate Æneas and the Sibyl quitted the abodes of the dead, and ascended without difficulty or adventure to the cave of the oracle, whence the hero hastened at once to his ships. Without loss of time he ordered the sails to be spread, and the ships were steered along the coast, drawing nearer ever hour to their final destination.

ÆNEAS'S FIRST GREAT BATTLE WITH THE LATINS

By Charles Henry Hanson

[Æneas finally lands in Italy, the country promised him by the Gods as a home for his race. The Italian king, Latinus, has been warned by signs and omens that the hand of his daughter Lavinia must not be given to an Italian prince, but to a stranger coming from a far country. He believes that Æneas is the hero chosen by the Fates as her husband, and greets him in most friendly manner. Queen Amata, however, is influenced by the Trojan-hating Juno to oppose this marriage. Turnus, chief of the Rutuli, a suitor of Lavinia, is next aroused, and soon the whole kingdom is in a turmoil. A fierce battle ensues.]

TURNUS, having brought the bulk of his forces from before the beseiged camp, hurled them against the army of Æneas before its ranks were properly formed, and a furious conflict at once began to rage. The Trojan hero, rejoicing to find himself once more on a field of battle, first encountered the Latian warriors, who chanced to be in his front. Their leader was Theron, a man of gigantic stature, who did not hesitate to engage Æneas hand to hand; but he paid dearly for his rashness, for the sword which Vulcan had forged —

so keen was its edge, so excellent its temper — pierced through his brazen buckler and his tunic stiffened by bars of gold, and penetrating his side, drained the life-blood. Next the hero struck down Lycas; and rushing onward, encountered two stalwart rustics, Cisseus and Gyas, who were making havoc among the Trojans by beating them down with ponderous clubs. On the divine armor the heavy blows of these rude weapons fell harmless, while the spear of Æneas proved fatal to both those who wielded them. An insolent warrior named Pharus was defying the hero from a short distance with taunting speech, when he hurled a javelin, which struck the boaster full in the mouth, and transfixing the throat, silenced him forever. Now a band of seven brothers, the sons of Phorcus, all at once attacked Æneas with darts, throwing them together. Some of the weapons struck his helmet and shield, and rebounded; others, turned aside by the care of Venus, grazed his skin. Æneas called to Achates to bring him more spears, and snatching one as soon as it was offered, hurled it against Mæon, one of the brothers, with such force that it penetrated his shield and corselet, and inflicted a mortal wound in his breast. Another brother, Alcanor, hurrying up to Mæon's assistance, he smote with a second spear, just where the arm and shoulder join, leaving the arm hanging to the body only by two or three shreds of skin and muscle. Seeing the slaughter that Æneas was spreading around him, Halæsus and Messapus hurried up with their bands to confront him, and so in that part of the field the battle grew still more furious.

BATTLE WITH THE LATINS

In another part, where Pallas was fighting at the head of his Arcadian horsemen, the ground had been rendered so uneven by the winter torrents that they were obliged to dismount, and being unaccustomed to fight on foot, they began to retreat before the fierce assault of the Rutulians. At this sight their brave young leader was overwhelmed with shame and mortification. "Whither," he cried, "my fellow countrymen, do you fly? I implore you, by the memory of your gallant deeds in the past, by the name of Evander, the king you love, by my own hopes of glory, not to flee. Your way lies through your foes, not from them; with your swords must you cut a passage where they crowd most densely. These are not gods who pursue us; they are mortals, like ourselves, and they are not stronger or more numerous than we. The ocean hems us in with an impassable barrier on the one side; the enemy confronts us on the other, and separates us from our friends. Whether shall we fly into the sea, or force our way toward the Trojans?" So saying, he turned, and dashed into the midst of the hostile ranks. Tagus was the first who fell a victim to his noble wrath; for as he was stooping to pick up a heavy stone, the spear of Pallas struck him in the middle of the back, and shattered the spine and ribs. As the young hero was withdrawing the weapon, Hisbon rushed on and struck at him from above; but the blow fell short, and before he could recover his guard Pallas buried his sword deep in his body. Warrior after warrior he struck down, restored the confidence of his followers, and spread confusion and dismay in the opposite ranks, raging among them as the flames lit by the husbandman in the autumn spread through the stubble, and destroy everything in their path. But now the Auruncian chief, Halæsus, summoned by some of his followers to their aid, opposed the advance of the Arcadians. He was a tried and fierce warrior, and he slew five of the bravest of Pallas's men before the young chief could confront him. Then, however, the son of Evander hurled a spear with such skill and certainty of aim that he pierced Halæsus's heart, and the grim leader of the Aurunci sank lifeless on the field. His fall was a sore discouragement to the troops of Turnus, which would have sought safety in flight, had not Lausus, the gallant son of Mezentius, — noble and upright offspring of an unworthy father, — suddenly come to their aid. First encountering Abas, leader of the Populonians, he slew him with a single blow of his sword, and followed up his success with a furious slaughter of Arcadians and Etrurians. Thus the battle continued: on the one side Pallas impetuously urged the attack; on the other Lausus not less obstinately maintained the defense. They were equal in years, and in beauty and grace of form; and to both alike the Fates had assigned a place among the victims of the war. But the Gods had ordained that they should not encounter hand to hand; each was destined to succumb to a superior foe.

Turnus was leading his troops in another quarter of the field, when he was summoned to hasten to the assistance of Lausus, who alone was bearing up the battle againt Pallas and his Arcadians. Quickly he turned his chariot in that direction, and as soon as he

reached the spot, called on his warriors to withdraw
from the conflict. "I alone," he said, "will encounter
Pallas; to me his life is given. Would to Heaven his
father were here to witness our combat." The Rutulians obeyed the command of their king, and fell back;
while Pallas, amazed at their retreat and the sudden
appearance of Turnus, gazed on his opponent. Then,
in reply to his vaunting speech, he said, "Now, either
by carrying off thy spoils or by a noble death at thy
hands, I shall be rendered famous. My sire knows how
to bear either extremity of fortune. Cease thy threaten-
ings and let us engage." As he spoke, the hearts of the
Arcadians, who loved him, were filled with fear and
sorrow. Turnus sprang from his chariot, and came
forward to the encounter on foot, advancing as a lion
bounds toward his prey. As soon as Pallas thought
him within reach of his spear, he prepared to throw it,
and uttered this prayer to Hercules: "By my father's
hospitality, and that abode which thou, his guest,
didst visit, O Alcides, aid, I implore thee, my arduous
attempt. May the dying eyes of Turnus behold me
strip him, expiring, of his bloody armor, and endure the
sight of a victorious foe." Hercules, from his place
on Olympus, heard the prayer, and knowing that the
decree of Fate was otherwise, answered with heavy
groans and unavailing tears. These were not unseen
by Jupiter, who strove to console his immortal son.
"To every one," he said, "his day is fixed; a short and
irretrievable term of life is given to all; but to lengthen
out fame by heroic deeds is the best that man can do.
Under the lofty walls of Troy many sons of gods them-

selves perished, — among them the heroic Sarpedon, my own offspring, perished; Turnus, too, is summoned by the Fates, and has nearly reached his term of life." He spoke, and turned away his gaze from the battle-field, himself pitying the untimely death of Pallas.

And now the brave son of Evander with his utmost force hurled his spear, and then hastened to draw his sword from its scabbard. The weapon struck Turnus where the shoulder was protected by the corselet, and piercing through the solid brass, slightly grazed the hero's body. Then Turnus, poising a steel-tipped javelin, darted it at Pallas, exclaiming, "See whether mine be not the more penetrating shaft." Cast with irresistible might, it tore its way through the youth's shield, composed though it was of thick plates of brass and iron, and through his cuirass, and inflicted a ghastly wound in his breast. In vain he wrenched out the deadly missile from his body; even as he withdrew it life deserted his quivering form, and he fell to the ground. Bestriding the corpse, Turnus cried, "Ye Arcadians, faithfully report to Evander this message, — I send him back his Pallas in such a plight as he deserved. Whatever honor is in a tomb, whatever solace in the performance of funeral rites, I freely grant him. His league with the Trojan intruder shall cost him dear." So saying, he pressed his foot on the body, and tore away a massive belt, adorned with figures richly carved in gold. This spoil Turnus exultingly clasped around his own body, little dreaming that the time would come when he would wish that he had never taken it, and that he and Pallas had never met. But now the lifeless corpse of the youth, stripped of its arms and still bleeding from the fatal wound inflicted by the Rutulian chief, was laid on a shield and borne away by his weeping followers. Thus the first day on which he took a part in war saw also the young hero's death, though not, indeed, before he had strewn the plain with Rutulian corpses.

Speedily the news of this sad disaster, and of the consequent retreat of his forces in that part of the field, was borne to Æneas. Rendered furious by the event, he impetuously mowed with his sword a bloody passage through the hostile ranks in search of Turnus, on whom he was eager to avenge the death of his friend. The thought of the bright youth who had thus perished in his cause, of the hoary father bereaved of all that made life dear to him, filled his heart with sorrow as he recalled the kindness which both had shown to him, and the pledges of enduring friendship he had exchanged with them. Eight Rutulian warriors he struck down, and captured them alive, destining them as victims to be offered to the shade of Pallas, and to drench with their blood the flames of the hero's funeral pyre. Next, Æneas having hurled a javelin at a Latian named Magus, the trembling wretch evaded the dart by stooping, and as Æneas rushed upon him with uplifted sword, he clasped his knees, and implored him to spare his life, proffering a large ransom of silver and gold which lay concealed underground in his house. Sternly the Trojan chief bade him keep his treasures for his sons; as for showing mercy, that was forbidden to him from the moment that Pallas fell by the hand of Turnus. Then grasping the suppliant's helmet, and forcing back his head so as to expose the neck, even as Magus renewed his petition he plunged the sword into his body to the hilt. Near by, the luckless Æmonides, a priest of Apollo and Diana, who wore a sacred fillet on his temples and shone in burnished armor, fell a victim to his relentless spear, and the splendid arms he had worn were carried off by Serestus as an offering to Mars. The Rutulians fled in terror before the raging chief; but King Cæculus of Præneste, and Umbro, the leader of the Marsians, renewed the struggle. A huge warrior named Tarquitus, the son of the nymph Dryope, dared to oppose himself to Æneas, but his fate was soon decided. The hero first pierced his corselet with a spear, and then, as he lay wounded and imploring mercy, smote off his head with his sword. Spurning the bleeding trunk, he furiously cried, "Lie there, haughty champion! Thee no tender mother shall lodge in the earth, or place a tomb above thy body; to birds of prey thou shalt be left, or cast in the sea to be devoured by fishes." Still insatiable of slaughter, he drove into terrified flight Antæus and Lycas, two of Turnus's bravest followers. But now the fierce Lucagus approached in a chariot drawn by two snow-white coursers. These were guided by his brother Liger, while he himself flourished his sword in the air, and prepared to encounter Æneas, who on his part rushed forward to meet them. "These," cried Liger, "are not the steeds of Diomedes, nor this the plain of Troy. Here an end shall be put at once to thy life and to the war." Against these insults Æneas prepared to give an answer otherwise than in words, and as

Lucagus bent forward in readiness for the fight, the Trojan javelin whizzed through the rim of his shield, smote him in the groin, and hurled him, quivering in the pangs of death, out of the chariot. Æneas assailed his dying ears with a bitter scoff: "It is not, O Lucagus, the slowness of thy steeds in flight that hath lost thee thy chariot, but thou thyself, springing from thy seat, hast abandoned it." So saying, he seized the chariot; and now the miserable Liger, extending his hands in supplication, begged for his life. "It was not in this fashion that thou spokest a little while since," replied the relentless hero. "It would not be fitting that thou shouldst desert thy brother. Die, therefore, and attend him to the shades." With that he thrust the avenging sword through his heart, whence the trembling soul fled with a shriek.

So Æneas spread havoc amid the hostile ranks, and drove the forces of Turnus back in headlong rout, so that Ascanius and those who had hitherto been shut up in the fortifications were able to issue forth into the field. Meanwhile Jupiter, watching from Olympus the fortunes of the day, accosted his consort. "Thou art in the right, my cherished queen, in alleging that Venus gives her aid to the Trojans; for without divine aid, how would it be possible for any mortal to achieve such deeds as Æneas is now accomplishing?" "Why," submissively answered Juno, "dost thou tease me, who am already oppressed with anguish for the fate of the people I befriend? Had I that share in your love which I once enjoyed, and which it is fitting for me to possess, thou surely couldst not refuse me this much, that I might have permission to rescue Turnus from the fate that threatens him, and restore him safe to his father Daunus. But since that cannot be, let him die, and glut the vengeance of the Trojan with his blood; yet his origin is divine, and often has he piled thy altars with sacrifices." Not unmoved, the ruler of the Gods replied, "If you plead for a respite from immediate death, and a little breathing-time for the youth, I grant you to bear him from the field, and for a short time to preserve him. So far I will indulge you; but if you hope to gain any greater favor, and imagine that the whole predetermined course of the war is to be altered at your entreaty, you delude yourself with empty hopes." With tears Juno responded, "What if thou shouldst grant in thy heart what in words thou dost refuse, and continue the life of Turnus for its natural duration? I fear much that a speedy end awaits the brave youth; but oh! I pray that I may be misled by groundless alarms, and that thou, to whom all power belongs, may alter thy purpose for the better."

Not daring to say more, the queen of heaven hastily descended from Olympus towards the contending armies. Then she devised an airy phantom, wearing armor which exactly resembled that of Æneas, and imitating to the life his walk and mien. This shadow she caused to flutter in the forefront of the battle, full in the view of Turnus, and to provoke him with darts and insolent words. The enraged Rutulian eagerly pressed upon it, and from a distance hurled against it a spear. Immediately the spectre, wheeling about, took to flight. Turnus, imagining that in very truth it was the Trojan chief who feared to meet him, and filled with baseless exultation, cried out, "Æneas, whither dost thou fly? Desert not thus thy promised bride; with this right hand will I bestow upon thee the settled abode thou hast sought in vain through so many lands and seas." Thus vociferating, he madly pursued the deceitful phantom. It chanced that near the shore there lay a vessel, joined to the land by a temporary bridge of planks. Hither Juno led the shadow, and caused it in seeming fear to leap on board and throw itself into a hiding-place. With not less speed Turnus followed, bounded along the bridge, and mounted to the lofty prow of the ship in search of the supposed fugitive. Instantly the goddess severed the cable, and drove the vessel over the foaming waves. Then the phantom melted into the air, and the Rutulian, utterly bewildered, gazed about him in despair, nor did he feel at all thankful to the guardian deity for having thus preserved him from the arms of Æneas.

"Almighty Father," he cried, raising his eyes and hands towards heaven, "why dost thou think me worthy of such shame as this? What have I done to merit such a punishment? whither am I borne? How shall I venture again to enter the walls of Laurentum or look upon my camp? What will be said of me by the warriors who have followed me into this war, and whom — unutterable shame! — I have abandoned to the bloodthirsty Trojans! O winds! take pity on me, I entreat you; dash this vessel on some rugged crag, and overwhelm me so that I can no longer be conscious either of my humiliation or of the reproaches of my Rutulians." While he thus lamented, he was uncertain whether he should put an end to his own life with his sword or plunge into the sea and endeavor to regain the land by swimming. Three times he attempted each expedient, and as often Juno, full of pity, restrained him. Carried along by a favorable wind, the ship bore him safely to the capital of his father, King Daunus.

Meanwhile Æneas raged through the battle-field in search of the victim whom the queen of the Gods had thus snatched from his conquering hands. Under his leadership the Trojans and their allies, flushed with success, pressed more eagerly on their discomfited foe; but Mezentius now advanced to restore the courage of the Rutulians. The Etrurians, as soon as they saw their expelled monarch, out of hostility to whom they had engaged in the war, rushed upon him with shouts of rage; but he, as fearless as he was wicked, stood as firmly against them as a great rock on the shore meets all the fury of the winds and waves. Three warriors he overthrew in quick succession: Hebrus he cut down with his sword, Latagus he slew by hurling a great stone which battered in his face, and at Palmus he threw a javelin which pierced his thigh and extended him helpless on the ground. Then the raging king slew Evas the Phrygian, and a Trojan named Mimas, who in former days had been the companion of Paris, having been born in Troy on the same night that gave to the light the ill-starred son of Priam. Paris now lay in eternal repose amid the ruins of his native city, while to Mimas the sword of Mezentius assigned an unknown grave on the distant shore of Italy. And just as when an old wild boar, chased from his retreat amid the wooded Alps, stands at bay among the underwood, and the hunters, afraid to approach him, ply him with darts from a distance, while he gnashes his tusks with rage and faces them undaunted, so stood Mezentius; while his former subjects, though filled with just anger against him, and eager for his destruction, dare not come within reach of his dreaded sword, but galled him with spears and useless clamor. It chanced that a Greek from Corytus, named Acron, presented himself in the front, conspicuous in nodding plumes, and in purple trappings that had been worked for him by his betrothed wife. His gay attire caught the eye of Mezentius, who rushed forward and smote down the luckless Greek; then, as the others fell back, he cut off the retreat of an Etrurian chief, Orodes, forced him to engage hand to hand, and speedily slew him. Pressing his foot on the expiring warrior to draw out his lance from his body, Mezentius cried to his followers, "Behold, friends! Orodes has fallen — not the meanest of our foes." The Rutulians raised a joyful shout, but the dying Orodes faintly answered, "Not long shalt thou rejoice with impunity over me; a similar fate awaits thyself, and soon shalt thou also be stretched lifeless on this same field." Smiling scornfully, Mezentius returned, "Die thou, and leave my fate to the Gods, in whose hands it rests." His example inspired other of the Rutulians; they pressed fiercely forward and drove back the troops of Æneas. Mezentius advanced at their head, and as he strode along, the

Trojan hero espied him, and hastened towards him. Un-
awed by the prospect of an encounter even with so
terrible a foe, Mezentius stood firm, and poising a huge
spear in his hand, exclaimed, — for he was a contemner
of the Gods, and never offered invocations to them, —
"Now let this right hand and this good dart be my aid;
and then I vow that my son, my dear Lausus, shall
be clad in the bright arms torn from the body of yon
Trojan pirate." With these words he drew the spear.
Sent with a true aim, it struck the shield of Æneas,
but glanced from the hardened surface, and turning
aside, pierced the side of Antores, a faithful follower
of Evander, who had come with Pallas to the war.
Thus died Antores, by a weapon never aimed at him,
but he was speedily avenged. Æneas, putting all his
might into the cast, now in his turn hurled his spear.
It tore its way through the triple plates of Mezentius'
shield, through his corselet, and inflicted a severe
wound in his groin, though its force was so far spent
that the injury was not mortal.

Overjoyed at the sight of his enemy's blood, Æneas
drew his sword from its sheath, and rushed upon Mezentius, who was as yet bewildered by the blow. When
Lausus saw his father in such peril he sprang forward
and stood before Æneas, while Mezentius fell back
among his friends, the Trojan lance still trailing in his
armor. Lausus received the first stroke of Æneas' sword
on his buckler, while the Rutulians with loud shouts
applauded him, and poured on the Trojan hero a tempest of darts. Against this he protected himself with
his shield, and meanwhile, pitying the youth and courage

of Lausus, spoke to him in words of warning: "Why do you thus rush on your own destruction, and attempt what is beyond your strength? Your filial devotion blinds you to your danger." But Lausus, resolute to defend his wounded sire, returned a haughty defiance. Then Æneas could no longer control his wrath; he exerted all his strength, and thrust his terrible sword up to the hilt through the body of the youth, who sank lifeless on the blood-steeped ground. When Æneas saw the comely young warrior stretched dead before him, his heart was filled with pity. "Ill-fated youth!" he cried, "how can I testify my reverence for thy filial piety and thy undaunted valor? Thou shalt at least retain those arms which it was thy delight to wear, and thy body shall be given up unspoiled to thy friends." With that he summoned the dismayed followers of Lausus, and with his own hands raised from the ground the comely body, all disfigured with blood and wounds.

Meantime Mezentius had retreated to the bank of the Tiber, where he took off his armor, and bathed his wound with water. While he was thus resting from the fatigues of the battle, he was full of anxiety for his son, and sent messenger after messenger to recall him from the fight. But too soon a crowd of weeping warriors appeared, carrying the corpse of Lausus in their arms. The sorrowing father divined what had occurred from their lamentations, even before the body was brought to him. He threw dust upon his head, he clasped the loved form in his arms, and bedewed the pallid face with his tears. "O my son," he exclaimed, "was I possessed with such a fond desire of life as to suffer thee to offer thyself in my place to the relentless foe? Am I preserved at the cost of these cruel wounds? Now, indeed, I feel the calamity of exile. My crimes have cost thee not only thy paternal throne and sceptre, but thy life also. It was I that owed expiation to my country, and should have satisfied my people by a deserved death. And yet I live! yet I do not quit the detested light! but I will quickly follow thee." Then he rose up, and though crippled by the wound in his thigh, and suffering anguish from its smart, he did not flinch, but ordered his attendants to bring his courser. This was a horse famous for its speed and its prompt obedience to the rein. When it was brought, he accosted it: "Long have we lived together, Rhœbus, and many great deeds have we accomplished. To-day we shall either bear away the head of Æneas and his arms all spattered with his blood, or we shall perish together; for I am assured that thou wilt never condescend to bear a Trojan lord." Then mounting the noble steed, he filled both hands with darts, and dashed recklessly into the midst of the battle. His heart swelling with rage and shame and grief, he thrice loudly summoned Æneas to the combat. Æneas heard, and rejoiced at the challenge; and with threatening spear advanced to meet his foe. "Barbarous wretch," cried Mezentius, "thinkest thou to affright me with thy weapons, now that thou hast robbed me of my son? That was the only means by which thou couldst destroy me. I fear neither death nor the anger of any of your gods. Forbear threats; now am I come hither to die, but first I bring you these gifts." So saying, he rapidly hurled

480

one dart after another at the hero, whirling swiftly round him on his horse; but the shield framed by Vulcan's hands received all the shafts and repelled them. Wearied at last of so unequal a fight, in which he had to endure ceaseless attacks without striking a blow, Æneas stepped forward, and hurled his spear against the charger, piercing its skull betwixt the ears. The fiery horse reared upward in the death agony, and then fell backward upon his rider, pressing him to the earth. The spectators of this fierce combat uplifted their voices in shouts, some in joy and others in sorrow, as Æneas rushed up to the fallen warrior, and lifting his sword to deal the fatal blow, cried, "Where is now the stern Mezentius?" The Etrurian, on the other hand, replied, "Spiteful foe, why dost thou threaten and insult before thou strikest? Thou wilt do me no wrong in slaying me. I sought thee expecting nothing else, and neither I nor my son has asked mercy at thy hands. One favor alone I implore of thee, that thou wilt give burial to my corpse. I know well that the hate of my former subjects would pursue me after death. Defend my remains, I entreat, from outrage, and grant me a grave along with my son." He said no more, but extended his throat to receive the fatal blow, which descended and drew forth his life as the blood poured over his armor.

The shades of night were now gathering, and as the Rutulians and Latins had quitted the field in confusion, the conflicts of that sanguinary day were at last ended.

ÆNEAS FINALLY CONQUERS THE LATINS

By Alfred J. Church

PRINCE TURNUS was filled with rage. Even as a lion which a hunter hath wounded breaketh the arrow wherewith he hath been stricken, and rouseth himself to battle, shaking his mane and roaring, so Turnus arose. And first he spake to King Latinus, saying, "I will meet this man face to face, and slay him while ye look on; or, if the Gods will that he vanquish me so, he shall rule over you, and have Lavinia to wife."

But King Latinus made answer, "Yet think awhile, my son. Thou hast the kingdom of thy father Daunus; and there are other noble virgins in Latium whom thou mayest have to wife. Wilt thou not then be content? For to give my daughter to any husband of this nation I was forbidden, as thou knowest. Yet did I disobey, being moved by love of thee, my wife also beseeching me with many tears. Thou seest what troubles I and my people, and thou more than all, have suffered from that time. Twice have we fled in the battle, and now the city only is left to us. If I must yield me to these men, let me yield whilst thou art yet alive. For what doth it profit me that thou shouldst die? Nay, but all men would cry shame on me if I gave thee to death!"

CONQUEST OF THE LATINS

Now for a space Turnus spake not for wrath. Then he said, "Be not troubled for me, my father. For I, too, can smite with the spear; and as for this Æneas, his mother will not be at hand to snatch him in a cloud from my sight."

Then Amata cried to him, saying, "Fight not, I beseech thee, with these men of Troy, my son; for surely what thou sufferest I also shall suffer. Nor will I live to see Æneas my son-in-law."

And Lavinia heard the voice of her mother, and wept. As a man stains ivory with crimson, or as roses are seen mixed with lilies, even so the virgin's face burned with crimson. And Turnus, regarding her, loved her exceedingly, and made answer, "Trouble me not with tears or idle words, my mother, for to this battle I must go. And do thou, Idmon the herald, say to the Phrygian king, 'To-morrow, when the sun shall rise, let the people have peace, but we two will fight together. And let him that prevaileth have Lavinia to wife.'"

Then first he went to the stalls of his horses. The wife of the North Wind gave them to Pilumnus. Whiter than snow were they, and swifter than the wind. Then he put the coat of mail about his shoulders, and fitted a helmet on his head, and took the great sword which Vulcan had made for Daunus his father, and had dipped it when it was white-hot in the river of Styx. His spear also he took where it stood against a pillar, saying, "Serve me well, my spear, that hast never failed me before, that I may lay low this womanish robber of Phrygia, and soil with dust his curled and perfumed hair."

The next day the men of Italy and the men of Troy measured out a space for the battle. And in the midst they builded an altar of turf. And the two armies sat on the one side and on the other, having fixed their spears in the earth and laid down their shields. Also the women and the old men stood on the towers and roofs of the city, that they might see the fight.

But Queen Juno spake to Juturna, the sister of Turnus, saying, "Seest thou how these two are now about to fight, face to face? And indeed Turnus goeth to his death. As for me, I endure not to look upon this covenant or this battle. But if thou canst do aught for thy brother, lo! the time is at hand." And when the nymph wept and beat her breast, Juno said, "This is no time for tears. Save thy brother, if thou canst, from death; or cause that they break this covenant."

After this came the kings, that they might make the covenant together. And King Latinus rode in a chariot with four horses, and he had on his head a crown with twelve rays of gold, for he was of the race of the sun; and Turnus came in a chariot with two white horses, having a javelin in either hand; and Æneas had donned the arms which Vulcan had made, and with him was the young Iulus. And after due offering Æneas sware, calling on all the Gods, "If the victory shall fall this day to Turnus, the men of Troy shall depart to the city of Evander, nor trouble this land any more. But if it fall to me, I will not that the Latins should serve the men of Troy. Let the nations be equal one with the other. The gods that I bring we will worship together, but King Latinus shall reign as before. A new city shall the men of Troy build for me, and Lavinia shall call it after her own name."

Then King Latinus sware, calling on the gods that are above and the gods that are below, saying, "This covenant shall stand forever, whatsoever may befall. As sure as this sceptre which I bear — once it was a tree, but a cunning workman closed it in bronze, to be the glory of the Latian kings — shall never again bear twig or leaf, so surely shall this covenant be kept."

But the thing pleased not the Latins; for before, indeed, they judged that the battle would not be equal between two; and now were they the more assured, seeing them when they came together, and that Turnus walked with eyes cast to the ground, and was pale and wan. Wherefore there arose a murmuring among the people, which when Juturna perceived, she took upon herself the likeness of Camertus, who was a prince and a great warrior among them, and passed through the host saying, "Are ye not ashamed, men of Italy, that one man should do battle for you all? For count these men; surely they are scarce one against two. And if he be vanquished, what shame for you! As for him, indeed, though he die, yet shall his glory reach to the heavens; but ye shall suffer disgrace, serving these strangers forever."

And when she saw that the people were moved, she gave also a sign from heaven. For lo! an eagle, that drave a crowd of sea-fowl before him, swooped down to the water, and caught a great swan; and even while the Italians looked, the birds that before had fled turned and pursued the eagle, and drave him before them, so that he dropped the swan and fled away. Which thing when the Italians perceived they shouted, and made them ready for battle. And the augur Tolumnius cried, "This is the token that I have looked for. For this eagle is the stranger, and ye are the birds, which before, indeed, have fled, but shall now make him to flee."

And he ran forward and cast his spear, smiting a man of Arcadia below the belt, upon the groin. One of nine brothers was he, sons of a Tuscan mother, but their father was a Greek; and they, when they saw him slain, caught swords and spears, and ran forward. And straightway the battle was begun. First they brake down the altars, that they might take firebrands therefrom; and King Latinus fled from the place. Then did Messapus drive his horses against King Aulestes of Mantua, who, being fain to fly, stumbled upon the altar and fell headlong on the ground. And Messapus smote him with a spear that was like a weaver's beam, saying, "This, of a truth, is a worthier victim." After this Coryneus, the Arcadian, when Ebysus would have smitten him, snatched a brand from the altar and set fire to the beard of the man, and, before he came to himself, caught him by the hair, and thrusting him to the ground, so slew him. And when Podalirius pursued Alsus the shepherd, and now held his sword over him ready to strike, the other turned, and with a battle-axe cleft the man's head from forehead to chin.

But all the while the righteous Æneas, having his head bare, and holding neither spear nor sword, cried to the people, "What seek ye? what madness is this? The covenant is established, and I only have the right to do battle." But even while he spake an arrow smote him, wounding him. But who let it fly no man knoweth; for who, of a truth, would boast that he had wounded Æneas? And he departed from the battle.

Now when Turnus saw that Æneas had departed from the battle he called for his chariot. And when he had mounted thereon he drave it through the host of the enemy, slaying many valiant heroes, as Sthenelus and Pholus, and the two sons of Imbrasus the Lycian, Glaucus and Lades. Then he saw Eumedes, son of that Dolon who would have spied out the camp of the Greeks, asking as his reward the horses of Achilles (but Diomed slew him). Him Turnus smote with a javelin from afar, and, when he fell, came near and put his foot upon him, and taking his sword drave it into his neck, saying, "Lo! now thou hast the land which thou soughtest. Lie there and measure out Italy for thyself." Many others he slew, for the army fled before him. Yet did one man, Phegeus by name, stand against him, and would have stayed the chariot, clutching the bridles of the horses in his hand. But as he clung to the yoke and was dragged along, Turnus broke his cuirass with his spear, and wounded him. And when the man set his shield before him, and made at Turnus with his sword, the wheels dashed him to the ground, and Turnus struck him between the helmet and the breastplate and smote off his head.

But in the meanwhile Mnestheus and Achates and Iulus led Æneas to the camp, leaning on his spear.

Very wroth was he, and strove to draw forth the arrow. And when he could not, he commanded that they should open the wound with the knife, and so send him back to the battle. Iapis also, the physician, ministered to him. Now this Iapis was dearer than all other men to Apollo, and when the god would have given him all his arts, even prophecy and music and archery, he chose rather to know the virtues of herbs and the art of healing, that so he might prolong the life of his father, who was even ready to die. This Iapis, then, having his garments girt about him in healer's fashion, would have drawn forth the arrow with the pincers, but could not. And while he strove, the battle came nearer, and the sky was hidden by clouds of dust, and javelins fell thick into the camp. But when Venus saw how grievously her son was troubled, she brought from Ida, which is a mountain of Crete, the herb dittany. A hairy stalk it hath and a purple flower. The wild goats know it well if so be that they have been wounded by arrows. This, then, Venus, having hidden her face, brought and dipped into the water, and sprinkled there with ambrosia and sweet-smelling panacea.

And Iapis, unawares, applied the water that had been healed; and lo! the pain was stayed and the blood was staunched and the arrow came forth, though no man drew it, and Æneas's strength came back to him as before. Then said Iapis, "Art of mine hath not healed thee, my son. The Gods call thee to thy work." Then did Æneas arm himself again, and when he had kissed Iulus and bidden him farewell, he went forth to the battle. And all the chiefs went with him, and the men

488

of Troy took courage and drave back the Latins. Then befell a great slaughter, for Gyas slew Ufens, who was the leader of the Æquians; also Tolumnius, the great augur, was slain, who had first broken the covenant, slaying a man with his spear. But Æneas deigned not to turn his hand against any man, seeking only for Turnus, that he might fight with him. But when the nymph Juturna perceived this she was sore afraid. Therefore she came near to the chariot of her brother, and thrust out Metiscus, his charioteer, where he held the reins, and herself stood in his room, having made herself like to him in shape and voice. Then as a swallow flies through the halls and arcades of some rich man's house, seeking food for its young, so Juturna drave the chariot of her brother hither and thither. And ever Æneas followed behind, and called to him that he should stay; but whenever he espied the man, and would have overtaken him by running, then again did Juturna turn the horses about and flee. And as he sped Messapus cast a spear at him. But Æneas saw it coming, and put his shield over him, resting on his knee. Yet did the spear smite him on the helmet-top and shear off the crest. Then indeed was his wrath kindled, and he rushed into the army of the enemy, slaying many as he went.

Then was there a great slaughter made on this side and on that. But after a while Venus put it into the heart of Æneas that he should lead his army against the city. Therefore he called together the chiefs, and, standing in the midst of them on a mound, spake, saying, "Hearken now to my words, and delay not to fulfill them, for of a truth Jupiter is on our side. I am purposed this day to lay this city of Latinus even with the ground, if they still refuse to obey. For why should I wait for Turnus till it please him to meet me in battle?"

Then did the whole array make for the walls of the city. And some carried firebrands, and some scaling-ladders, and some slew the warders at the gates, and cast javelins at them who stood on the walls. And then there arose a great strife in the city, for some would have opened the gates that the men of Troy might enter, and others made haste to defend the walls. Hither and thither did they run with much tumult, even as bees in a hive in a rock which a shepherd hath filled with smoke, having first shut all the doors thereof.

Then also did other ill fortune befall the Latins, for when Queen Amata saw from the roof of the palace that the enemy were come near to the walls, and saw not anywhere the army of the Latins, she supposed Turnus to have fallen in the battle. Whereupon, crying out that she was the cause of all these woes, she made a noose of the purple garment wherewith she was clad, and hanged herself from a beam of the roof. Then did lamentation go through the city, for the women wailed and tore their hair, and King Latinus rent his clothes and threw dust upon his head.

But the cry that went up from the city came to the ears of Turnus where he fought in the farthest part of the plain. And he caught the reins and said, "What meaneth this sound of trouble and wailing that I hear?" And the false Metiscus, who was in truth his sister, made answer, "Let us fight, O Turnus, here where the Gods give us victory. There are enough to defend the city." But Turnus spake, saying, "Nay, my sister, for who thou art I have known even from the beginning; it must not be so. Why camest thou down from heaven? Was it to see thy brother die? And now what shall I do? Have I not seen Murranus die, and Ufens the Æquian? And shall I suffer this city to be destroyed? Shall this land see Turnus flee before his enemies? Be ye kind to me, O gods of the dead, seeing that the gods of heaven hate me. I come down to you a righteous spirit, and not unworthy of my fathers."

And even as he spake came Saces, riding on a horse that was covered with foam, and on his face was the wound of an arrow. And he cried, "O Turnus, our last hopes are in thee. For Æneas is about to destroy the city, and the firebrands are cast upon the roofs. And King Latinus is sore tried with doubt, and the Queen hath laid hands upon herself and is dead. And now only Messapus and Atinas maintain the battle, and the fight grows fierce around them, whilst thou drivest thy chariot about these empty fields."

Then for a while Turnus stood speechless, and shame and grief and madness were in his soul; and he looked to the city, and lo! the fire went up even to the top of the tower which he himself had builded upon the walls to be a defense against the enemy. And when he saw it, he cried, "It is enough, my sister; I go whither the Gods call me. I will meet with Æneas face to face, and endure my doom."

And as he spake he leapt down from his chariot,

and ran across the plain till he came near to the city, even where the blood was deepest upon the earth, and the arrows were thickest in the air. And he beckoned with the hand and called to the Italians, saying, "Stay now your arrows. I am come to fight this battle for you all." And when they heard it they left a space in the midst. Æneas also, when he heard the name of Turnus, left attacking the city, and came to meet him, mighty as Athos, or Eryx, or Father Apenninus, that raiseth his snowy head to the heavens. And the men of Troy and the Latins and King Latinus marveled to see them meet, so mighty they were.

First they cast their spears at each other, and then ran together, and their shields struck one against the other with a crash that went up to the sky. And Jupiter held the balance in heaven, weighing their doom. Then Turnus, rising to the stroke, smote fiercely with his sword. And the men of Troy and the Latins cried out when they saw him strike. But the treacherous sword brake in the blow. And when he saw the empty hilt in his hand he turned to flee. They say that when he mounted his chariot that day to enter the battle, not heeding the matter in his haste, he left his father's sword behind him, and took the sword of Metiscus, which, indeed, served him well while the men of Troy fled before him, but brake, even as ice breaks, when it came to the shield which Vulcan had made. Thereupon Turnus fled, and Æneas, though the wound which the arrow had made hindered him, pursued. Even as a hound follows a stag that is penned within some narrow space, for the beast flees hither and thither, and the staunch Umbrian hound follows close upon him, and almost holds him, and snaps his teeth, yet bites him not, so did Æneas follow hard on Turnus. And still Turnus cried out that some one should give him his sword, and Æneas threatened that he would destroy the city if any should help him. Five times about the space they ran; not for some prize they strove, but for the life of Turnus. Now there stood in the plain the stump of a wild olive-tree. The tree was sacred to Faunus, but the men of Troy had cut it, and the stump only was left. Herein the spear of Æneas was fixed, and now he would have drawn it forth that he might slay Turnus therewith, seeing that he could not overtake him by running. Which when Turnus perceived, he cried to Faunus, saying, "O Faunus, if I have kept holy for thee that which the men of Troy have profaned, hold fast this spear." And the god heard him; nor could Æneas draw it forth. But while he strove, Juturna, taking again the form of Metiscus, ran and gave to Turnus his sword. And Venus, perceiving it, wrenched forth the spear from the stump. So the two stood again face to face.

Then spake Jupiter to Juno, where she sat in a cloud watching the battle, "How long wilt thou fight against fate? What purpose hast thou now in thy heart? Was it well that Juturna — for what could she avail without thy help? — should give back to Turnus his sword? Thou hast driven the men of Troy over land and sea, and kindled a dreadful war, and mingled the song of marriage with mourning. Further thou mayest not go."

And Juno humbly made answer, "This is thy will, great Father; else had I not sat here, but stood in the battle smiting the men of Troy. And indeed I spake to Juturna that she should help her brother; but aught else I know not. And now I yield. Yet grant me this. Suffer not that the Latins should be called after the name of Troy, nor change their speech, nor their garb. Let Rome rule the world, but let Troy perish forever."

Then spake with a smile the Maker of all things, "Truly thou art a daughter of Saturn, so fierce is the wrath of thy soul. And now what thou prayest I give. The Italians shall not change name, nor speech, nor garb. The men of Troy shall mingle with them, and I will give them a new worship, and call them all Latins. Nor shall any race pay thee more honor than they."

Then Jupiter sent a fury from the pit. And she took the form of a bird, even of an owl that sitteth by night on the roof of a desolate house, and flew before the face of Turnus and flapped her wings against his shield. Then was Turnus stricken with great fear, so that his hair stood up and his tongue clave to the roof of his mouth. And when Juturna knew the sound of the false bird what it was, she cried aloud for fear, and left her brother and fled, hiding herself in the river of Tiber.

But Æneas came on, shaking his spear that was like unto a tree, and said, "Why delayest thou, O Turnus? Why drawest thou back? Fly now if thou canst through the air, or hide thyself in the earth." And Turnus made answer, "I fear not thy threats, but the Gods and Jupi-

494

ter, that are against me this day." And as he spake
he saw a great stone which lay hard by, the landmark
of a field. Scarce could twelve chosen men, such as
men are now, lift it on their shoulders. This he caught
from the earth and cast it at his enemy, running forward as he cast. But he knew not, so troubled was he
in his soul, that he ran or that he cast, for his knees
tottered beneath him and his blood grew cold with
fear. And the stone fell short, nor reached the mark.
Even as in a dream, when dull sleep is on the eyes of
a man, he would fain run but cannot, for his strength
faileth him, neither cometh there any voice when he
would speak; so it fared with Turnus. For he looked
to the Latins and to the city, and saw the dreadful
spear approach, nor knew how he might fly, neither
how he might fight, and could not spy anywhere his
chariot or his sister. And all the while Æneas shook
his spear and waited that his aim should be sure. And
at the last he threw it with all his might. Even as a
whirlwind it flew, and brake through the seven folds of
the shield and pierced the thigh. And Turnus dropped
with his knee bent to the ground. And all the Latins
groaned aloud to see him fall. Then he entreated
Æneas, saying, "I have deserved my fate. Take thou
that which thou hast won. Yet perchance thou mayest
have pity on the old man, my father, even Daunus,
for such an one was thy father Anchises, and give me
back to my own people, if it be but my body that thou
givest. Yet hast thou conquered, and the Latins have
seen me beg my life of thee, and Lavinia is thine.
Therefore I pray thee, stay now thy wrath."

Then for a while Æneas stood doubting; aye, and might have spared the man, when lo! he spied upon his shoulders the belt of Pallas, whom he had slain. And his wrath was greatly kindled, and he cried with a dreadful voice, "Shalt thou who art clothed with the spoils of my friends escape me? 'T is Pallas slays thee with this wound, and takes vengeance on thy accursed blood." And as he spake he drave the steel into his breast. And with a groan the wrathful spirit passed into darkness.

. . . .

According to the old legends Æneas wedded the fair Lavinia, founded his city of Lavinium, and ruled over it for three years. Then in a battle with the Rutulians, or some other Italian people, he disappeared; and as his body was not found after the conflict was over, it was believed that the Gods had taken him up to heaven. His son Ascanius peacefully succeeded him, and removed the capital of his kingdom to Alba Longa, which city again, after the lapse of centuries, gave birth to mighty Rome.

END OF VOLUME III